CIGARETTE C

2014/15 Catalogue
other Trade Cards

"My catalogue is long, through every passion ranging"
W. S. Gilbert (The Mikado)

Published by
LODDON AUCTIONS LTD
PO Box 6223, Newbury, RG14 9JU
Tel: 0118 976 1372
E-mail: Info@loddonauctions.co.uk
Web site: www.loddonauctions.co.uk

Reprint

Printed by Blueprint and Design Unit 5 Dulwich Business Centre, Malham Road, London SE23 1AG
020 8699 8759

ISBN 978-0-946942-32-9

Loddon Auctions Ltd

Live Auctions

2014

Sunday 1st June

Wednesday 13th &
Thursday 14th August

Sunday 7th September

Sunday 2nd November

Postal Auctions

2014

Monday 7th July

Monday 6th October

We are always interested in items for our
forthcoming Auctions including cigarette cards,
postcards, beer labels etc.

Please do not hesitate to contact us for
further information.

0118 976 1372

INTRODUCTION

It is now several years since the last edition of Cigarette Card Values was published. Indeed Murray Cards (International) Ltd. ceased trading in February 2012. The 2011/12 edition was the 46th consecutive catalogue, and during the course of time it has steadily been enlarged and fine-tuned so that it has come to be regarded as THE guide. Recently many collectors and dealers have indicated how much they miss the presence of an accurate and current price list showing both cigarette and trade cards under one convenient cover.

I have therefore been persuaded to participate in the production of a catalogue, which although new is based on familiar lines. All prices have been carefully considered in the light of changes in the marketplace that have occurred in the last three years. I have not this time, however, added to the considerable number of sets that are included – bearing in mind that all British tobacco issues and most of the commonly available overseas and trade cards have always been listed.

Determining prices or values is always a difficult decision. However since we are no longer inhibited by the consideration of stock holdings we have been able to arrive at the values solely on the basis of our perception of the current market forces. We have nevertheless looked at the figures from the point of view of a dealer rather than a collector. It should be remembered that a fair selling price has to take into account all the associated costs, such as cash invested, storage costs, insurance and travel, as well as Value Added Tax. For this reason exchanges between collectors and auction prices realized will often vary considerably from the prices shown herein. Therefore the figures shown should be taken as indicative of relative rather than absolute values It should also be understood that condition will play a major role in determining prices; at one extreme a modern commercial production would be expected to be in perfect condition, while at the other for the single card known from the Craigmillar Creamery Co. condition would hardly be a consideration at all. So the best advice for readers would be to examine the prices herein and apply your own yardstick to them.

The publication of the book has now been taken over by Loddon Auctions Ltd. Gary Arkell is well known as a collector and an auctioneer, and I anticipate that with his finger on the cartophilic pulse he will be able to carry this essential work forward into the future. Plans are already in place to introduce yet more features into the next edition, and I trust that the Murray Guide will continue into the foreseeable future, with the help of you, the collecting public.

Martin Murray

HOW TO USE THE CATALOGUE

The Catalogue is in three parts.

Part 1 contains all known issues by British-based tobacco companies. Thus all cards by the firm W.D & H.O. Wills, which was located in Bristol, are shown, even though they may have been issued in a Wills brand abroad. Issues from the Channel Islands and the Republic of Ireland are included in this part. Excluded are most post cards and larger non-insert items.

Part II contains tobacco issues by most of the major manufacturers in the English-speaking world, and a selection of other series, including all the sets readily available to collectors.

Part III comprises series issued with commodities other than tobacco (commonly known as "trade cards"). Although mainly British issues, there are a number of overseas sets included. Each issuer's name is followed by the commodity with which the cards were issued; where the set was not given away free, but produced in order to be sold, the issuer is described as "commercial".

Parts I and III commence with an index of brand names, and the issuer's name under which that item appears. Series are listed in alphabetical order of series title under the issuing firm, regardless of country of origin. Where the issuer was not normally located in the United Kingdom the country of origin is given. In the case of certain larger issuers series have been listed in logical groups so that they may be more readily found.

For each set the following information is given:-

(1) **Size** information. Cards are assumed to be standard size unless otherwise stated. Sizes used generally correspond to the page sizes used for plastic albums i.e. when a letter is used it may be assumed that at least one dimension is greater than the size shown by the previous letter.
Abbreviations used are:-

K	smaller than standard	51 x 41 mm
M	medium size	80 x 52 mm
L	large size	80 x 71 mm
T	Typhoo/Doncella size	106 x 52 mm
X	extra large size	80 x 113 mm
P	postcard size	165 x 110 mm
G	cabinet size	228 x 165 mm
E	too large for Nostalgia albums	
D	dual (more than one) size	
S	stereoscopic series	
F	photographic production	

(2) Number of cards in set. When there are several rare numbers in a set the quantity normally available is shown. Thus 35/37 means that the series consists of 37 cards, but that only 35 are usually obtainable.

(3) Series title. Where the set has no name, then the title accepted by common usage is given. Sect. = sectional series. Silk = silk, satin or canvas. P/C = playing card.

(4) Year of issue. This is approximate only, and should in no way be considered to be binding. Particularly in the case of overseas and pre-1900 issues the date should be treated as merely an indication of the era in which the set was produced.

(5) Price of odd cards. Because of high labour costs and overheads it is not an economic proposition to offer odd cards from many post-1945 series. Where shown the price is that of normal cards in the set. End numbers (e.g. numbers 1 and 50 from a set of 50 cards) are DOUBLE the prices shown. Known scarce subjects from a series (e.g. cricketers from a general interest series) would be more expensive than the price shown here.

It must be borne in mind that many of these prices are only approximate, since the discovery of just a few cards from a scarcer series could greatly affect the price.

(6) Price of complete sets. Prices shown are for sets in clean, undamaged condition. Where mint sets are specified there might be a premium added.

ALIKE SERIES

There are many instances where affiliated companies, or indeed completely independent groups issued identical series, where the pictures are the same, and only the issuer's name is altered. Examples are Fish & Bait issued by Churchman, I.T.C. (Canada) and Wills; British Cavalry Uniforms of the Nineteenth Century issued by Badshah, Browne, Empson, Rington and Wilcocks & Wilcocks; or even Interesting Animals by Hignett or Church & Dwight.

The Cartophilic Society of Great Britain

Est. 1938

'Devoted to propagating, enhancing and preserving the hobby of cigarette and trade card collecting'

Join the society and:
- meet collectors across the UK at one of our 20 branches
- receive our colour magazine – 'Card World', filled with up-to-date research and articles
- get preferential rates on all our reference books
- get free admission to any of our national events
- bid in our members only postal auctions

Full membership 2014 (1 Year) –
Home – £24.50
Europe - £27.00
International - £35.00
Under 21 years of age - £10

Family Membership 2014 (one magazine to one address)
Two members - £27.00
Three or more members - £32.00

For more information about joining the society please visit our website www.card-world.co.uk or contact our membership secretary:

Colin Fawcett
Sherwood, Trafford Road, Wisbech, Cambs., PE13 2EJ
Tel: 01945 583656
email: clnfa@aol.com

INDEX OF BRANDS (Tobacco). These appear on cards without the Manufacturer's name.

ADMIRAL CIGARETTES	See National Cigarette & Tobacco Co. (Part 2)
AIRMAIL CIGARETTES	See Hill (Part 1)
ALBERT CIGARETTES	See British American Tobacco Co. (Part 2)
ALL ARMS CIGARETTES	See Carreras (Part 1)
S.ANARGYROS	See American Tobacco Co. (Part 2)
ATLAS	See American Tobacco Co. (Part 2)

BANDMASTER CIGARETTES	See Cohen Weenen (Part 1)
BATTLE-AXE	See American Tobacco Co (Part 2)
B.D.V CIGARETTES	See Godfrey Phillips (Part 1)
BEAUTY BRIGHT CIGARETTES	See Asheville Tobacco Works (Part 2)
BETWEEN THE ACTS	See American Tobacco Co (Part 2)
BIG GUN CIGARETTES	See Sandorides (Part 1)
BLACK CAT CIGARETTES	See Carreras (Part 1)
BLACK SPOT CIGARETTES	See Scerri (Part 2)
BORNEO QUEEN CIGARS	See B.Morris (Part 1)
BOUQUET CIGARETTES	See I.T.C. (Canada) (Part 2)
BRIDE LONG CUT TOBACCO	See Mrs G B Miller (Part 2)
BRITISH CONSULS	See Macdonald (Part 2)
BROADWAY NOVELTIES	See Teofani (Part 1)
BULLDOG CIGARS	See Elliott (Part 1)

CAIRO MONOPOL CIGARETTES	See American Tobacco Co. (Part 2)
CAKEWALK CIGARETTES	See Pezaro (Part 1)
CAMEO CIGARETTES	See British American Tobacco Co (Part 2)
CAPS THE LOT	See Bewlay (Part 1)
CASKET CIGARETTES	See Pattreiouex (Part 1)
CASTELLA CIGARS	See Wills (Part 1)
CHAIRMAN CIGARETTES	See Lea (Part 1)
CHALLENGE FLAT BRILLIANTES	See Gloag (Part 1)
CITAMORA CIGARETTES	See Gloag (Part 1)
CLUB MEMBER etc	See Pattreiouex (Part 1)
CLUB MIXTURE	See Continental Cigarette Factory (Part 1)
COCKADE	See Venable (Part 2)
COLIN CAMPBELL CIGARS	See Robinson & Barnsdale (Part 1)
COPAIN	See British American Tobacco Co. (Part 2)
CORONET CIGARETTES	See Sniders & Abrahams (Part 2)
CROWFOOT CIGARETTES	See Hill (Part 1)
CYMAX CIGARETTES	See Coudens (Part 1)

DERBY LITTLE CIGARS	See American Tobacco Co. (Part 2)
DE RESZKE CIGARETTES	See Millhoff (Part 1)
DOMINO CIGARETTES	See British American Tobacco Co (Part 2)
DOUBLE ACE CIGARETTES	See Ardath (Part 1)
DOUBLE 5	See American Eagle Tobacco Co. (Part 2)

EAGLE BIRD	See British American Tobacco Co. (Part 2)
EDWARD VII	See Cabana Cigar Co. (Part 1)
EGYPTIENNE LUXURY	See American Tobacco Co. (Part 2)
ELDONA	See Drapkin & Millhoff (Part 1)
EMBLEM CIGARETTES	See Westminster (Part 1) or
	American Tobacco Co. (Part 2)
EMPRESS CIGARETTES	See Burstein Isaacs (Part 1)
ERINMORE CIGARETTES	See Murray (Part 1)
EXPLORER CIGARETTES	See Drapkin & Millhoff (Part 1)

F. FARRUGIA MALTA	See Omega (Part 2)
FAVOURITE CIGARETTES	See Teofani (Part 1)
FORECASTA	See B. Morris (Part 1)
FOUR SQUARE	See Dobie (Part 1)
FRESHER CIGARETTES	See Challis (Part 1)

G.P.	See G. Phillips (Part 1)
GAINSBOROUGH	See Cohen Weenen (Part 1)
GIBSON GIRL	See Hill (Part 1)
GOLD COIN TOBACCO	See Buchner (Part 2)
GOLD DOLLAR	See B.A.T. (Part 2)
GOLDEN GRAIN	See Brown & Williamson (Part 2)
GOLD FLAKE HONEYDEW	See Hill (Part 1)
GRAND DUKE CIGARETTES	See American Tobacco Co. (Part 2)
GREYS CIGARETTES	See United Kingdom Tobacco Co. (Part 1)
GREYS TOBACCO	See Drapkin (Part 1)

GUARDS CIGARETTES	See Carreras (Part 1)
HAVELOCK CIGARETTES	See Wills (Part 1)
HAWSER Etc	See Wholesale Tobacco Co. (Part 1)
HEARTS DELIGHT CIGARETTES	See Pritchard & Burton (Part 1)
HERBERT TAREYTON CIGARETTES	See American Tobacco Co. (Part 2)
HOFFMAN HOUSE MAGNUMS	See American Tobacco Co. (Part 2)
HONEST LONG CUT	See Duke or American Tobacco Co. (Part 2)
HUDAVEND CIGARETTES	See Teofani (Part 1)
HUSTLER LITTLE CIGARS	See American Tobacco Co. (Part 2)
ISLANDER, FAGS, SPECIALS, CLUBS	See Bucktrout (Part 1)
JACK ROSE LITTLE CIGARS	See American Tobacco Co. (Part 2)
JERSEY LILY CIGARETTES	See Bradford (Part 1)
JUNIOR MEMBER CIGARETTES	See Pattreiouex (Part 1)
KENSITAS CIGARETTES	See J.Wix (Part 1)
KONG BENG	See American Tobacco Co. (Part 2)
LENOX CIGARETTES	See American Tobacco Co. (Part 2)
LE ROY CIGARS	See L Miller (Part 2)
LEVANT FAVOURITES	See B.Morris (Part 1)
LIFEBOAT CIGARETTES	See United Tobacco Co. (Part 2)
LIFE RAY CIGARETTES	See Ray (Part 1)
LITTLE RHODY CUT PLUG	See Geo.F.Young (Part 2)
LOTUS CIGARETTES	See United Tobacco Co. (Part 2)
LUCANA CIGARETTES	See Sandorides (Part 1)
LUCKY STRIKE CIGARETTES	See American Tobacco Co. (Part 2)
LUXURY CIGARETTES	See American Tobacco Co. (Part 2)
MAGPIE CIGARETTES	See Schuh (Part 2)
MANIKIN CIGARS	See Freeman (Part 1)
MASCOT CIGARETTES	See B.A.T. (Part 2)
MATTOSSIANS IMPORTED EGYPTIAN CIGARETTES	See Henly & Watkins (Part 1)
MAX CIGARETTES	See A. & M. Wix (Part 1)
MAYBLOSSOM CIGARETTES	See Lambert & Butler (Part 1)
MECCA CIGARETTES	See American Tobacco Co. (Part 2)
MILLBANK CIGARETTES	See Imperial Tobacco Co. (Canada) (Part 2)
MILLS CIGARETTES	See Amalgamated Tobacco Corporation (Part 1)
MILO CIGARETTES	See Sniders & Abrahams (Part 2)
MINERS EXTRA SMOKING TOBACCO	See American Tobacco Co. (Part 2)
MOGUL CIGARETTES	See American Tobacco Co. (Part 2)
MOTOR	See American Tobacco Co. (Part 2)
MURAD CIGARETTES	See American Tobacco Co. (Part 2)
NASSA CIGARETTES	See Policansky Bros. (Part 2)
NEBO CIGARETTES	See American Tobacco Co. (Part 2)
OK CIGARETTES	See Hartleys T.C. (Part 2)
OBAK CIGARETTES	See American Tobacco Co. (Part 2)
OFFICERS MESS CIGARETTES	See African Tobacco Mfrs. (Part 2)
OLD GOLD CIGARETTES	See American Tobacco Co. (Part 2)
OLD JUDGE CIGARETTES	See B.A.T or Goodwin (Part 2)
ONE OF THE FINEST	See Buchner (Part 2)
ORACLE CIGARETTES	See Tetley (Part 1)
OUR LITTLE BEAUTIES	See Allen & Ginter (Part 2)
OXFORD CIGARETTES	See American Tobacco Co. (Part 2)
PALACE CIGARETTES	See Teofani (Part 1)
PAN HANDLE SCRAP	See American Tobacco Co. (Part 2)
PEDRO	See American Tobacco Co. (Part 2)
PETER PAN CIGARETTES	See Sniders & Abrahams (Part 2)
PHAROAH'S DREAM CIGARETTES	See Teofani (Part 1)
PIBROCH VIRGINIA	See Fryer (Part 1)
PICADILLY LITTLE CIGARS	See American Tobacco Co. (Part 2)
PICK-ME-UP CIGARETTES	See Drapkin & Millhoff (Part 1)
PIEDMONT CIGARETTES	See American Tobacco Co. (Part 2)
PINHEAD CIGARETTES	See British American Tobacco Co. (Part 2)
PINNACE	See G.Phillips (Part 1)
PIONEER CIGARETTES	See Richmond Cavendish (Part 1)
PIRATE CIGARETTES	See Wills (Part 1)
POLO MILD CIGARETTES	See Murray (Part 1)

PURITAN LITTLE CIGARS	See American Tobacco Co. (Part 2)
PURPLE MOUNTAIN CIGARETTES	See Wills (Part 1)
R.S	See R. Sinclair (Part 1)
RECRUIT LITTLE CIGARS	See American Tobacco Co. (Part 2)
RED CROSS	See Lorillard or American Tobacco Co. (Part 2)
REINA REGENTA CIGARS	See B.Morris (Part 1)
RICHMOND GEM CIGARETTES	See Allen & Ginter (Part 2)
RICHMOND STRAIGHT CUT CIGARETTES	See American Tobacco Co. (Part 2)
ROSELAND CIGARETTES	See Glass (Part 1)
ROYAL BENGALS LITTLE CIGARS	See American Tobacco Co. (Part 2)
RUGGER CIGARETTES	See United Tobacco Companies (Part 2)
ST.DUNSTANS CIGARETTES	See Carreras (Part 1)
ST. LEGER LITTLE CIGARS	See American Tobacco Co. (Part 2)
SCOTS CIGARETTES	See African Tobacco Mfrs. (Part 2)
SCRAP IRON SCRAP	See American Tobacco Co. (Part 2)
SEAL OF NORTH CAROLINA PLUG CUT OF TOBACCO	See Marburg Bros. (Part 2)
SENATOR CIGARETTES	See Scerri (Part 2)
SENIOR SERVICE CIGARETTES	See Pattreiouex (Part 1)
SENSATION CUT PLUG	See Lorillard (Part 2)
SHANTUNG CIGARETTES	See British American Tobacco Co. (Part 2)
SILKO CIGARETTES	See American Tobacco Co. (Part 2)
SMILE AWAY TOBACCO	See Carreras (Part 1)
SOVEREIGN CIGARETTES	See American Tobacco Co. (Part 2)
SPANISH FOUR	See W.R.Gresh (Part 2)
SPANISH PUFFS	See Mandelbaum (Part 2)
SPINET CIGARETTES	See Hill (Part 1)
SPOTLIGHT TOBACCOS	See Hill (Part 1)
SPRINGBOK CIGARETTES	See United Tobacco Co. (Part 2)
STAG TOBACCO	See American Tobacco Co. (Part 2)
STANDARD CIGARETTES	See Carreras (Part 1) or Sniders & Abrahams (Part 2)
STATE EXPRESS CIGARETTES	See Ardath (Part 1)
SUB ROSA	See Pacholder (Part 2)
SUB ROSA CIGARROS	See American Tobacco Co. (Part 2)
SUMMIT	See Internationational Tobacco Co. (Part 1)
SUNFLOWER CIGARETTES	See B.A.T (Part 2)
SUNRIPE CIGARETTES	See Hill (Part 1)
SUNSPOT CIGARETTES	See Theman (Part 1)
SWEET CAPORAL	See Kinney or American Tobacco Co. (Part 2)
SWEET LAVENDER	See Kimball (Part 2)
TATLEY CIGARETTES	See Walkers (Part 1)
TEAL CIGARETTES	See British American Tobacco Co. (Part 2)
THREE BELLS CIGARETTES	See Bell (Part 1)
THREE CASTLES CIGARETTES	See Wills (Part 1)
THREE DOGS CIGARETTES	See Sandorides (Part 1)
THREE STAR CIGARETTES	See Teofani (Part 1)
TIGER CIGARETTES	See British American Tobacco Co. (Part 1)
TIPSY LOO CIGARETTES	See H.C.Lloyd (Part 1)
TOKIO CIGARETTES	See American Tobacco Co. (Part 2)
TRAWLER CIGARETTES	See Pattreiouex (Part 1)
TRUMPS LONG CUT	See Moore & Calvi (Part 2)
TURF CIGARETTES	See Carreras (Part 1)
TURKEY RED CIGARETTES	See American Tobacco Co. (Part 2)
TURKISH TROPHY CIGARETTES	See American Tobacco Co. (Part 2)
TWELFTH NIGHT CIGARETTES	See American Tobacco Co. (Part 2)
U.S. MARINE	See American Tobacco Co. (Part 2)
UZIT CIGARETTES	See American Tobacco Co. (Part 2)
VANITY FAIR CIGARETTES	See B.A.T. or Kimball (Part 2)
VICE REGAL CIGARETTES	See Wills (Part 1)
VICTORY TOBACCO	See Buchner (Part 2)
VIRGINIA BRIGHTS CIGARETTES	See Allen & Ginter (Part 2)
WEST END CIGARETTES	See Teofani (Part 1)
WINGS CIGARETTES	See Brown & Williamson (Part 2)
YANKEE DOODLE	See British Australasian Tobacco Co. (Part 2)
ZIRA CIGARETTES	See American Tobacco Co. (Part 2)

Part 1

BRITISH TOBACCO MANUFACTURERS

(Including Channel Islands, Eire, and Overseas Issues
by British-based firms)

ABDULLA & CO. LTD.

Qty		Date	Odds	Sets
50	Beauties Of To-Day	1938	£3.60	£180.00
L1	Bridge Rule Cards (Several Printings)	1936	–	£15.00
25	British Butterflies	1935	£1.20	£30.00
F52	Cinema Stars	1932	£3.85	£200.00
30	Cinema Stars (Brown Back)	1932	£5.00	–
30	Cinema Stars (Black Back)	1933	£3.70	£110.00
32	Cinema Stars (Brown Glossy Front)	1933	£2.65	£85.00
32	Cinema Stars (Hand Coloured)	1934	£2.65	£85.00
30	Cinema Stars (Hand Coloured)	1934	£3.30	–
P2	Commanders Of The Allies	1914	£85.00	–
25	Feathered Friends	1935	£1.20	£30.00
50	Film Favourites	1934	£3.70	£185.00
50	Film Stars	1934	£6.75	–
P24	Film Stars (Series Of Cards)	1934	£7.75	–
P24	Film Stars (Series Of 24 Cards)	1934	£7.75	–
P24	Film Stars, 2nd (25-48)	1934	£7.75	–
M3	Great War Gift Packing Cards	1916	£85.00	£250.00
18	Message Cards (Blue Printing)	1936	£12.50	–
18	(Green Printing)	1936	£13.00	–
18	(Orange Printing)	1936	£13.00	–
K18	Message Cards(Two Wordings)	1936	£15.00	–
25	Old Favourites	1936	£0.90	£22.50
L1	Princess Mary Gift Card	1914	–	£22.50
40	Screen Stars (No Successors Clause)	1939	£1.75	£70.00
40	(With Successors Clause)	1939	£2.50	£100.00
50	Stage And Cinema Beauties	1935	£3.50	–
30	Stars Of The Stage And Screen (Black And White)	1934	£4.00	–
30	(Hand Coloured)	1934	£5.00	-

GERMAN ISSUES

Qty		Date	Odds	Sets
M150	Autobilder Serie I	1931	£1.80	–
M150	Autobilder Serie II+B281	1932	£1.80	–
M160	Im Auto Mit Abdulla Durch Die Welt	1930	£1.20	£192.00
M110	Landerwappen-Sammlung	1932	£1.25	–
M110	Landerwappen-Sammlung Serie II	1932	£1.25	–
M150	Landerwappen-Sammlung Serie III	1932	£1.25	£187.50
M200	Nationale/Internationale Sportrekorde	1931	£3.00	–
M50	Soldatenbilder Europaischer Armeen	1928	£2.50	–
X80	Wappenkarten	1928	£1.20	£96.00

ADCOCK & SON

Qty		Date	Odds	Sets
11/12	Ancient Norwich	1928	£3.60	£40.00

ADKIN & SONS

Qty		Date	Odds	Sets
25	Actresses-French	1898	£215.00	–
12	A Living Picture (Adkin & Sons Back)	1897	£7.75	£93.00
12	(These Cards Back)	1897	£7.75	£93.00
P12	A Living Picture	1897	£100.00	–
12	A Royal Favourite	1900	£12.50	£150.00
15	Beauties "PAC"(7 Brands)	1898	£335.00	–
50	Butterflies & Moths	1924	£2.00	£100.00
12	Character Sketches (Black Back)	1897	£7.50	£90.00
12	(Green Back)	1897	£7.50	£90.00
P12	Character Sketches	1897	£110.00	–
P4	Games By Tom Browne	1909	£300.00	–

2

ADKIN & SONS – cont.

Qty		Date	Odds	Sets
25	Notabilities	1915	£4.60	£115.00
12	Pretty Girl Series (Actresses)	1897	£60.00	£720.00
12	Pretty Girl Series (12 Calendar Backs)	1900	£60.00	–
12	(6 Verse Backs)	1900	£40.00	–
12	(32 Other Backs)	1900	£35.00	–
	Soldiers Of The Queen	1899	–	–
24	("Series Of 50, Issued Exclusively")	1899	£27.50	–
50	("Series Of 50")	1900	£5.50	£325.00
59	("Series Of 60")	1900	£4.75	–
31	Soldiers Of The Queen & Portraits	1901	£6.25	£195.00
30	Sporting Cups & Trophies	1914	£16.75	£560.00
25	War Trophies	1917	£4.25	£105.00
50	Wild Animals Of The World	1923	£1.65	£82.50

AIKMAN'S (TOBACCONIST)

Qty		Date	Odds	Sets
30	Army Pictures, Cartoons, etc.	1916	£150.00	–

H.J. AINSWORTH (TOBACCONIST)

Qty		Date	Odds	Sets
30	Army Pictures, Cartoons, etc.	1916	£130.00	–

ALBERGE & BROMET

Qty		Date	Odds	Sets
25	Boer War & General Interest			
	(Brown Bridal Bouquet)	1900	£120.00	–
	(Brown La Optima)	1900	£200.00	–
	(Green Bridal Bouquet)	1900	£160.00	–
	(Green La Optima)	1900	£120.00	–
40	Naval & Military Phrases (Bridal Bouquet)	1904	£100.00	–
40	(La Optima)	1904	£100.00	–
30	Proverbs	1903	£100.00	–

PHILLIP ALLMAN & CO. LTD.

Qty		Date	Odds	Sets
50	Coronation Series	1953	£0.80	£40.00
	Pin Up Girls, 1st Series			
12	(Numbered)	1953	£5.00	£60.00
12	(Unnumbered, "Ask For Allman-Always")	1953	£3.75	£45.00
12	(Unnumbered, "For Men Only")	1953	£3.25	£40.00
L12	Pin Up Girls, 1st Series	1953	£4.25	£50.00
12	Pin Up Girls, 2nd Series	1953	£4.00	£48.00
L12	Pin Up Girls, 2nd Series	1953	£4.00	£48.00
24	Pin Up Girls, Combined Series			
	(Numbered "First Series of 24")	1953	£8.00	–

AMALGAMATED TOB. CORP. LTD. (Mills)

Qty		Date	Odds	Sets
25	Aircraft Of The World	1958	£1.00	–
25	A Nature Series	1958	–	£3.00
25	Animals Of The Countryside	1958	£0.30	£7.50
25	Aquarium Fish	1961	–	£3.00
25	Army Badges-Past And Present	1961	£1.20	£30.00
25	British Coins And Costumes	1958	£0.60	£15.00
25	British Locomotives	1961	–	£8.00
25	British Uniforms Of The 19th Century	1957	£0.80	£20.00
25	Butterflies And Moths	1957	£0.30	£7.50
25	Cacti	1961	£0.50	£12.50
25	Castles Of Britain	1961	–	£27.50
25	Coins Of The World	1961	–	£5.00

3

AMALGAMATED TOB. CORP. LTD. (Mills) - cont.

Qty		Date	Odds	Sets
25	Communications	1961	–	£25.00
25	Dogs	1958	–	£22.00
25	Evolution Of The Royal Navy	1957	–	£20.00
M25	Famous British Ships, Series No.1	1952	–	£4.00
M25	Famous British Ships, Series No.2	1952	–	£4.00
25	Football Clubs And Badges	1961	£1.60	£40.00
25	Freshwater Fish	1958	–	£6.00
25	Guerriers A Travers Les Ages (French)	1961	–	£16.00
25	Histoire De L'Aviation, Premiere Serie	1961	–	£4.00
25	Histoire De L'Aviation, Seconde Serie	1962	–	£25.00
25	Historical Buildings	1959	–	£17.50
M25/50	History Of Aviation	1952	–	£5.00
M50	History Of Aviation	1952	–	£50.00
25	Holiday Resorts	1957	–	£3.00
25	Interesting Hobbies	1959	£0.50	£12.50
25	Into Space	1959	–	£8.50
25	Kings Of England	1954	£1.70	£42.50
25	Les Autos Modernes (French Text)	1961	–	£12.50
25	Medals Of The World	1959	–	£6.00
25	Merchant Ships Of The World	1961	£0.60	£15.00
25	Merveilles Modernes (French Text)	1961	–	£8.00
25	Miniature Cars & Scooters	1958	£1.20	£30.00
25	Naval Battles	1959	£0.50	£12.50
25	Ports Of The World	1959	–	£3.00
25	Propelled Weapons	1953	–	£5.00
25	Ships Of The Royal Navy	1961	–	£10.00
25	Sports And Games	1958	£1.20	£30.00
25	The Wild West	1960	–	£30.00
25	Tropical Birds	1958	–	£25.00
25	Weapons Of Defence	1961	–	£25.00
25	Wild Animals	1958	–	£5.00
25	World Locomotives	1959	£1.00	£25.00

THE ANGLO-AMERICAN CIG MAKING CO. LTD.

20	Russo-Japanese War Series	1904	£400.00	–

ANGLO CIGARETTE MFG. CO. LTD.

36	Tariff Reform Series	1909	£32.50	–

ANONYMOUS ISSUES - TOBACCO
PRINTED BACKS

?33	Beauties "KEWA" ("England Expects" Back)	1899	£130.00	–
25	Boer War And General Interest (Design Back)	1901	£45.00	–
41	V.C. Heroes	1916	£8.50	£350.00
50	War Portraits	1915	£26.00	–

PLAIN BACKS

25	Actors & Actresses "FROGA C"	1900	£12.50	–
?9	Actresses "ANGLO"	1896	£85.00	–
?23	Actresses "ANGOOD" (Brown Front)	1898	£37.50	–
?23	(Green Front)	1898	£50.00	–
?30	(Grey Front)	1898	£27.50	–
20	Actresses "BLARM"	1900	£12.50	£250.00
50	Actresses "DAVAN"	1902	£36.50	–
26	Actresses "FROGA A" (Brown)	1900	£10.00	£260.00

4

ANONYMOUS ISSUES - TOBACCO – cont.

Qty		Date	Odds	Sets
26	Actresses "FROGA A" (Coloured)	1900	£11.50	–
25	Actresses "HAGG"	1900	£9.50	–
25	Beauties "BOCCA"	1900	£16.00	–
50	Beauties "CHOAB" (Brown)	1902	£10.00	–
50	(Coloured)	1902	£11.00	–
50	Beauties "FECKSA"	1903	£10.00	–
24	Beauties "FENA"	1899	£50.00	–
25	Beauties "GRACC"	1898	£18.00	–
26	Beauties "HOL"	1900	£12.00	–
?14	Beauties "KEWA"	1898	£35.00	–
20	Beauties "PLUMS"	1898	£42.50	–
25	Boer War & General Interest	1901	£30.00	–
20	Boer War Cartoons	1900	£15.00	–
20	Boer War Generals "CLAM"	1901	£13.00	–
12	Boer War Generals "FLAC"	1901	£13.00	–
25	Boxer Rebellion-Sketches	1904	£11.00	–
M108	British Naval Crests	1916	£3.50	–
16	British Royal Family	1902	£9.50	–
F12	Celebrities Of The Great War	1915	£18.00	–
50	Colonial Troops	1902	£9.00	–
M108	Crests & Badges Of The British Army	1916	£4.00	–
20	Cricketers Series	1902	£230.00	–
50	Dogs (as Taddy)	1900	£26.50	–
30	Flags & Flags With Soldiers (Draped)	1902	£8.00	–
15	Flags & Flags With Soldiers (Undraped)	1902	£8.50	–
24	Flags Arms & Types Of Nations	1904	£7.50	£180.00
40	Home & Colonial Regiments	1900	£9.00	–
2	King Edward & Queen Alexandra	1902	£18.00	£36.00
1	Lord Kitchener	1915	–	£22.50
40	Naval & Military Phrases	1904	£8.00	–
F30	Photographs (Animal Studies)	1935	£1.75	£52.00
?42	Pretty Girl Series "BAGG"	1898	£18.00	–
12	Pretty Girl Series "RASH"	1899	£16.00	–
30	Proverbs	1901	£11.00	–
19	Russo Japanese Series	1904	£16.00	–
20	Russo Japanese War Series	1904	£18.00	–
25	Star Girls	1900	£10.00	–
20	The European War Series	1915	£7.00	£140.00
25	Types Of British & Colonial Troops	1900	£17.50	–
25	Types Of British Soldiers	1914	£10.00	£250.00
24	Views And Yachts	1900	£13.00	–

E & W ANSTIE

Qty		Date	Odds	Sets
25	Aesop's Fables	1934	£3.25	£80.00
16	British Empire Series	1904	£13.00	£208.00
10	Clifton Suspension Bridge (Sect)	1938	£2.75	£27.50
M36	Flags (Silk)	1915	£2.00	–
X10	Flags (Silk)	1915	£11.00	–
40	Nature Notes	1939	£8.00	–
50	People Of Africa	1926	£3.50	£175.00
50	People Of Asia	1926	£3.50	£175.00
50	People Of Europe	1925	£3.00	£150.00
40	Places Of Interest (Matt Front)	1939	£3.00	–
40	(Varnished Front)	1939	£1.00	£40.00

5

E & W. ANSTIE – cont.

Qty		Date	Odds	Sets
8	Puzzle Series	1900	£220.00	–
25	Racing Series (1-25)	1922	£3.80	£95.00
25	Racing Series (26-50)	1922	£6.00	£150.00
60/85	Regimental Badges (Silk)	1915	£2.00	–
M5	Royal Mail Series	1900	£320.00	–
X5	Royal Standard & Portraits (Silk)	1915	£15.00	–
2	Royal Portraits (Silk)	1915	£50.00	–
50	Scout Series	1923	£3.30	£165.00
10	Stonehenge (Sect)	1936	£3.00	£30.00
10	The Victory (Sect)	1936	£3.00	£30.00
50	The World's Wonders	1924	£1.50	£75.00
20	Wells Cathedral (Sect)	1935	£2.00	£40.00
40	Wessex	1938	£1.60	£64.00
20	Wiltshire Downs (Sect)	1935	£2.00	£40.00
10	Windsor Castle (Sect)	1937	£3.00	£30.00

HENRY ARCHER & CO.

Qty		Date	Odds	Sets
51	Actresses "FROGA" (Multi-Backed)	1900	£70.00	–
50	Beauties "CHOAB" (Brown)	1900	£30.00	£1,500.00
25	Beauties "CHOAB" (Coloured, Vari-Backed)	1900	£75.00	–
20	Prince Of Wales Series	1912	£28.00	–

ARDATH TOBACCO CO. LTD.

Qty		Date	Odds	Sets
50	Animals At The Zoo (Descriptive Back)	1924	£2.50	£125.00
50	(Double Ace Back)	1924	£22.00	–
F54	Beautiful English Women	1930	£3.50	£190.00
25	Big Game Hunting (Descriptive Back)	1930	£4.00	–
25	(Double Ace Back)	1930	£15.00	–
L30	Boucher Series	1915	£3.00	£90.00
50	Britain's Defenders	1936	£0.80	£40.00
50	British Born Film Stars	1934	£1.65	£82.50
M50	British Born Film Stars	1934	£2.80	£140.00
X1	Calendar 1942	1941	–	£2.75
X1	Calendar 1942-3	1942	–	£4.50
X1	Calendar 1943	1942	–	£10.00
X1	Calendar 1943-4	1943	–	£2.00
X1	Calendar 1944	1943	–	£2.00
P2	Calendars (Silk)	1937	£135.00	–
MF36	Camera Studies	1939	£1.35	£48.00
LF45	Camera Studies	1939	£1.35	£60.00
L8	Christmas Greeting Cards (Folders)	1943	£3.25	£26.00
X25	Champion Dogs	1934	£2.20	£55.00
X?97	Contract Bridge Contest Hands	1930	£32.50	–
50	Cricket, Tennis & Golf Celebrities (Brown, N.Z. Issue)	1935	£2.50	£125.00
50	(Grey, G.B. Issue)	1935	£1.70	£85.00
X25	Dog Studies (State Express etc.)	1938	£5.20	£130.00
X25	(Firm's Name Only, N.Z.)	1938	£13.00	–
25	Eastern Proverbs	1932	£1.70	£42.50
48	Empire Flying-Boat (Sect)	1938	£1.60	£75.00
50	Empire Personalities	1937	£0.70	£35.00
50	Famous Film Stars	1934	£1.00	£50.00
50	Famous Footballers	1934	£1.65	£82.50
25	Famous Scots	1935	£1.50	£37.50
X25	Fighting & Civil Aircraft	1936	£2.80	£70.00

Qty		Date	Odds	Sets
50	Figures Of Speech	1936	£1.50	£75.00
50	Film,Stage And Radio Stars	1935	£1.00	£50.00
X25	Film,Stage & Radio Stars (Different)	1935	£1.60	£40.00
PF?12	Film Stars (State Express)	1938	£32.00	–
PF?10	Film Stars (Straight Cut)	1938	£32.00	–
P?1	Film Stars (Three Threes)	1938	£40.00	–
M50	Flags 4th Series (Silk)	1914	£40.00	–
M50	Flags 5th Series (Silk)	1914	£40.00	–
M25	Flags 6th Series (Silk)	1914	£50.00	–
L40	Franz Hals Series (No Overprint)	1916	£13.00	£520.00
L40	(2.5 Cents Overprint)	1916	£27.50	
X50	From Screen And Stage	1936	£1.30	£65.00
L30	Gainsborough Series (Multi-Backed)	1915	£2.85	£85.00
L30	Girls Of All Nations	1916	£18.00	–
50	Great War Series	1916	£5.20	£260.00
P12	Great War Bookmarks (3 Types)	1916	£55.00	–
50	Great War Series "B"	1916	£5.20	£260.00
50	Great War Series "C"	1916	£5.75	–
35	Hand Shadows	1930	£35.00	–
X25	Historic Grand Slams	1936	£32.50	–
L25	Hollandsche Oude Meesters (4 Backs)	1916	£15.00	–
L25	Hollandsche Oude Meesters (26-50)	1916	£16.00	–
X48	How To Recognise The Service Ranks	1940	£5.00	–
X2	Industrial Propaganda Cards (Black)	1943	£7.00	–
X4	Industrial Propaganda Cards (Coloured)	1943	£7.00	–
X11	Industrial Propaganda Cards (White)	1943	£5.00	–
X?171	Information Slips	1940	£3.50	–
L24/25	It All Depends On ME	1940	£1.70	£40.00
50	Life In The Services (Adhesive)	1938	£0.90	£45.00
50	(Non-Adhesive NZ)	1938	£1.25	£62.00
96	Modern School Atlas	1936	£1.50	£144.00
50	National Fitness (Adhesive)	1938	£0.50	£25.00
50	(Non-Adhesive NZ)	1938	£1.00	£50.00
50	New Zealand Views	1928	£2.60	£130.00
L1	On The Kitchen Front	1942	–	£3.00
50	Our Empire	1937	£1.50	£75.00
LF110	Photocards "A" (Lancs. Football Teams)	1936	£2.00	£220.00
LF110	Photocards "B" (N.E. Football Teams)	1936	£2.30	–
LF110	Photocards "C" (Yorks. Football Teams)	1936	£1.80	£200.00
LF165	Photocards "D" (Scots. Football Teams)	1936	£1.50	£250.00
LF110	Photocards "E" (Midland Football Teams)	1936	£2.00	£220.00
LF110	Photocards "F" (Southern Football Teams)	1936	£1.80	£200.00
LF99	Photocards "Z" (Sport & General Interest)	1936	£0.85	£85.00
LF11	Photocards "Supplementary"	1936	£5.50	–
LF22	Photocards Group "A" (Sports)	1937	£1.35	£30.00
LF21/22	Photocards Group "B" (Coronation,Sport)	1937	£0.85	£18.00
L22	Complete Set	1937	–	£32.00
LF21/22	Photocards Group "C" (Lancs. Celebrities)	1937	£1.10	£23.00
L22	Complete Set	1937	–	£38.00
LF22	Photocards Group "D" (Irish Celebrities)	1937	£1.45	£32.00
LF22	Photocards Group "E" (Films, Sports)	1938	£1.10	£24.00
LF22	Photocards Group "F" (Films, Sports)	1938	£1.50	£33.00
LF11	Photocards Group "G" (Cricketers)	1938	£19.00	–
LF66	Photocards Group "G"+B354" (Various)	1938	£2.60	–
LF22	Photocards Group "H" (Films, Sports)	1938	£1.10	£24.00

ARDATH TOBACCO CO. LTD. – cont.

Qty		Date	Odds	Sets
LF22	Photocards Group "I" (Films, Various)	1938	£1.10	£24.00
LF22	Photocards Group "J" (Films, Various)	1939	£1.25	£27.50
LF22	Photocards Group "K" ("KINGS" Clause)	1939	£0.90	£20.00
LF22	(No Clause)	1939	£1.65	–
LF44	Photocards Group "L" (Various)	1939	£0.70	£30.00
F45	Photocards Group "M" (Films, Various)	1939	£0.90	£40.00
LF45	Photocards Group "M" ("KINGS" Clause)	1939	£0.90	£40.00
LF45	(No Clause)	1939	£0.85	£38.00
F45	Photocards Group "N" (Films)	1939	£0.90	£40.00
LF45	Photocards Group "N" (Films)	1939	£0.70	£32.00
LF66	Photocards Views Of The World	1938	£0.95	£62.00
25	Proverbs (1-25)	1936	£1.70	£42.50
25	Proverbs (26-50)	1936	£3.20	–
L30	Raphael Series	1916	£3.00	£90.00
LF45	Real Photographs Group "O" (Films)	1939	£0.60	£27.00
F45	Real Photographs 1st Series	1939	£1.00	£45.00
XF18	Real Photographs 1st Series (Views)	1937	£2.50	£45.00
F54	Real Photographs 2nd Series	1939	£1.10	£60.00
XF18	Real Photographs 2nd Series	1937	£2.50	£45.00
XF18	Real Photographs 3rd Series (Views)	1937	£2.50	£45.00
XF18	Real Photographs 4th Series	1938	£2.50	£45.00
XF18	Real Photographs 5th Series (Views)	1938	£2.50	£45.00
XF18	Real Photographs 6th Series	1938	£2.50	£45.00
LF44	Real Photographs Series 1-GP1	1939	£0.90	£40.00
LF44	Real Photographs Series 2-GP2	1939	£0.50	£22.00
LF44	Real Photographs Series 3-GP3	1939	£3.10	–
LF44	Real Photographs Series 3-CV3 (Views)	1939	£0.85	£37.00
LF44	Real Photographs Series 4-CV4 (Views)	1939	£0.40	£18.00
XF36	Real Photographs Series 7	1938	£0.70	£25.00
XF36	Real Photographs Series 8	1938	£0.60	£32.00
LF54	Real Photographs Series 9	1938	£0.80	£43.00
XF54	Real Photographs Series 9	1938	£0.60	£32.50
LF54	Real Photographs Series 10	1939	£0.65	£35.00
XF54	Real Photographs Series 10	1939	£1.00	£55.00
LF54	Real Photographs Series 11	1939	£0.55	£30.00
XF54	Real Photographs Series 11	1939	£1.00	£54.00
LF54	Real Photographs Series 12	1939	£0.60	£32.00
LF54	Real Photographs Series 13	1939	£0.55	£30.00
LF36	Real Photographs Of Famous Landmarks	1939	£3.35	£120.00
XF36	Real Photographs Of Famous Landmarks	1939	£1.75	£63.00
LF36	Real Photographs Of Modern Aircraft	1939	£4.40	–
XF36	Real Photographs Of Modern Aircraft	1939	£3.35	£120.00
L30	Rembrandt Series	1914	£3.90	–
L40	Ditto (Splendo Cigarettes)	1914	£15.50	£600.00
X30	Rembrandt Series	1914	£6.50	–
L30	Rubens Series	1916	£3.00	£90.00
L30	("N.Z." At Base)	1916	£20.00	–
L30	(Splendo Cigarettes)	1916	£18.00	–
L30	(Winfred Cigarettes)	1916	£18.00	–
100	Scenes From Big Films	1935	£2.00	£200.00
M100	Scenes From Big Films	1935	£4.25	–
X20	Ships Of The Royal Navy (Package)	1953	£22.50	–
50	Silver Jubilee	1935	£0.70	£35.00
50	Speed Land Sea & Air (State Express)	1935	£1.50	£75.00
50	("Ardath"-NZ)	1935	£2.20	£110.00

8

Sports & Pastimes
T.P. & R. Goodbody, Hudden, Taddy

Transvaal Series
Wills

Types Of London
Carreras Limited

Regimental Mascots
E. Robinson & Sons

Footballers (coloured)
W.A & A.C. Churchman

War Portraits
Themans & Co

V.C. Heroes
Thomson & Porteous

Girls, Flags & Arms Of
Countries
I. Rutter & Co

Military Series
John Player & Sons

ARDATH TOBACCO CO. LTD. – cont.

Qty		Date	Odds	Sets
X25	Speed Land Sea & Air (Different)	1938	£1.70	£42.50
50	Sports Champions (Title In 1 Line)	1935	£1.30	£65.00
50	(Title In 2 Lines-NZ)	1935	£2.20	£110.00
6	Sportsmen (Double Ace)	1953	£5.50	—
50	Stamps Rare & Interesting	1939	£1.50	£75.00
50	Swimming Diving And Life-Saving	1937	£1.90	£95.00
50	Tennis	1938	£2.20	£110.00
L?	The Beauty Of State Express (Circular)	1928	£100.00	—
9	The Office Of Chief Whip	1955	£3.25	—
X?3	Theatre Actresses Smoking (2 Sizes)	1915	£42.50	—
48	Trooping The Colour (Sect)	1939	£2.10	£100.00
L?12	Types Of English Manhood (Circular)	1935	£80.00	—
X12	Types Of Smokers	1914	£80.00	—
M1	Union Jack Folder	1943	—	£8.00
L30	Velasquez Series	1916	£3.70	£110.00
X30	Velasquez Series	1916	£6.50	—
50	Who Is This? (Film Stars)	1936	£2.20	£110.00
X?5	Wonderful Handcraft	1935	£50.00	—
X24/25	World Views (2 Printings)	1937	£0.50	£12.00
50	Your Birthday Tells Your Fortune	1937	£0.85	£42.50

ASSOCIATED TOBACCO MANUFACTURERS

Qty		Date	Odds	Sets
25	Cinema Stars (5 Backs)	1926	£35.00	—

ATKINSON (TOBACCONIST)

Qty		Date	Odds	Sets
30	Army Pictures, Cartoons, etc."	1916	£135.00	—

AVISS BROS. LTD.

Qty		Date	Odds	Sets
40	Naval & Military Phrases	1904	£225.00	—

J.A. BAILEY

Qty		Date	Odds	Sets
40	Naval & Military Phrases	1904	£275.00	—

A. BAKER & CO. LTD.

Qty		Date	Odds	Sets
25	Actresses, 3 Sizes"	1901	£33.00	£825.00
P25	Actresses, 3 Sizes (As Small)	1901	£240.00	—
L25	Actresses, 3 Sizes (Different)	1901	£50.00	—
20	Actresses BLARM (Back Design 58mm Long)	1900	£30.00	—
20	(Back Design 64mm Long)	1900	£32.00	—
10	Actresses "HAGG"	1900	£32.00	£320.00
41	Baker's Tobacconists Shops			
	(Cigar etc. Manufacturers)	1901	£150.00	—
	(Try Our 3 1/2d Tobaccos)	1901	£250.00	—
25	Beauties Of All Nations (Albert Baker)	1898	£22.00	£550.00
25	(A.Baker)	1899	£16.00	£400.00
16	British Royal Family	1902	£45.00	—
20	Cricketers Series	1902	£300.00	—
25	Star Girls	1898	£220.00	—

BAYLEY AND HOLDSWORTH

Qty		Date	Odds	Sets
26	Flag Signalling Code Series	1912	£180.00	—

THOMAS BEAR & SONS LTD.

Qty		Date	Odds	Sets
50	Aeroplanes	1926	£4.25	—
50	Cinema Artistes,Set 2"	1936	£3.60	—
50	Cinema Artistes,Set 4"	1937	£3.85	—
50	Cinema Stars "BAMT" (2 Printings)	1928	£2.80	—
50	Do You Know?	1923	£1.80	£90.00
270	Javanese Series (Blue)	1925	£1.75	—
100	Javanese Series (Yellow)	1925	£7.00	—
50	Stage And Film Stars	1926	£4.00	—

E.C.BEESTON

30	Army Pictures,Cartoons,etc.	1916	£135.00	—

BELFAST SHIP STORES CO LTD

?10	Dickens Characters Burlesqued	1893	£1,000.00	—

J.& F.BELL LTD

10	Actresses "HAGG"	1900	£80.00	—
25	Beauties (Scotia Back)	1897	£120.00	—
25	(Three Bells Back)	1897	£120.00	—
25	Colonial Series	1901	£45.00	—
30	Footballers	1902	£67.50	—
60	Rigsvaabner	1925	£25.00	—
25	Scottish Clan Series	1903	£16.00	£475.00
60	Women Of All Nations (Printed Back)	1925	£25.00	£1,500.00
60	(Plain Back)	1925	£15.00	—

R. BELLWOOD

18	Motor Cycle Series	1913	£130.00	—

RICHARD BENSON LTD.

L23/24	Old Bristol Series	1925	£3.20	£75.00
X24	Old Bristol Series (Re-Issue)	1946	£2.00	£48.00

BENSON & HEDGES LTD.

1	Advertisement Card, Original Shop	1973	—	£2.00
48	Ancient & Modern Fire Fighting Equipment	1947	£6.25	£300.00
L10	B.E.A. Aircraft	1958	£8.50	—
50	Friendly Games	1970	£1.25	—
X?12	"Oxford" University Series"	1912	£35.00	—

FELIX S. BERLYN

25	Burline Mixture (Golfers Blend) Series	1910	£400.00	—
P25	Burline Mixture (Golfers Blend) Series	1910	£650.00	—

BERRY'S

20	London Views	1904	£260.00	—

BEWLAY & CO.

6	Comic Advertisement Cards (7 Backs)	1909	£150.00	—
P6	Comic Advertisement Cards	1909	£110.00	£660.00
12	War Series (Portraits, Multi-Backed)	1915	£12.50	£150.00
12	(Portraits, Plain Backed)	1915	£11.00	—

BEWLAY & CO. – cont.

Qty		Date	Odds	Sets
25	War Series (Scenes, Modern Man Cigarettes)	1915	£13.00	£325.00
25	(Scenes, Modern Man Mixture)	1915	£13.00	£325.00
25	(Scenes, Two Great Favourites)	1915	£13.00	£325.00

W.O. BIGG & CO.

37	Flags Of All Nations (Horizontal Back)	1904	£8.75	—
37	(Vertical Back)	1904	£8.75	—
50	Life On Board A Man Of War	1905	£11.00	£550.00

JAS. BIGGS & SONS

26	Actresses "FROGA A" (Brand In Black)	1900	£50.00	—
26	(Brand In White)	1900	£40.00	—
26	Actresses "FROGA B"	1900	£50.00	—
25	Beauties "BOCCA" (Black Back)	1900	£75.00	—
25	(Blue Back)	1900	£75.00	—
25	Beauties "CHOAB" (Blue Back)	1902	£75.00	—
50	(Black Overprint)	1902	£75.00	—
30	Colonial Troops	1901	£35.00	—
30	Flags & Flags With Soldiers	1903	£32.50	—
25	Star Girls	1900	£260.00	—

J.S. BILLINGHAM

30	Army Pictures,Cartoons,etc.	1916	£135.00	—

R. BINNS

?17	Halifax Town Footballers	1924	£160.00	—

BLANKS CIGARETTES

50	Keystrokes In Break-Building	1910	£600.00	—

BOCNAL TOBACCO CO.

25	Luminous Silhouettes Of Beauty &Charm	1938	£3.00	£75.00
25	Proverbs Up-To-Date	1938	£2.00	£50.00

ALEXANDER BOGUSLAVSKY LTD.

P12	Big Events On The Turf	1924	£45.00	—
25	Conan Doyle Characters (Black Back)	1923	£7.00	£175.00
25	(Green Back)	1923	£6.50	£162.50
25	Mythological Gods And Goddesses	1924	£2.80	£70.00
25	Sports Records (1-25)	1925	£1.90	£47.50
25	Sports Records, 2nd Series (26-50)	1925	£2.20	£55.00
25	Winners On The Turf (Name No Serifs)	1925	£3.60	£90.00
25	(Name With Serifs)	1925	£5.25	—
L25	Winners On The Turf	1925	£5.60	£140.00

R. & E. BOYD LTD.

25	Places Of Interest	1938	£75.00	—
M25	Places Of Interest	1938	£65.00	—
L25	Wild Birds At Home	1938	£70.00	—

11

WM. BRADFORD

Qty		Date	Odds	Sets
50	Beauties "CHOAB"	1902	£36.00	—
?7	Beauties, Jersey Lily"	1900	£550.00	—
20	Boer War Cartoons	1901	£120.00	—

THOS. BRANKSTON & CO. LTD.

30	Colonial Troops (Golf Club Mixture)	1901	£32.50	—
30	(Red Virginia)	1901	£32.50	—
30	(Sweet As The Rose)	1901	£32.50	—
12	Pretty Girl Series "RASH"	1900	£375.00	—

BRIGHAM & CO.

L16	Down The Thames From Henley To Windsor	1912	£160.00	—
16	Reading Football Players	1912	£425.00	—
X3	Tobacco Growing In Hampshire, England	1928	£15.00	£45.00

BRITANNIA ANONYMOUS SOCIETY

?31	Beauties & Couples	1914	£80.00	—

BRITISH & COLONIAL TOBACCO CO.

25	Armies Of The World	1900	£210.00	—

J.M. BROWN

30	Army Pictures, Cartoons, etc.	1916	£120.00	—

ROBERT BRUCE LTD.

18	Motor Cycle Series	1913	£300.00	—

JOHN BRUMFIT

50	The Public Schools Ties Series (Old Boys)	1925	£4.00	£200.00

BUCKTROUT & CO.LTD.(Channel Isles)

M416	Around The World/Places Of Interest	1924	£0.50	£210.00
24	Birds Of England	1924	£3.25	£75.00
50	Cinema Stars,1st	1926	£2.00	£100.00
50	Cinema Stars,S econd Series	1927	£2.20	£110.00
M50	Football Teams	1928	£3.40	£170.00
L22	Football Teams Of The Bailiwick	1927	£1.10	£24.00
123	Guernsey Footballers (Multi-Backed)	1923	£3.25	—
20	Inventors Series	1924	£1.40	£28.00
25	Marvels Of The Universe Series	1919	£2.60	£65.00
M54	Playing Cards	1930	£0.75	£40.00
25	Sports & Pastimes	1926	£5.00	£150.00

G.A.BULLOGH (Tobacconist)

30	Army Pictures,Cartoons,etc.	1916	£130.00	—

BURSTEIN ISAACS & CO. LTD.

50	Famous Prize Fighters (Names Capitals)	1923	£7.50	—
50	(Mixed Letters)	1923	£6.80	£340.00
F27/28	London View Series	1922	£3.75	£105.00

BYRT WOOD & CO.

Qty		Date	Odds	Sets
?35	Pretty Girl Series "BAGG"...	1900	£150.00	—

CABANA CIGAR CO.

40	Home & Colonial Regiments (C.C.C.).................................	1901	£375.00	—
M1	Little Manturios Advert Card (4 Types)..............................	1904	—	£350.00

PERCY E. CADLE & CO.

20	Actresses "BLARM"..	1900	£37.50	—
26	Actresses "FROGA" (Brown, Printed Back)........................	1900	£37.00	—
26	(Brown, Stamped Back)......................	1900	£220.00	—
26	Actresses "FROGA" (Coloured)...	1900	£50.00	—
?12	Boer War & Boxer Rebellion Sketches	1901	£65.00	—
10	Boer War Generals..	1901	£75.00	—
20	Footballers..	1904	£67.50	£1,350.00

CARRERAS LTD.

F24	Actresses And Their Pets (2 Printings)	1926	£5.25	£125.00
50	A Kodak At The Zoo, A Series	1924	£0.70	£35.00
50	A Kodak At The Zoo, 2nd Series	1925	£0.65	£32.50
48	Alice In Wonderland (Round Corners)	1930	£1.60	£80.00
48	(Square Corners)................................	1930	£3.20	£150.00
L48	Alice In Wonderland...	1930	£1.85	£92.00
X1	Alice In Wonderland (Instructions)	1930	—	£14.00
50	Amusing Tricks & How To Do Them...................................	1937	£1.50	£75.00
22	Battle Of Waterloo	1934	£1.50	—
L15	Battle Of Waterloo	1934	£2.50	—
M1	Battle Of Waterloo (Instructions).......................................	1934	—	£12.50
M50	Believe It Or Not..	1934	£0.70	£35.00
50	Birds Of The Countryside	1939	£1.10	£55.00
200	Black Cat Library	1913	£12.50	—
50	Britains Defences..	1938	£0.70	£35.00
25	British Costumes	1927	£1.30	£32.50
L25	British Costumes	1927	£1.30	£32.50
F27	British Prime Ministers..	1928	£1.85	£50.00
1	Calendar	1934	—	£32.00
L24	Canada's Corvettes, 1st Series	1943	£16.00	—
L24	Canada's Corvettes, 2nd Series	1944	£17.00	—
50	Celebrities Of British History...	1935	£1.00	£50.00
25	Christie Comedy Girls..	1928	£2.00	£50.00
30	Cricketers..	1934	£3.50	£105.00
50	Cricketers (A Series Of 50, Brown)	1934	£3.40	£170.00
50	(A Series Of 50, Black)	1934	£40.00	—
F50	Dogs & Friend	1936	£0.50	£25.00
50	Do You Know?...	1939	£0.40	£20.00
50	Famous Airmen & Airwomen	1936	£1.70	£85.00
25	Famous Escapes	1926	£1.50	£37.50
L25	Famous Escapes	1926	£1.60	£40.00
P10	Famous Escapes	1926	£3.20	£32.00
96	Famous Film Stars	1935	£1.35	£130.00
48	Famous Footballers	1935	£1.60	£77.00
24	(25-48 Redrawn)	1935	£1.85	£44.00
25	Famous Men	1927	£1.50	£37.50
LF24	Famous Naval Men..	1929	£2.25	£55.00
X6	Famous Posters (St. Dunstan's)	1923	£26.00	—

CARRERAS LTD. – cont.

Qty		Date	Odds	Sets
LF12	Famous Soldiers	1928	£5.75	£70.00
F27	Famous Women	1929	£1.30	£35.00
25	Figures Of Fiction	1924	£2.20	£55.00
F54	Film & Stage Beauties	1939	£0.50	£27.00
LF54	Film And Stage Beauties (2 Printings)	1939	£0.65	£35.00
LF36	Film And Stage Beauties (2 Printings)	1939	£0.95	£34.00
XF36	Film And Stage Beauties	1939	£1.60	£58.00
50	Film Favourites	1938	£1.50	£75.00
F54	Film Stars, A Series"	1937	£0.85	£45.00
F54	Film Stars, 2nd Series (3 Printings)	1938	£0.55	£30.00
LF54	Film Stars (As 2nd Series)	1938	£1.10	£60.00
XF36	Film Stars (Different)	1936	£3.00	£108.00
XF36	Film Stars, Second Series (Different)	1936	£2.80	£100.00
XF36	Film Stars, Third Series"	1937	£2.80	£100.00
XF36	Film Stars, Fourth Series"	1938	£2.80	£100.00
50	Film Stars (By Desmond)	1936	£1.10	£55.00
72	Film Stars (Oval, Half-Tone)	1934	£1.60	£115.00
F72	(Oval, "Real Photos")	1934	£2.80	–
60	Flags Of All Nations	Unissued	–	£36.00
28	Flag Dominoes (Unissued)	Unissued	£13.00	–
K6	Flags & Arms (Circular)	1915	£55.00	–
K7	Flags Of The Allies (Shaped)	1915	£55.00	–
K?6	Flags Of The Allies (Pin As Mast)	1915	£100.00	–
50	Flowers	1936	£0.50	£25.00
75	Footballers (Large Titles)	1934	£2.25	£168.00
75	(Small Titles)	1934	£2.20	£165.00
36	Fortune Telling (Card Inset)	1926	£0.30	£11.00
36	(Head Inset, Black No.)	1926	£0.25	£9.00
36	B662(Head Inset, Brown No.)	1926	£0.90	£32.50
L36	Fortune Telling (Card Inset)	1926	£0.30	£11.00
L36	(Head Inset)	1926	£0.35	£12.00
X1	Fortune Telling (Instructions)	1926	–	£13.00
F54	Glamour Girls Of Stage And Films	1939	£0.60	£33.00
LF54	Glamour Girls Of Stage And Films	1939	£0.75	£40.00
LF36	Glamour Girls Of Stage And Films	1939	£1.25	£45.00
XF36	Glamour Girls Of Stage And Films	1939	£1.60	£58.00
M50	Gran-Pop	1934	£0.65	£32.00
L50	Gran-Pop	1934	£0.50	£25.00
M16	Guards Series (Sectional)	1970	£0.70	£11.00
M8	Guards Series (Full Length)	1970	£0.70	£6.00
M4	Guards Series (Mugs)	1971	£0.75	£3.00
48	Happy Family	1925	£0.25	£12.00
L48	Happy Family	1925	£0.25	£12.00
25	Highwaymen	1924	£2.50	£62.50
50	History Of Army Uniforms	1937	£1.40	£70.00
50	History Of Guards Uniforms	Unissued	£6.00	–
50	History Of Naval Uniforms	1937	£1.00	£50.00
25	Horses And Hounds	1926	£2.20	£55.00
L20	Horses And Hounds	1926	£2.25	£45.00
P10	Horses And Hounds	1926	£4.20	£42.00
50	Kings & Queens Of England	1935	£1.65	£82.50
L50	Kings & Queens Of England	1935	£2.50	£125.00
L?79	Lace Motifs	1915	£7.25	–
P?15	Lace Motifs (Double Size)	1915	£36.00	–
G?7	Lace Motifs (Quadruple Size)	1915	£80.00	–

CARRERAS LTD. – cont.

Qty		Date	Odds	Sets
F27	Malayan Industries	1929	£0.90	£24.00
F24	Malayan Scenes	1928	£3.50	–
LF24	Malayan Scenes	1928	£0.75	£18.00
7	Millionaire Competition	1971	£2.00	–
K53	Miniature Playing Cards	1934	£0.20	£9.00
50	Notable M.P.s	1929	£1.40	£70.00
L50	Notable M.P.s	1929	£0.85	£42.50
F25	Notable Ships Past & Present	1929	£1.40	£35.00
24	Old Staffordshire Figures	1926	£1.30	£31.50
P12	Old Staffordshire Figures	1926	£2.85	£34.00
L24	Old Staffordshire Figures (Different)	1926	£1.50	£37.50
24	Orchids	1925	£1.25	£30.00
L24	Orchids	1925	£1.15	£28.00
P24	Orchids	1925	£3.35	£80.00
50	Our Navy	1937	£1.10	£55.00
50	Palmistry	1933	£0.70	£35.00
F27	Paramount Stars	1929	£2.10	£56.00
25	Picture Puzzle Series	1923	£1.50	£37.50
52	Playing Cards	1926	£1.20	–
52	Playing Cards & Dominoes (Numbered)	1929	£0.30	£15.00
52	(Unnumbered)	1929	£0.25	£13.00
L26	Playing Cards & Dominoes (Numbered)	1929	£0.50	£13.00
L26	(Unnumbered)	1929	£0.75	£20.00
48	Popular Footballers	1936	£1.30	£62.50
72	Popular Personalities (Oval)	1935	£1.00	£72.00
10	Irish Subjects (1-10)	1935	£18.00	–
E12	Premium Silks (Assorted Subjects)	1914	£180.00	–
25	Races-Historic & Modern	1927	£2.30	£57.50
L25	Races-Historic & Modern	1927	£2.50	£62.50
P12	Races-Historic & Modern	1927	£5.25	£63.00
50	Radio & Television Favourites (Unissued)	Unissued	£8.50	–
140	Raemaekers War Cartoons (Black Cat)	1916	£1.15	£160.00
140	(Carreras)	1916	£3.85	–
25	Regalia Series	1925	£0.60	£15.00
L20	Regalia Series	1925	£0.60	£12.00
P10	Regalia Series	1925	£2.20	£22.00
L50	Round The World Scenic Models	1925	£0.85	£42.50
50	School Emblems	1929	£0.85	£42.50
L40	School Emblems	1929	£0.80	£32.00
P20	School Emblems	1929	£2.40	£48.00
M20	Sport Fish (Canada)	1986	£3.30	–
L216	Sportsman's Guide-Fly Fishing (Canada)	1950	£1.70	–
48	Tapestry Reproductions Of Paintings (Sect.)	1938	£0.50	£24.00
52	The Greyhound Racing Game	1926	£0.22	£11.00
L52	The Greyhound Racing Game	1926	£0.22	£11.00
X1	The Greyhound Racing Game (Instructions)	1926	–	£13.00
M5	The Handy English-French Dictionary	1915	£25.00	–
50	The Nose Game	1927	£0.45	£22.50
L50	The Nose Game	1927	£0.45	£22.50
X1	The Nose Game (Instructions)	1927	–	£13.00
50	The Science Of Boxing (Black Cat)	1914	£2.60	£130.00
50	(Carreras)	1914	£5.25	–
50	Tools And How To Use Them	1935	£2.20	£110.00
80	Types Of London	1919	£1.50	£120.00
F27	Views Of London	1929	£0.50	£13.50

CARRERAS LTD. – cont.

Qty		Date	Odds	Sets
F27	Views Of The World	1927	£0.75	£20.00
M15/20	Wild Animals (Canada)	1985	£0.45	£7.00
25	Wild Flower Art Series	1923	£1.30	£32.50
50	Women On War Work	1916	£7.25	£362.50

TURF SLIDES (Cut to Size - Uncut slides available at double price)

Qty		Date	Odds	Sets
50	British Aircraft	1953	£0.85	£42.50
50	British Fish	1954	£0.35	£17.50
50	British Railway Locomotives	1952	£0.85	£42.50
50	Celebrities Of British History	1951	£0.70	£35.00
50	Famous British Fliers	1956	£3.25	–
50	Famous Cricketers	1950	£3.20	£160.00
50	Famous Dog Breeds	1952	£1.00	£50.00
50	Famous Film Stars	1949	£1.70	£85.00
50	Famous Footballers	1951	£2.50	£125.00
50	Film Favourites	1948	£2.20	£110.00
50	Film Stars	1947	£1.70	£85.00
50	Footballers	1948	£2.50	£125.00
50	Olympics 1948	1948	£3.20	£160.00
50	Radio Celebrities	1950	£0.65	£32.50
50	Sports	1949	£1.90	£95.00
50	Zoo Animals	1954	£0.20	£10.00

"BLACK CAT" MODERN ISSUES

Qty		Date	Odds	Sets
50	British Birds	1976	£0.20	£5.00
50	Flowers All The Year Round	1977	£0.20	£10.00
50	Kings & Queens Of England	1977	£0.25	£12.50
50	Military Uniforms	1976	£0.15	£5.00
50	Palmistry	1979	£1.40	£70.00
50	Sport Fish	1978	£0.20	£8.00
50	Vintage Cars (With "Filter")	1976	£0.20	£8.00
50	(Without "Filter")	1976	£0.20	£8.00

AUSTRALIAN ISSUES

Qty		Date	Odds	Sets
72	Film Stars Series (Smile Away)	1933	£3.25	–
72	(Standard)	1933	£1.50	£108.00
72	Football Series	1933	£3.00	£216.00
24	Personality Series	1933	£2.60	£62.00
72	Personality Series, Film Stars"	1933	£1.25	£90.00
72	Personality Series, Footballers"	1933	£3.00	£216.00

CARRERAS & MARCIANUS

Qty		Date	Odds	Sets
1	Photo Miniatures Folder (3 Printings)	1909	–	£110.00
100	War Series	1915	£85.00	–

CARRICK

Qty		Date	Odds	Sets
12	Military Terms	1900	£80.00	–

P.J. CARROLL & CO.

Qty		Date	Odds	Sets
25	Birds	1939	£0.90	£22.50
25	British Naval Series	1915	£42.50	–
25	Derby Winners (Black Back)	1914	£110.00	–
25	(Green Back)	1914	£130.00	–
K26	Grand Slam Spelling Bee Cards	1936	£16.50	–
24	Jig - Saw Puzzles	1935	£18.00	–

P.J. CARROLL & CO. – cont.

Qty		Date	Odds	Sets
20	Louth All-Ireland Champions	1912	£32.50	—
25	Ship Series	1934	£10.00	£250.00
M24	The Irish Open Golf Championship ....Unissued		£12.50	—

THE CASKET TOBACCO & CIG. CO. LTD.

?1	Bowling Fixture Cards	1909	£500.00	—
?5	Cricket Fixture Cards	1905	£500.00	—
?2	Cyclists Lighting Up Table	1909	£500.00	—
?17	Football Fixture Cards	1909	£500.00	—
?49	Road Maps	1909	£450.00	—

S. CAVANDER & CO.

?50	Beauties "PLUMS"	1898	£600.00	—

CAVANDERS LTD.

25	Ancient Chinese	1926	£1.70	£42.50
25	Ancient Egypt	1928	£1.50	£37.50
L25	Ancient Egypt (Different)	1928	£1.60	£40.00
F36	Animal Studies	1936	£0.40	£15.00
F50	Beauty Spots Of Great Britain	1927	£0.30	£15.00
MF50	Beauty Spots Of Great Britain	1927	£0.30	£15.00
F54	Camera Studies	1926	£0.20	£11.00
MF56	Camera Studies	1926	£0.20	£12.00
30	Cinema Stars	1934	£1.35	£40.00
MS50	Coloured Stereoscopic	1931	£0.65	£32.50
25	Feathered Friends	1926	£2.60	£65.00
25	Foreign Birds (Same Subjects As Above)	1926	£1.60	£40.00
MS50	Glorious Britain	1930	£0.60	£30.00
25	Little Friends	1924	£1.00	£25.00
FS72	Peeps Into Many Lands, A Series"	1927	£0.45	£32.00
MFS72	Peeps Into Many Lands, A Series (Different)	1927	£0.85	£62.00
XFS36	Peeps Into Many Lands, A Series (Different)	1927	£2.20	£80.00
FS72	Peeps Into Many Lands 2nd Series	1928	£1.10	£80.00
MFS72	Peeps Into Many Lands 2nd Series (Different)	1928	£1.10	£80.00
FS48	Peeps Into Many Lands 3rd Series	1929	£0.40	£20.00
MFS48	Peeps Into Many Lands 3rd Series (Different)	1929	£1.10	£52.50
MFS48	(Reprinted)	1929	£1.60	£78.00
FS48	Peeps Into Prehistoric Times 4th Series	1930	£0.80	£40.00
MFS48	Peeps Into Prehistoric Times 4th Series (Different)	1930	£1.50	£72.00
F33	Photographs	1935	£1.50	£50.00
L48	Regimental Standards	1923	£12.00	—
25	Reproductions Of Celebrated Oil Paintings	1925	£1.30	£32.50
F108	River Valleys	1926	£0.25	£26.00
MF108	River Valleys	1926	£0.30	£31.50
25	School Badges (Dark Blue Back)	1928	£1.00	£25.00
25	(Light Blue Back)	1928	£1.00	£25.00
MF30	The Colonial Series (Large Captions)	1925	£0.45	£13.50
MF30	(Small Captions)	1925	£0.35	£10.50
F54	The Homeland Series (Black Back)	1924	£0.30	£17.50
F50	(Blue Back)	1924	£1.10	£55.00
MF50	The Homeland Series "Hand Coloured"	1924	£0.35	£17.50
MF56	"Real Photos"	1924	£0.55	£32.00
MF56	Uncoloured	1924	£0.70	£40.00
MF56	"Reprinted"	1925	£0.55	£32.00

Qty		Date	Odds	Sets
M25	The Nation's Treasures..	1925	£0.50	£12.50
MF30	Wordsworth's Country..	1926	£0.85	£25.00

R.S. CHALLIS & CO. LTD.

Qty		Date	Odds	Sets
50	Comic Animals...	1936	£0.80	£40.00
?44	Flickits (Fresher Cigarettes)	1936	£38.50	–
36	Wild Birds At Home (Baldric Cigarettes).....................	1935	£0.70	£25.00
36	(Baldric Deleted)	1935	£1.30	–

H CHAPMAN & CO

Qty		Date	Odds	Sets
30	Army Pictures, Cartoons, etc..............................	1916	£210.00	–

CHARLESWORTH & AUSTIN

Qty		Date	Odds	Sets
50	Beauties "BOCCA"	1900	£33.00	£1,650.00
16	British Royal Family	1902	£48.00	–
50	Colonial Troops (Black Back)................................	1901	£38.00	–
30	(Brown Back)	1901	£36.00	–
20	Cricketers Series..	1902	£320.00	–
30	Flags & Flags With Soldiers	1903	£35.00	–

CHESTERFIELD CIGARETTES

Qty		Date	Odds	Sets
M6	Chesterfield Cocktails..	1980	£0.50	£3.00

A. CHEW & CO.

Qty		Date	Odds	Sets
30	Army Pictures, Cartoons, etc..............................	1916	£150.00	–

CHING & CO. (Channel Isles)

Qty		Date	Odds	Sets
L24	Around & About In Jersey, 1st Series.....................	1963	£0.30	£7.50
L24	Around & About In Jersey, 2nd Series....................	1964	£0.60	£15.00
25	Do You Know?...	1962	–	£3.00
M48	Flowers...	1962	£1.00	£48.00
L24	Jersey Past & Present, A Series	1960	–	£6.50
L24	Jersey Past & Present, Second Series	1962	£0.80	£20.00
L24	Jersey Past & Present, Third Series	1963	–	£6.50
25	Ships And Their Workings	1961	–	£3.00
50	Veteran And Vintage Cars (Mauve)........................	1960	£0.60	£30.00
25	(Blue, 26-50)	1960	£1.25	–

W.A. & A.C. CHURCHMAN

Qty		Date	Odds	Sets
24	Actresses, Unicoloured (Blue Printing)	1897	£85.00	–
24	(Brown Printing)	1897	£85.00	–
26	Actresses, "FROGA A"	1900	£36.00	–
26	Actresses, "FROGA B"	1900	£45.00	–
M48	Air-Raid Precautions...	1938	£0.25	£12.00
25	Army Badges Of Rank	1916	£4.60	£115.00
50	Association Footballers, A Series	1938	£0.85	£42.50
50	Association Footballers, 2nd Series	1939	£1.25	£62.50
50	A Tour Round The World	1911	£7.00	£350.00
12	Beauties "CERF"..	1899	£65.00	£780.00
25	Beauties "CHOAB"	1900	£125.00	–
M?25	Beauties "CHOAB" (Circular).................................	1900	£1,500.00	–
25	Beauties "FECKSA"..	1903	£95.00	–

W.A. & A.C. CHURCHMAN – cont.

Qty		Date	Odds	Sets
25	Beauties "GRACC"	1898	£100.00	—
50	Birds & Eggs	1906	£7.00	£350.00
20	Boer War Cartoons	1901	£110.00	—
41	Boer War Celebrities & Actresses	1901	£21.00	£860.00
20	Boer War Generals "CLAM" (Black)	1901	£36.00	—
20	Boer War Generals "CLAM" (Brown)	1901	£35.00	£700.00
25	Boxing	1922	£5.20	£130.00
50	Boxing Personalities	1938	£1.60	£100.00
50	Boy Scouts, A Series"	1916	£7.20	£360.00
50	Boy Scouts, 2nd Series"	1916	£7.20	£360.00
50	Boy Scouts, 3rd Series (Blue Back)	1916	£11.00	—
50	(Brown Back)	1916	£7.20	£360.00
25	British Film Stars	1934	£2.50	£62.50
54/55	Can You Beat Bogey At St. Andrews?	1934	£2.10	£190.00
54/55	(Red Overprint)	1934	£2.25	£200.00
25	Cathedrals & Churches	1924	£2.00	£50.00
X12	Cathedrals & Churches	1924	£11.00	£132.00
50	Celebrated Gateways	1925	£1.90	£95.00
M1	Christmas Greeting Card	1938	—	£2.00
25	Civic Insignia And Plate	1926	£2.00	£50.00
50	Contract Bridge	1935	£0.90	£45.00
50	Cricketers	1936	£3.20	£160.00
25	Curious Dwellings	1926	£2.20	£55.00
L12	Curious Dwellings	1926	£6.50	£78.00
25	Curious Signs	1925	£2.20	£55.00
38	Dogs And Fowls	1908	£7.75	£295.00
25	Eastern Proverbs A Series	1931	£0.80	£20.00
L12	Eastern Proverbs A Series	1931	£4.20	£50.00
25	Eastern Proverbs 2nd Series	1932	£0.80	£20.00
L12	Eastern Proverbs 2nd Series	1932	£2.50	£30.00
L12	Eastern Proverbs 3rd Series	1933	£3.00	£36.00
L12	Eastern Proverbs 4th Series	1934	£2.00	£24.00
50	East Suffolk Churches (Black Front)	1912	£1.90	£95.00
50	(Sepia Front)	1917	£1.60	£80.00
50	Empire Railways	1931	£2.60	£130.00
25	Famous Cricket Colours	1928	£3.80	£95.00
50	Famous Golfers	1927	£10.00	£700.00
L12	Famous Golfers, A Series	1927	£30.00	—
L12	Famous Golfers, 2nd Series	1928	£30.00	—
25	Famous Railway Trains	1929	£2.60	£65.00
L12	Famous Railway Trains, A Series	1929	£7.50	£90.00
L12	Famous Railway Trains, 2nd Series	1929	£5.50	£66.00
50	Fish & Bait	1914	£6.70	£335.00
50	Fishes Of The World	1912	—	£275.00
30/50	Fishes Of The World (as above)	1924	£1.60	£48.00
50	Flags & Funnels Of Leading Steamship Lines	1912	£7.00	£350.00
50	Football Club Colours	1909	£11.00	—
50	Footballers (Brown)	1914	£35.00	£1,750.00
50	Footballers (Coloured)	1914	£17.00	£850.00
52	Frisky	1935	£3.60	£185.00
1	Frisky (Instructions)	1935	—	£12.00
50	History & Development Of The British Empire	1934	£2.00	£100.00
M48	Holidays In Britain (Views & Maps)	1937	£0.25	£12.00
M48	Holidays In Britain (Views Only)	1938	£0.20	£10.00
40	Home & Colonial Regiments	1902	£55.00	—

W.A. & A.C. CHURCHMAN – cont.

Qty		Date	Odds	Sets
40	Howlers	1937	£0.30	£12.00
L16	Howlers	1937	£0.50	£8.00
50	Interesting Buildings	1905	£7.75	£387.50
25	Interesting Door-Knockers	1928	£2.50	£62.50
25	Interesting Experiments	1929	£1.60	£40.00
50	In Town To-Night	1938	£0.50	£25.00
L12	Italian Art Exhibition, 1930, 1st Series	1930	£2.75	£33.00
L12	Italian Art Exhibition, 1930, 2nd Series	1931	£1.50	£18.00
50	Kings Of Speed	1939	£0.65	£32.50
50	Landmarks In Railway Progress	1931	£2.80	£140.00
L12	Landmarks In Railway Progress, 1st Series	1932	£5.25	£63.00
L12	Landmarks In Railway Progress, 2nd Series	1932	£6.25	£75.00
50	Lawn Tennis	1928	£4.00	£200.00
L12	Lawn Tennis	1928	£12.50	£150.00
50	Legends Of Britain	1936	£0.90	£45.00
L12	Legends Of Britain	1936	£1.50	£18.00
25	Life In A Liner	1930	£1.70	£42.50
L12	Life In A Liner	1930	£5.70	£68.00
50	Medals	1910	£7.20	£360.00
50	Men Of The Moment In Sport	1928	£2.60	£260.00
L12	Men Of The Moment In Sport, 1st Series	1928	£8.50	£300.00
L12	Men Of The Moment In Sport, 2nd Series	1928	£8.75	—
M48	Modern Wonders	1938	£0.25	£12.00
25	Musical Instruments	1924	£3.60	£90.00
25	Nature's Architects	1930	£1.30	£32.50
L12	Nature's Architects	1930	£2.00	£24.00
D55	Olympic Winners Through The Years	1960	£1.80	—
50	Phil May Sketches (Gold Flake)	1912	£6.80	£340.00
50	(No Brand)	1912	£7.80	£390.00
25	Pipes Of The World	1927	£3.00	£75.00
50	Prominent Golfers	1931	£8.50	£525.00
L12	Prominent Golfers	1931	£20.00	£400.00
50	Racing Greyhounds	1934	£2.70	£135.00
25	Railway Working, A Series	1926	£3.80	£95.00
L12	Railway Working, A Series	1926	£10.00	—
25	Railway Working, 2nd Series	1927	£2.50	£62.50
L13	Railway Working, 2nd Series	1926	£10.00	—
L12	Railway Working, 3rd Series	1927	£9.50	£115.00
50	Regimental Colours & Cap Badges	1912	£7.20	£360.00
50	Rivers & Broads	1921	£6.00	£300.00
50	Rivers & Broads Of Norfolk & Suffolk	1922	£4.20	£210.00
50	Rugby Internationals	1935	£1.90	£95.00
50	Sectional Cycling Map	1913	£6.00	£300.00
50	Silhouettes Of Warships	1915	£9.00	£450.00
50	Sporting Celebrities	1931	£2.60	£180.00
25	Sporting Trophies	1927	£2.50	£62.50
L12	Sporting Trophies	1927	£6.25	£75.00
25	Sports & Games In Many Lands	1929	£3.25	£160.00
25	The Houses Of Parliament & Their Story	1931	£2.20	£55.00
25	The Inns Of Court	1922	£2.90	£72.50
50	The King's Coronation	1937	£0.20	£10.00
L15	The King's Coronation	1937	£0.80	£12.00
M48	The Navy At Work	1937	£0.50	£24.00
50	The Queen Mary	1936	£1.60	£80.00
L16	The Queen Mary	1936	£3.25	£52.00

Qty		Date	Odds	Sets
M48	The RAF At Work	1937	£1.00	£48.00
50	The Story Of London	1934	£1.80	£90.00
L12	The Story Of London	1934	£3.00	£36.00
50	The Story Of Navigation	1937	£0.55	£27.50
L12	The Story Of Navigation	1937	£1.25	£15.00
D40	The World Of Sport	1961	£1.80	–
36	3 Jovial Golfers	1934	£3.75	£135.00
73	3 Jovial Golfers (Irish Issue)	1934	£8.00	–
50	Treasure Trove	1937	£0.35	£17.50
L12	Treasure Trove	1937	£1.35	£16.00
25	Types Of British & Colonial Troops	1899	£45.00	–
25	Warriors Of All Nations	1929	£3.00	£75.00
L12	Warriors Of All Nations A Series	1929	£3.90	£47.00
L12	Warriors Of All Nations 2nd Series	1931	£4.15	£50.00
50	Well-Known Ties, A Series	1934	£0.80	£40.00
L12	Well-Known Ties, A Series	1934	£2.00	£24.00
50	Well-Known Ties, Second Series	1935	£0.75	£37.50
L12	Well-Known Ties, 2nd Series	1935	£1.65	£20.00
25	Wembley Exhibition (2 Printings)	1924	£2.50	£62.50
50	West Suffolk Churches	1919	£1.60	£80.00
50	Wild Animals Of The World	1907	£7.50	£375.00
M48	Wings Over The Empire	1939	£0.60	£26.50
50	Wonderful Railway Travel	1937	£0.50	£25.00
L12	Wonderful Railway Travel	1937	£1.60	£20.00
50	World Wonders Old And New ....Unissued		–	£20.00

OVERSEAS ISSUES (NO I.T.C CLAUSE)

Qty		Date	Odds	Sets
M48	Air-Raid Precautions	1938	£1.80	–
M48	Holidays In Britain (Views & Maps)	1937	£1.80	–
M48	Holidays In Britain (Views Only)	1938	£1.80	–
M48	Modern Wonders (Plain Base)	1938	£1.80	£86.00
M48	(Silver Line At Base)	1938	£5.00	–
M48	The Navy At Work	1937	£2.00	£96.00
M48	The R.A.F. At Work	1937	£2.00	–
25	Warriors Of All Nations (No Name on Front)	1929	£9.00	–
M48	Wings Over The Empire	1939	£2.00	–

CIGARETTE COMPANY (Channel Isles)

Qty		Date	Odds	Sets
72	Jersey Footballers (Blue Background)	1910	£6.50	–
50	Jersey Footballers (Grey Background)	1910	£6.50	–
?53	Jersey Footballers (No Frame For Name)	1910	£16.50	–

WM. CLARKE & SON

Qty		Date	Odds	Sets
25	Army Life	1915	£13.00	£325.00
16	Boer War Celebrities	1901	£25.00	£400.00
50	Butterflies & Moths	1912	£8.50	£425.00
30	Cricketer Series	1901	£165.00	–
66	Football Series	1902	£32.00	–
25	Marine Series	1907	£15.00	£375.00
50	Royal Mail	1914	£12.00	£600.00
50	Sporting Terms (Multi-Backed)	1900	£50.00	–
20	Tobacco Leaf Girls	1898	£400.00	–
25	Well-Known Sayings	1900	£26.00	£650.00

J.H. CLURE & SON

Qty		Date	Odds	Sets
30	Army Pictures, Cartoons, Etc (No Brands)	1916	£125.00	—
30	(Havana Mixture)	1916	£125.00	—
50	War Portraits	1916	£110.00	—

J. LOMAX COCKAYNE

Qty		Date	Odds	Sets
50	War Portraits	1916	£100.00	—

COHEN WEENEN & CO.

Qty		Date	Odds	Sets
F40	Actresses, Footballers & Jockeys	1901	£52.50	—
26	Actresses "FROGA"	1900	£65.00	—
?119	Bandmaster Conundrums	1907	£11.00	—
25	Beauties "BOCCA"	1899	£75.00	—
25	Beauties "GRACC"	1899	£110.00	—
65	Celebrities, Black & White ("250"Back)	1900	£5.50	—
20	("500"Back)	1900	£11.00	—
45	Boer War Celebrities, Coloured ("100" Back)	1901	£5.00	£225.00
45	("250" Back)	1901	£9.00	—
76	Celebrities, Coloured ("250", Different)	1901	£6.00	£450.00
30	Celebrities, Gainsborough ("400"Back)	1902	£13.00	£390.00
M39	("250"Back)	1902	£50.00	—
M40	(Metal Frame)	1902	£70.00	—
MF?177	Celebrities, Gainsborough (No Frame)	1901	£5.00	—
MF?177	(Metal Frame)	1901	£16.50	—
25	Cricketers	1926	£16.00	£400.00
20	Cricketers, Footballers & Jockeys	1900	£23.00	£460.00
25	Famous Boxers (Black Back)	1912	£17.00	—
25	(Green Back)	1912	£11.50	£460.00
25	(Anonymous)	1912	£18.00	—
40	Fiscal Phrases (Copyright Registered)	1902	£12.00	£480.00
40	(No Copyright Clause)	1902	£12.00	£480.00
60	Football Captains 1907-8	1908	£14.50	£870.00
100	Heroes Of Sport	1897	£90.00	—
40	Home & Colonial Regiments ("100"Back)	1901	£9.00	£360.00
40	("250"Back)	1901	£13.00	—
40	(Gold Border)	1901	£165.00	—
20	Interesting Buildings & Views (Plain)	1902	£12.00	£240.00
20	(Gold Surround)	1902	£130.00	—
K52	Miniature Playing Cards (Bandmaster)	1910	£4.25	£220.00
20	Nations (Non Descriptive)	1902	£12.50	£250.00
20	(Descriptive)	1923	£4.75	£95.00
40	Naval & Military-Phrases (Blue Back)	1904	£28.00	—
40	(Red Back)	1906	£17.00	£680.00
40	(Gold Border)	1906	£125.00	—
50	Owners, Jockeys, Footballers, Cricketers Series 2	1906	£15.00	£750.00
20	Owners, Jockeys, Footballers, Cricketers Series 3	1907	£16.00	£320.00
30	Proverbs	1903	£16.00	£480.00
20	Russo Japanese War Series	1904	£20.00	£400.00
25	Silhouettes Of Celebrities	1903	£13.00	£375.00
50	Star Artistes	1907	£11.50	£575.00
L16	Victoria Cross Heroes (Silk)	1915	£40.00	—
50	Victoria Cross Heroes (51-100)	1916	£11.50	£575.00
25	(51-75, Anonymous)	1916	£15.00	—
50	War Series	1916	£11.00	£550.00

COHEN WEENEN & CO. – cont.

Qty		Date	Odds	Sets
25	War Series (26-50, Anonymous)	1916	£15.00	—
30	Wonders Of The World (Green Back)	1908	£7.50	£225.00
30	(Grey Back)	1923	£3.00	£90.00

T. H. COLLINS

Qty		Date	Odds	Sets
25	Homes Of England (Black Front)	1924	£22.50	—
25	(Mauve Front)	1924	£5.00	£125.00
25	Sports & Pastimes	1923	£7.00	£200.00

F. COLTON JR

Qty		Date	Odds	Sets
30	Army Pictures, Cartoons, etc. ("Best Brands")	1916	£130.00	—
30	("Trade Supplied")	1916	£130.00	—
50	War Portraits	1916	£115.00	—

T. W. CONQUEST (Tobacconist)

Qty		Date	Odds	Sets
30	Army Pictures, Cartoons, etc.	1916	£150.00	—

CONTINENTAL CIGARETTE FACTORY

Qty		Date	Odds	Sets
25	Charming Portraits (Firm's Name)	1920	£5.00	£125.00
25	(Club Mixture, Blue)	1920	£7.00	—
4	(Club Mixture, Brown)	1920	£12.50	£50.00
25	(Plain Back)	1920	£3.75	—

COOPER & CO.

Qty		Date	Odds	Sets
25	Boer War Celebrities "STEW" (Alpha)	1901	£160.00	—
25	(Gladys)	1901	£160.00	—

CO-OPERATIVE WHOLESALE SOCIETY(C.W.S)

Qty		Date	Odds	Sets
6	Advertisement Cards	1915	£425.00	—
24	African Types	1936	£0.60	£15.00
X2	Beauties	1925	£70.00	—
M50	Beauty Spots Of Britain	1936	£0.45	£22.50
50	Boy Scout Badges	1939	£1.50	£72.00
25	Boy Scout Series	1912	£35.00	£875.00
48	British And Foreign Birds	1938	£0.80	£40.00
50	British Sport Series (Multi-Backed)	1904	£32.50	—
25	Cooking Recipes	1923	£2.40	£60.00
28	Co-Operative Buildings & Works	1916	£15.00	£420.00
24	English Roses	1924	£4.00	£96.00
50	Famous Bridges	1937	£0.85	£42.50
48	Famous Buildings	1935	£0.90	£43.50
25	How To Do It (Mixed Backs)	1924	—	£65.00
25	(Anglian Mixture)	1924	£2.75	—
25	(Equity Tobacco)	1924	£2.75	—
25	(Jaycee Brown Flake)	1924	£2.75	—
25	(Raydex Gold Leaf)	1924	£2.75	—
48	Musical Instruments	1934	£4.00	£190.00
25	Parrot Series	1910	£37.50	—
48	Poultry	1927	£8.00	£375.00
48	Railway Engines	1936	£3.50	£168.00
24	Sailing Craft	1935	£1.50	£36.00
18	War Series	1914	£27.50	—
48	Wayside Flowers (Brown Back)	1923	£2.20	£105.00
48	Wayside Flowers (Green Back, Different)	1928	£1.00	£48.00
48	Wayside Woodland Trees	1924	£2.50	£120.00
24	Western Stars	1957	£0.75	£18.00

COPE BROS. & CO. LTD.

Qty		Date	Odds	Sets
KF?47	Actors & Actresses	1900	£30.00	—
20	Actresses "BLARM" (Plain Back)	1902	£36.00	—
20	(Printed Back, 63mm Long)	1902	£36.00	—
20	(Printed Back, 70mm Long)	1902	£35.00	£700.00
6	Actresses "COPEIS"	1898	£300.00	—
26	Actresses "FROGA"	1900	£90.00	—
F50	Actresses & Beauties	1900	£16.00	£800.00
P6	Advertising Postcards	1924	£85.00	—
52	Beauties, Playing Card Inset	1899	£42.50	—
15	Beauties "PAC"	1898	£75.00	—
50	Boats Of The World	1912	£15.00	£750.00
25	Boxers (1-25)	1915	£18.50	£475.00
25	Boxers (26-50)	1915	£16.00	£400.00
25	Boxers (51-75)	1915	£16.00	£400.00
25	Boxers (76-100)	1915	£22.00	£550.00
25	Boxers (101-125)	1915	£16.00	£400.00
1	Boxers (New World's Champion)	1915	—	£48.00
25	Boxing Lessons	1935	£4.40	£110.00
35	Boy Scouts & Girl Guides (English)	1910	£13.00	£455.00
35	(Scandinavian)	1910	£32.00	—
X25	Bridge Problems	1924	£30.00	—
25	British Admirals	1915	£14.00	£350.00
50	British Warriors (Black Printing)	1912	£8.50	£425.00
50	(Grey Printing)	1912	£11.00	—
25	Castles	1939	£1.20	£30.00
25	Cathedrals	1939	£1.50	£37.50
50	Characters From Scott	1900	£13.00	£650.00
20	Chinese Series (1-20)	1903	£12.50	£250.00
20	Chinese Series (21-40, Bond Of Union)	1903	£12.00	—
20	(21-40, Cope's Courts)	1903	£12.00	—
20	(21-40, Golden Cloud)	1903	£12.00	—
20	(21-40, Golden Magnet)	1903	£12.00	—
20	(21-40, Solace)	1903	£12.00	—
25	Chinese Series (41-65, 2 Printings)	1903	£12.00	—
50	Chinese Series (66-115, Multi-Backed)	1903	£15.00	—
X6	Comic Hunting Scenes	1885	£300.00	—
P?2	Comic Scenes With Dog (Folders)	1885	£400.00	—
50	Cope's Golfers	1900	£85.00	—
L25	Dickens Character Series	1939	£1.10	£27.50
50	Dickens Gallery (Back-Listed)	1900	£11.50	£575.00
50	(Solace Back)	1900	£110.00	—
E1	Dickens Gallery Album	1900	—	£160.00
50	Dogs Of The World (English)	1912	£13.00	£650.00
50	(Scandinavian)	1912	£37.50	—
25	Eminent British Regiments Officers			
	(English, Brown Back)	1908	£13.00	£325.00
	(English, Claret back)	1908	£13.00	£325.00
	(Scandinavian)	1908	£32.50	—
24	Flags, Arms & Types Of All Nations (Numbered)	1904	£8.00	£192.00
24	(Unnumbered)	1904	£100.00	—
30	Flags Of Nations (Black Back)	1903	£13.00	£390.00
30	(Indian, Blue Back)	1903	£85.00	—
30	(Plain Back)	1903	£8.50	£255.00
M50	General Knowledge	1925	£4.00	£200.00
M32	Golf Strokes	1923	£15.00	—

Beauties
E. Robinson & Sons

Sports & Pastimes
Cope Bros & Co

British Beauties
Godfrey Phillips

Puzzle Pictures
Major Drapkin & Co

Music Hall Celebrities
R & J Hill

Nautical Expressions
T.S.S. & Others

National & Colonial Arms
B. Morris

Mining
Edwards, Ringer & Bigg
also Wills

King Lud Problems
E. Robinson & Sons,
Pattreiouex

Qty		Date	Odds	Sets
60	Happy Families	1937	£1.65	£100.00
M50	Household Hints	1925	£1.70	£85.00
X20	Kenilworth Phrases	1910	£500.00	–
25	Lawn Tennis Strokes	1924	£6.00	£150.00
5	Lawn Tennis Strokes (26-30)	1925	£22.50	–
L50	Modern Dancing	1926	£14.00	–
50	Music Hall Artistes ("Series Of 50")	1913	£32.50	£1,625.00"
50	(No Quantity)	1913	£12.00	£600.00
120	Noted Footballers (Clips, 120 Subjects)	1910	£22.00	–
162	Noted Footballers (Clips, 282 Subjects)	1910	£22.00	–
471	Noted Footballers (Clips, 500 Subjects)	1910	£22.00	
1	Noted Footballers (Clips, Unnumbered)	1910	–	£60.00
195	Noted Footballers (Solace Cigarettes)	1910	£22.00	–
24	Occupations For Women	1897	£100.00	–
X6	Phases Of The Moon	1885	£300.00	–
T12	Photo Albums For The Million (Buff)	1902	£16.50	£200.00
T12	Photo Albums For The Million (Green)	1902	£16.00	£192.00
25	Pigeons	1926	£9.00	£225.00
52	Playing Cards (Rounded Corners)	1902	£11.00	–
52	(Squarer Corners)	1902	£11.00	–
30	Scandinavian Actors & Actresses	1910	£40.00	£1,200.00"
50	Shakespeare Gallery	1900	£13.00	£650.00
G14	Smoke Room Booklets	1890	£25.00	–
25	Song Birds	1926	£7.00	£175.00
25	Sports & Pastimes	1925	£4.40	£110.00
L25	The Game Of Poker	1936	£0.50	£12.50
X7	The Seven Ages Of Man	1885	£350.00	–
25	The World's Police	1937	£5.00	£125.00
L25	Toy Models-The Country Fair	1925	£0.50	£12.50
25	Uniforms (Circular Medallion Back)	1898	£28.00	£700.00
25	(Square Medallion Back, Narrow)	1898	£25.00	£625.00
25	(Square Medallion Back, Wide)	1898	£60.00	–
50	VC & DSO Naval & Flying Heroes (Unnumbered)	1917	£9.00	£600.00
25	VC & DSO Naval & Flying Heroes (51-75)	1917	£11.00	–
20	War Pictures	1915	£13.00	£260.00
25	War Series	1915	£13.50	–
25	Wild Animals & Birds (English)	1907	£17.00	£425.00
25	(Scandinavian)	1907	£37.50	–

E. CORONEL

25	Types Of British & Colonial Troops	1900	£65.00	–

DAVID CORRE & CO.

40	Naval & Military Phrases (With Border)	1904	£90.00	–
40	(No Border)	1904	£85.00	–

JOHN COTTON LTD.

L50	Bridge Hands	1934	£12.00	–
50	Golf Strokes A/B	1936	£9.00	£450.00
50	Golf Strokes C/D	1937	£10.00	–
50	Golf Strokes E/F	1938	£13.50	–
50	Golf Strokes G/H	1939	£400.00	–
50	Golf Strokes I/J	1939	£400.00	–

A. & J. COUDENS LTD.

Qty		Date	Odds	Sets
F60	British Beauty Spots (Numbered)	1923	£1.65	£100.00
F60	(Unnumbered)	1923	£2.75	—
F60	(Rubber Stamped)	1923	£4.00	—
F60	(Plain Back, Anon)	1923	£4.00	—
F60	Holiday Resorts In East Anglia	1924	£1.30	£78.00
25	Sports Alphabet	1924	£10.00	£250.00

THE CRAIGMILLAR CREAMERY CO.

Qty		Date	Odds	Sets
M?1	Scottish Views	1901	£1,500.00	—

W. R. DANIEL

Qty		Date	Odds	Sets
30	Colonial Troops (Black Back)	1902	£90.00	—
30	(Brown Back)	1902	£100.00	—
25	National Flags & Flowers-Girls	1901	£160.00	—

W F DANIELL

Qty		Date	Odds	Sets
X?1	Puzzle Cards	1895	£750.00	

W.T. DAVIES & SONS

Qty		Date	Odds	Sets
50	Actresses	1902	£95.00	—
30	Aristocrats Of The Turf, A Series (1-30)	1924	£6.00	£180.00
12	Aristocrats Of The Turf (31-42)	1924	£20.00	—
36	Aristocrats Of The Turf, Second Series	1924	£5.00	£180.00
25	Army Life	1915	£12.00	£300.00
12	Beauties	1903	£65.00	—
25	Boxing	1924	£4.00	£100.00
50	Flags & Funnels Of Leading Steamship Lines	1913	£12.00	—
?13	Newport Football Club	1904	£425.00	—
?5	Royal Welsh Fusiliers	1904	£425.00	—

S.H. DAWES (Tobacconist)

Qty		Date	Odds	Sets
30	Army Pictures, Cartoons, etc.	1916	£160.00	—

J.W. DEWHURST

Qty		Date	Odds	Sets
30	Army Pictures, Cartoons, etc.	1916	£135.00	—

R.I. DEXTER

Qty		Date	Odds	Sets
30	Borough Arms	1900	£1.65	£50.00

DIANELLOS & VERGOPOULOS

Qty		Date	Odds	Sets
XF?7	Views Of Cyprus	1926	£65.00	—

GEORGE DOBIE & SON LTD.

Qty		Date	Odds	Sets
M?28	Bridge Problems	1933	£50.00	—
M32	Four Square Books (1-32)	1959	£2.50	—
M32	Four Square Books (33-64)	1960	£2.20	£70.00
M32	Four Square Books (65-96)	1960	£2.20	£70.00
25	Weapons Of All Ages	1924	£8.00	£200.00

DOBSON & CO LTD

Qty		Date	Odds	Sets
8	The European War Series	1917	£47.50	—

DOMINION TOBACCO CO. (1929) LTD.

Qty		Date	Odds	Sets
25	Old Ships, 1st Series	1934	£2.60	£65.00
25	Old Ships, 2nd Series	1935	£1.20	£30.00
25	Old Ships, 3rd Series	1936	£1.20	£30.00
25	Old Ships, 4th Series"	1936	£2.20	£55.00

JOSEPH W. DOYLE LTD.

Qty		Date	Odds	Sets
F12	Beauties (Series CC.D)	1928	£30.00	—
F12	Beauties (Series CC.E)	1928	£30.00	—
F12	British Views (Series CC.B)	1928	£30.00	—
F12	Castles (Series CC.C)	1928	£30.00	—
XF18	Children	1928	£14.00	—
F12	Dirt Track Riders (Series CC.A)	1928	£50.00	—

DOYLE'S (Reading)

Qty		Date	Odds	Sets
?	Merry Miniatures (Booklets)	1924	£135.00	

MAJOR DRAPKIN & CO

Qty		Date	Odds	Sets
12	Actresses	1910	£8.00	—
8	Advertisement Cards	1926	£7.50	£60.00
M1	Army Insignia	1915	£1,000.00	—
50	Around Britain	1929	£1.40	£70.00
L50	Around Britain	1929	£2.75	—
50	Around The Mediterranean	1926	£1.50	£75.00
L50	Around The Mediterranean	1926	£3.00	—
F40	Australian & English Test Cricketers	1928	£2.40	£96.00
25	British Beauties	1930	£3.00	£75.00
F36	Celebrities Of The Great War (Printed)	1916	£0.70	£25.00
F34	(Plain Back)	1916	£0.65	£22.00
M96	Cinematograph Actors	1913	£13.50	—
15	Dogs And Their Treatment	1924	£5.50	£82.50
L15	Dogs And Their Treatment	1924	£6.50	£100.00
50	Girls Of Many Lands	1929	£4.00	—
M50	Girls Of Many Lands	1929	£0.65	£32.50
25	How To Keep Fit (Crayol Cigarettes)	1912	£17.00	£425.00
25	(Drapkin's Cigarettes)	1912	£17.00	£425.00
54	Life At Whipsnade Zoo	1934	£0.50	£27.00
50	Limericks	1929	£1.70	£85.00
F36	National Types Of Beauty	1928	£0.70	£25.00
25	Optical Illusions (Panel 23 X 7mm)	1926	£3.50	£87.50
25	(Panel 26 X 9mm)	1926	£3.20	£80.00
L25	Optical Illusions	1926	£3.80	£95.00
25	Palmistry	1927	£3.00	£75.00
L25	Palmistry	1927	£3.20	£80.00
48	Photogravure Masterpieces	1915	£10.00	—
25	Puzzle Pictures	1926	£4.50	£112.50
L25	Puzzle Pictures	1926	£4.50	£112.50
M40	Regimental Colours & Badges Of The Indian Army			
	(Silk, No Vertical Pillars)	1915	£4.50	—
	(Silk, With Vertical Pillars on Back)	1915	£40.00	—
?26	Shots From The Films (Package Issue)	1934	£25.00	—
T25	Soldiers & Their Uniforms (Die-Cut)	1914	—	£80.00
T25	(Crayol)	1914	£1.00	—
T25	(Drapkin)	1914	£1.00	—
T22/25	(Die-Cut)	1914	—	£22.00

MAJOR DRAPKIN & CO – cont.

Qty		Date	Odds	Sets
F35/36	Sporting Celebrities In Action	1930	£3.00	£220.00
40	The Game Of Sporting Snap	1928	£4.25	£170.00
1	The Greys Advertisement Card	1935	−	£3.00
12	Views Of The World	1910	£5.00	£60.00
6/8	Warships	1912	£12.00	£72.00

DRAPKIN & MILLHOFF

?2	Beauties "KEWA" (Eldona Cigarettes)	1899	£350.00	−
?1	(Explorer Cigarettes)	1899	£350.00	−
25	Boer War Celebrities "PAM" (Multibacked)	1901	£32.00	−
25	(Plain Backs)	1901	£60.00	−
30	Colonial Troops (Multi-Backed)	1902	£55.00	−
X?6	Pick-Me-Up Paper Inserts	1900	£300.00	−
?3	Pretty Girl Series "BAGG"	1898	£350.00	−

DU MAURIER CIGARETTES

X?50	Advertising Inserts	1931	£7.50	−

J. DUNCAN & CO. LTD.

47/50	Evolution Of The Steamship	1925	£0.85	£40.00
48	Flags, Arms & Types Of Nations (Blue)	1911	£30.00	−
48	(Green)	1911	£45.00	−
20	Inventors & Their Inventions	1915	£60.00	−
30	Scottish Clans,Arms Of Chiefs (Black)	1912	£250.00	−
30	(Green)	1912	£17.50	£525.00
L72	Scottish Gems (Coloured)	1912	£13.00	−
L50	Scottish Gems 2nd Series	1913	£14.00	−
L50	Scottish Gems 3rd Series	1914	£12.00	£600.00
L50	Scottish Gems (Reissue, Black & White)	1925	£0.60	£30.00
25	Types Of British Soldiers	1910	£50.00	−

GEO. DUNCOMBE (Tobacconist)

30	Army Pictures, Cartoons, etc.	1916	£140.00	−

ALFRED DUNHILL LTD

M25	Dunhill King Size Ransom	1985	£1.65	−

EDWARDS, RINGER & CO.

X50	How To Count Cribbage Hands	1908	£350.00	−

EDWARDS, RINGER & BIGG

25	Abbeys & Castles (Exmoor Hunt Back)	1912	£8.50	£212.50
25	(New York Back)	1912	£8.50	£212.50
25	Abbeys And Castles (Type Set Back)	1912	£9.00	£225.00
25	Alpine Views (Exmoor Hunt Back)	1912	£8.50	£212.50
25	(New York Back)	1912	£8.50	£212.50
50	A Tour Round The World	1909	£12.00	£600.00
12	Beauties "CERF"	1905	£70.00	£840.00
25	Beauties "FECKSA"	1900	£40.00	−
50	Birds & Eggs	1906	£13.00	−
?25	Boer War Sketches	1901	£175.00	−
25	Boer War Celebrities "STEW"	1901	£42.50	−
25	British Trees & Their Uses	1933	£2.50	£62.50

EDWARDS, RINGER & BIGG – cont.

Qty		Date	Odds	Sets
1	Calendar & Lighting Up Table	1899	–	£600.00
1	Calendar	1905	–	£450.00
1	Calendar (Empire Back)	1910	–	£450.00
1	Calendar (New York Back)	1910	–	£500.00
50	Celebrated Bridges	1924	£2.50	£125.00
50	Cinema Stars	1923	£1.75	£87.50
L25	Cinema Stars	1923	£2.20	£55.00
25	Coast And Country (Exmoor Hunt Back)	1911	£8.50	£212.50
25	(New York Back)	1911	£8.50	£212.50
23	Dogs Series (Exmoor Hunt Back)	1908	£9.00	–
23	(Klondyke Back)	1908	£4.50	£100.00
3	Easter Manoeuvres Of Our Volunteers	1897	£300.00	£900.00
25	Flags Of All Nations (1st Series)	1907	£9.00	£225.00
12	Flags Of All Nations (2nd Series)	1907	£8.50	£100.00
37	(Exmoor Hunt)	1907	£8.50	£315.00
37	(Globe & Flags)	1907	£9.00	–
37	(Stag Design)	1907	£8.50	£315.00
37	(Vertical Back)	1907	£9.00	£335.00
25	Garden Life	1934	£3.20	£80.00
25	How To Tell Fortunes	1929	£4.00	£100.00
50	Life On Board A Man Of War	1905	£11.00	£550.00
1	Miners Bound For Klondyke	1897	–	£450.00
50	Mining	1925	£2.50	£125.00
25	Musical Instruments	1924	£4.00	£100.00
25	Optical Illusions	1936	£3.20	£80.00
25	Our Pets, A Series	1926	£2.50	£62.50
25	Our Pets, 2nd Series	1926	£2.40	£60.00
25	Past & Present	1928	£3.60	£90.00
10	Portraits Of His Majesty The King	1902	£40.00	£400.00
25	Prehistoric Animals	1924	£5.00	£125.00
25	Sports & Games In Many Lands	1935	£4.25	£160.00
56	War Map, Western Front"	1916	£11.00	£615.00
54	War Map Of The Western Front,			
	Series 2 (Exmoor Hunt Back)	1917	£11.00	–
54	(New York Back)	1917	£11.00	£595.00

S. EISISKI

Qty		Date	Odds	Sets
?26	Actresses "ANGOOD"	1900	£400.00	–
6	Actresses "COPEIS"	1899	£400.00	–
?23	Beauties "FENA" (Printed Back)	1899	£400.00	–
?23	(Rubber Stamped Back)	1899	£400.00	–
?2	Beauties "KEWA" (Birds Eye Back)	1900	£400.00	–
?2	New Gold Back)	1900	£400.00	–
?2	(Rubber Stamped Back)	1900	£400.00	–

R J ELLIOTT & CO LTD

Qty		Date	Odds	Sets
1	Bulldog Advertisement Card (2 Types)	1910	–	£300.00

EMPIRE TOBACCO CO.

Qty		Date	Odds	Sets
6	Franco British Exhibition	1907	£375.00	–

ENCHANTERESSE EGYPTIAN CIG. CO.

Qty		Date	Odds	Sets
?23	Actresses "ANGOOD"	1898	£350.00	–
K52	Miniature Playing Cards	1931	£6.00	–

THE EXPRESS TOBACCO CO. LTD.

Qty		Date	Odds	Sets
M50	How It Is Made (Motor Cars)	1939	£3.25	£175.00

L. & J. FABIAN

F24	The Elite Series (Numbered LLF1-24)	1932	£37.50	–
F?47	The Elite Series (Plain Numerals)	1932	£37.50	–

FAIRWEATHER & SONS

50	Historic Buildings Of Scotland	1914	£50.00	£2,500.00

W. & F. FAULKNER

26	Actresses "FROGA"	1900	£55.00	–
25	Angling	1929	£9.00	£225.00
12	'Ation Series	1901	£25.00	£300.00
25	Beauties (Coloured)	1898	£75.00	–
49	Beauties "FECKSA"	1901	£26.00	£1,175.00
16	British Royal Family	1901	£40.00	£640.00
50	Celebrated Bridges	1925	£2.50	£125.00
12	Coster Series	1900	£32.00	–
20	Cricketers Series	1902	£300.00	–
12	Cricket Terms	1899	£85.00	–
12	Football Terms, 1st Series	1900	£35.00	£420.00
12	Football Terms, 2nd Series	1900	£35.00	£420.00
12	Golf Terms	1901	£100.00	–
12	Grenadier Guards	1899	£30.00	£360.00
40	Kings & Queens	1902	£25.00	–
12	Kipling Series	1900	£27.50	£330.00
12	Military Terms, 1st Series	1899	£25.00	£300.00
12	Military Terms, 2nd Series	1899	£26.00	£310.00
12	Nautical Terms, 1st Series (2 Printings)	1900	£25.00	£300.00
12	Nautical Terms, 2nd Series (Grenadier)	1900	£25.00	£300.00
12	(Union Jack)	1900	£25.00	£300.00
25	Old Sporting Prints	1930	£3.80	£95.00
25	Optical Illusions	1935	£3.20	£80.00
90	Our Colonial Troops (Grenadier)	1900	£16.00	£1,440.00
30	(Grenadier,With "Copyright",1-30)	1900	£32.00	–
60	(Union Jack,31-90)	1900	£18.50	–
20	Our Gallant Grenadiers (No I.T.C.Clause)	1902	£17.00	£340.00
20	Our Gallant Grenadiers (I.T.C.Clause)	1903	£28.00	£560.00
20	Our Gallant Grenadiers (Numbered 21-40)	1902	£25.00	£500.00
25	Our Pets, A Series	1926	£3.20	£80.00
25	Our Pets, 2nd Series	1926	£2.80	£70.00
12	Policemen Of The World (Grenadier)	1899	£225.00	–
12	(Nosegay)	1899	£36.00	£430.00
12	Police Terms	1899	£30.00	£360.00
25	Prominent Racehorses Of The Present Day	1923	£3.40	£85.00
25	Prominent Racehorses Of The Present Day, 2nd Series	1924	£5.00	£125.00
12	Puzzle Series (Grenadier)	1898	£250.00	–
12	(Nosegay)	1898	£65.00	–
25	South African War Series	1901	£17.00	£425.00
12	Sporting Terms	1900	£36.00	£432.00
12	Street Cries	1902	£26.00	–
12	The Language Of Flowers (Grenadier)	1900	£32.00	£384.00
12	(Nosegay)	1900	£32.00	£384.00

FIELD FAVORITES CIGARETTES

Qty		Date	Odds	Sets
F?	Footballers	1893	£2,000.00	—

THE FIGARO CIGARETTE

| X?12 | Caricatures | 1880 | £1,000.00 | — |

FINLAY & CO. LTD.

| ?27 | Our Girls | 1910 | £160.00 | — |
| 30 | World's Aircraft | 1912 | £70.00 | — |

FLYNN

| 26 | Beauties "HOL" | 1899 | £600.00 | |

C D FOTHERGILL

| M? | Football Shields | 1900 | £130.00 | — |

FRAENKEL BROS.

?2	Beauties - Don Jorge (2 Printings)	1897	£800.00	—
?23	Beauties - "FENA"	1899	£130.00	—
25	Beauties - "GRACC"	1898	£160.00	—
24	Beauties - "HUMPS"	1899	£140.00	—
26	Music Hall Artistes (Pink Card)	1900	£110.00	—
26	(White Card)	1900	£120.00	—
25	Types Of British & Colonial Troops	1900	£70.00	—

FRANKLYN DAVEY & CO.

12	Beauties "CERF"	1905	£70.00	£840.00
50	Birds	1896	£70.00	—
10	Boer War Generals	1901	£90.00	—
25	Boxing	1924	£3.40	£85.00
25	Ceremonial And Court Dress	1915	£12.00	£300.00
50	Children Of All Nations	1934	£0.90	£45.00
1	Comic Dog Folder	1898	—	£700.00
50	Football Club Colours	1909	£16.50	—
50	Historic Events	1924	£2.60	£130.00
25	Hunting	1925	£1.10	£27.50
50	Modern Dance Steps A Series	1930	£5.00	—
50	Modern Dance Steps 2nd Series	1931	£1.10	£55.00
50	Naval Dress & Badges	1916	£12.00	—
50	Overseas Dominions (Australia)	1923	£5.00	—
25	Star Girls	1901	£250.00	—
10	Types Of Smokers	1898	£52.00	£520.00
50	Wild Animals Of The World	1902	£12.50	—

A.H. FRANKS & SONS

56	Beauties	1901	£75.00	—
24	Nautical Expressions	1902	£80.00	—
25	Types Of British & Colonial Troops	1900	£65.00	—

J.J. FREEMAN & CO.

| 12 | Actresses "FRAN" | 1915 | £50.00 | — |
| 12 | Views Of The World | 1910 | £45.00 | — |

J R FREEMAN

Qty		Date	Odds	Sets
33	Football Challenge (3 Printings)	1969	£6.00	—
M12	Manikin Cards	1915	£85.00	—

C. FRYER & SONS LTD.

Qty		Date	Odds	Sets
25	Boer War & General Interest (3 Backs)	1900	£175.00	—
X50	Clan Sketches	1930	£13.00	£650.00
40	Naval & Military Phrases	1904	£65.00	—
?14	Vita Berlin Series	1901	£450.00	—

FRYER & COULTMAN

Qty		Date	Odds	Sets
X12	Almanack	1893	£850.00	—
?50	Beauties "PLUMS"	1896	£850.00	—

J. GABRIEL

Qty		Date	Odds	Sets
10	Actresses "HAGG"	1900	£80.00	—
25	Beauties "GRACC"	1898	£200.00	—
20	Cricketers Series	1902	£400.00	—
40	Home & Colonial Regiments	1902	£85.00	—
?53	Pretty Girl Series "BAGG"	1898	£75.00	—
25	Types Of British & Colonial Troops	1899	£70.00	—

GALA CIGARETTES

Qty		Date	Odds	Sets
1	Stamp Cards	1910	—	£175.00

GALLAHER LTD.

Qty		Date	Odds	Sets
F110	Actors & Actresses (2 Printings)	1901	£5.50	—
P3	Advertising Postcards	1923	£85.00	—
48	Aeroplanes	1939	£1.00	£48.00
25	Aesop's Fables ("Series of 25")	1931	£1.50	£37.50
25	("Series of 50")	1931	£1.60	£40.00
100	Animals & Birds Of Commercial Value	1921	£0.65	£65.00
48	Army Badges	1939	£0.75	£36.00
L24	Art Treasures Of The World	1930	£1.25	£30.00
100	Association Football Club Colours	1910	£8.50	£850.00
52	Beauties (Playing Card Inset)	1905	£12.00	£624.00
52	(No Inset)	1905	£12.50	£650.00
MF48	Beautiful Scotland	1939	£1.00	£48.00
50	Birds & Eggs (Gallaher Ltd Only Label)	1905	£50.00	—
50	("Manufactured By" Label)	1905	£8.50	—
100	Birds Nests & Eggs	1919	£1.50	£150.00
100	Boy Scout Series (Green, Belfast & London)	1911	£2.75	£275.00
86	(Green, London & Belfast)	1911	£2.75	—
100	Boy Scout Series (Brown Back, Redrawn)	1922	£2.25	£225.00
48	British Birds	1937	£0.50	£24.00
100	British Birds By George Rankin	1923	£1.60	£160.00
100	By Rankin	1923	£20.00	—
75	British Champions Of 1923	1924	£1.80	£135.00
50	British Naval Series	1914	£5.50	£275.00
48	Butterflies & Moths	1938	£0.50	£24.00
25	Champion Animals & Birds Of 1923	1924	£1.80	£45.00
48	Champions A Series (No Captions Front)	1934	£0.90	£45.00
48	(Captions On Front)	1934	£0.65	£31.50
48	Champions 2nd Series	1935	£0.50	£24.00

GALLAHER LTD. – cont.

Qty		Date	Odds	Sets
48	Champions Of Screen & Stage (Red Back)	1934	£0.75	£36.00
48	(Blue Back, Gallaher's Cigarettes)	1934	£1.20	£57.50
48	(Blue Back, Gallaher Ltd)	1934	£2.00	–
100	Cinema Stars	1926	£1.60	£160.00
MF48	Coastwise	1938	£1.35	£67.50
24	Dogs (Caption In Block)	1934	£1.40	£35.00
24	(Caption In Script)	1934	£2.40	£57.50
L24	Dogs (Caption In Block)	1934	£1.60	£40.00
L24	(Caption In Script)	1934	£2.75	£66.00
48	Dogs, A Series	1936	£0.80	£40.00
48	Dogs, 2nd Series	1938	£0.50	£24.00
F100	English & Scotch Views	1910	£3.00	£300.00
100	Fables & Their Morals (No. By Caption)	1912	£1.50	£150.00
100	(Thick Numerals)	1922	£0.75	£75.00
100	(Thin Numerals)	1922	£0.75	£75.00
100	Famous Cricketers	1926	£3.00	£300.00
48	Famous Film Scenes	1935	£0.75	£36.00
50	Famous Footballers (Brown Back)	1926	£2.60	£130.00
100	Famous Footballers (Green Back)	1925	£2.50	£250.00
48	Famous Jockeys (Blue Printing)	1936	£1.35	£65.00
48	Mauve Printing)	1936	£3.00	–
48	Film Episodes	1936	£0.65	£31.00
48	Film Partners	1935	£0.90	£42.00
M24/25	Flags (Silk)	1915	£8.00	£192.00
MF48	Flying	1938	£1.75	–
50	Footballers (1-50)	1928	£3.20	£160.00
50	Footballers (51-100)	1928	£3.20	£160.00
50	Footballers In Action	1927	£2.70	£135.00
48	Garden Flowers	1938	£0.20	£10.00
100	How To Do It	1916	£3.75	£375.00
F100	Interesting Views (Black & White)	1923	£1.40	£140.00
F100	(Coloured)	1923	£2.40	£240.00
400	Irish Views Scenery (Numbered On Back)	1908	£1.50	–
400	Irish View Scenery ("Ltd" Block Letters)	1908	£0.75	£300.00
F400	(Chocolate Front)	1910	£3.50	–
F400	(Plain Back)	1910	£3.00	–
F400	("Ltd" In Script)	1910	£0.80	£320.00
F200	Irish View Scenery (401-600)	1910	£2.00	–
LF48	Island Sporting Celebrities	1938	£2.75	£132.00
100	Kute Kiddies Series	1916	£4.00	£400.00
F50	Latest Actresses (Black & White)	1909	£13.00	£650.00
F50	Chocolate Front)	1909	£22.50	–
50	Lawn Tennis Celebrities	1928	£5.00	£250.00
24	Motor Cars	1934	£4.50	£110.00
48	My Favourite Part	1939	£0.75	£36.00
MF48	Our Countryside	1938	£1.40	–
100	Plants Of Commercial Value	1917	£0.75	£75.00
48	Portraits Of Famous Stars	1935	£1.00	£48.00
48	Racing Scenes	1938	£0.75	£36.00
50	Regimental Colours & Standards	1899	£7.00	£350.00
100	Robinson Crusoe	1928	£1.80	£180.00
50	Royalty Series	1902	£7.00	£350.00
LF48	Scenes From The Empire	1939	£0.30	£15.00
48	Shots From Famous Films	1935	£0.60	£30.00
MF24	Shots From The Films	1936	£3.60	–

GALLAHER LTD. – cont.

Qty		Date	Odds	Sets
48	Signed Portraits Of Famous Stars	1935	£2.50	£120.00
M20	Silk Cut Advertisement Cards	1993	–	£10.00
48	Sporting Personalities	1936	£0.50	£24.00
100	Sports Series	1912	£6.00	£700.00
?98	Stage & Variety Celebrities (Multi-Backed)	1899	£90.00	–
48	Stars Of Screen & Stage (Brown Back)	1935	£1.75	£85.00
48	(Green Back)	1935	£0.60	£29.00
25	The Allies Flags	1914	£4.00	£100.00
100	The Great War Series	1915	£2.60	£260.00
100	The Great War Second Series	1915	£2.80	£280.00
25	The Great War V.C. Heroes, 1st Series	1915	£4.50	£112.50
25	The Great War V.C. Heroes, 2nd Series	1915	£5.00	£125.00
25	The Great War V.C. Heroes, 3rd Series	1915	£4.50	£112.50
25	The Great War V.C. Heroes, 4th Series	1916	£4.50	£112.50
25	The Great War V.C. Heroes, 5th Series	1916	£4.50	£112.50
25	The Great War V.C. Heroes, 6th Series	1917	£4.50	£112.50
25	The Great War V.C. Heroes, 7th Series	1917	£4.50	£112.50
25	The Great War V.C. Heroes, 8th Series	1918	£4.50	£112.50
48	The Navy (Gallaher)	1937	£1.40	£70.00
48	(Park Drive)	1937	£0.75	£36.00
100	The Reason Why	1924	£0.65	£65.00
111	The South African Series	1901	£6.00	£665.00
100	The Zoo Aquarium	1924	£1.00	£100.00
48	Trains Of The World	1937	£1.00	£48.00
100	Tricks & Puzzles Series (Green Back)	1913	£5.50	£600.00
100	Tricks & Puzzles Series (Black Back)	1933	£1.35	£135.00
50	Types Of The British Army			
	(Battle Honours Back)	1897	£11.00	–
	(Green Back)	1898	£10.00	£500.00
	(1-50, "Three Pipe Tobaccos" In Brown)	1898	£8.50	£425.00
	(1-50, "Now In Three Strengths")	1898	£8.50	£425.00
50	Types Of The British Army, 51-100"			
	"Three Pipe Tobaccos" (2 Printings)	1898	£8.50	£425.00
	"Now In Three Strengths	1898	£8.50	£425.00
100	Useful Hints Series	1915	£3.25	£325.00
25	Views In North Of Ireland	1912	£60.00	£1,500.00
50	Votaries Of The Weed	1916	£7.00	£350.00
100	Why Is It? (Brown Back)	1915	£3.25	£325.00
100	(Green Back)	1915	£3.25	£325.00
48	Wild Animals	1937	£0.50	£24.00
48	Wild Flowers	1939	£0.60	£30.00
100	Woodland Trees Series	1912	£4.75	£475.00
50	Zoo Tropical Birds, 1st Series"	1928	£1.40	£70.00
50	Zoo Tropical Birds, 2nd Series"	1929	£1.40	£70.00

GASPA

?14	Our Great Novelists	1930	£175.00	–

SAMUEL GAWITH

X25	The English Lakeland	1926	£24.00	£600.00

F. GENNARI

50	War Portraits	1916	£120.00	–

LOUIS GERARD LTD.

Qty		Date	Odds	Sets
50	Modern Armaments (Numbered)	1938	£1.25	£62.50
50	(Unnumbered)	1938	£1.60	£80.00
24	Screen Favourites (Gerard & Co)	1937	£4.00	—
24	(Gerard Ltd)	1937	3.75	£90.00
48	Screen Favourites & Dancers (Matt)	1937	£2.50	£120.00
48	(Varnished)	1937	£4.00	—

GLASS & CO. LTD.

Qty		Date	Odds	Sets
20	Actresses "BLARM"	1900	£75.00	—
10	Actresses "HAGG"	1900	£80.00	—
25	Beauties "FECKSA"	1903	£125.00	—
20	Boer War Cartoons	1901	£130.00	—
25	Boer War Celebrities "STEW"	1901	£90.00	—
16	British Royal Family	1901	£75.00	—
20	Cricketers Series	1902	£375.00	—
40	Naval & Military Phrases	1902	£115.00	—
19	Russo Japanese Series	1904	£70.00	—

R.P. GLOAG & CO.

Qty		Date	Odds	Sets
?9	Actresses "ANGLO" (The Challenge Flat)	1896	£450.00	—
?9	(Citamora)	1896	£450.00	—
?10	Beauties "PLUMS" (Black/White, Citamora)	1896	£120.00	—
?60	(B & W, Challenge Flat)	1896	£100.00	—
?10	(Brown, Plain Back)	1896	£250.00	—
?10	(Brown, Printed Back)	1896	£250.00	—
40	Home & Colonial Regiments	1900	£45.00	—
30	Proverbs	1901	£110.00	—
25	Types Of British & Colonial Troops	1900	£60.00	—

THE GLOBE CIGARETTE CO.

Qty		Date	Odds	Sets
25	Actresses-French	1898	£350.00	—

GOLDS LTD.

Qty		Date	Odds	Sets
1	Advertisement Card	1905	£750.00	—
18	Motor Cycle Series (Blue Back)	1914	£50.00	—
18	(Grey Back, Numbered)	1914	£55.00	—
18	(Grey Back, Unnumbered)	1914	£65.00	—
L?21	Prints From Noted Pictures (3 Brands)	1908	£140.00	—
L?21	(5 Brands)	1908	£140.00	—
L?21	(No Firm's Name)	1908	£140.00	—

T.P. & R. GOODBODY

Qty		Date	Odds	Sets
?23	Actresses "ANGOOD"	1898	£350.00	—
?10	Beauties "KEWA" (Mauve Back)	1898	£300.00	—
?10	(Red Back)	1898	£300.00	—
25	Boer War Celebrities (Multi-Backed)	1901	£35.00	—
16	Boer War Celebrities (Different)			
	(Complete Frame, Multi-Backed)	1900	£35.00	—
	(No Vertical Lines, Multi-Backed)	1900	£35.00	—
	(2 Horizontal Lines, Multi-Backed)	1900	£35.00	—
50	Colonial Forces (Black Back)	1900	£75.00	—
50	(Brown Back)	1900	£80.00	—
M50	Colonial Forces	1900	£500.00	—

T.P. & R. GOODBODY – cont.

Qty		Date	Odds	Sets
67	Dogs (Multi-Backed)	1898	£90.00	–
26	Eminent Actresses (Name At Bottom)	1900	£50.00	£1,300.00
26	(Name At Top)......................................	1900	£250.00	–
20	Irish Scenery (Donore Castle Cigarettes)............................	1905	£45.00	–
20	Furze Blossom Cigarettes).........................	1905	£45.00	–
20	(Primrose Cigarettes)	1905	£45.00	–
20	(Royal Wave Cigarettes)............................	1905	£45.00	–
20	(Straight Cut Cigarettes)	1905	£45.00	–
?14	Pretty Girl Series"BAGG" (Grey Back).................................	1898	£300.00	–
?14	(Mauve Back)...........................	1898	£300.00	–
?14	(Red Back)	1898	£300.00	–
?14	(No Brands)...............................	1898	£300.00	–
50	Questions & Answers In Natural History.............................	1924	£2.40	£120.00
25	Sports & Pastimes	1925	£7.00	£200.00
25	Types Of Soldiers	1914	£60.00	–
20	War Pictures	1915	£35.00	£700.00
12	With The Flag To Pretoria	1901	£110.00	–

GORDON'S

?4	Billiards	1912	£1,000.00	–

F GOUGH

M?	Play Up Sporting Shields..	1900	£80.00	–

GRAVESON

30	Army Pictures, Cartoons, etc. (3 Backs)...............................	1916	£140.00	–

FRED GRAY

25	Types Of British Soldiers	1914	£160.00	–

GRIFFITHS BROS.

XF18	Beauties	1928	£150.00	–

GUERNSEY TOBACCO CO. (Channel Isles)

49	And When Did You Last See Your Father? (Sect.)	1936	£2.40	–
K52	Miniature Playing Cards...	1933	£1.00	–
48	The Laughing Cavalier (Sect)..	1935	£2.40	–
48	The Toast (Sect, Black Back)...	1936	£2.40	£115.00
48	(Sect, Green Back)...	1936	£7.50	–

HARRIS & SONS

26	Beauties "HOL"..	1900	£36.50	–
30	Colonial Troops..	1901	£100.00	–
25	Star Girls (6 Backs)	1899	£300.00	–

JAS. H. HARRISON

18	Motor Cycle Series	1914	£95.00	–

HARVEY'S NAVY CUT

M?	Play Up Sporting Shields..	1900	£100.00	–

HARVEY & DAVY

Qty		Date	Odds	Sets
50	Birds & Eggs	1905	£4.50	£225.00
35	Chinese & South African Series	1901	£140.00	—
30	Colonial Troops	1902	£80.00	—
25	Types Of British & Colonial Troops	1901	£90.00	—

W. HEATON

Qty		Date	Odds	Sets
?6	Birkby Views	1912	£400.00	—

HENLY & WATKINS LTD.

Qty		Date	Odds	Sets
25	Ancient Egyptian Gods (Plain Back)	1924	£7.50	£187.50
25	(Printed Back)	1924	£7.50	£187.50

HIGNETT BROS & CO.

Qty		Date	Odds	Sets
50	Actors Natural & Character Studies	1938	£1.80	£90.00
26	Actresses "FROGA"	1900	£60.00	—
25	Actresses, Photogravure	1900	£65.00	—
28	Actresses, "PILPI I"	1901	£17.50	£490.00
F50	Actresses, "PILPI II"	1901	£12.00	£600.00
P1	Advertisement Card, Calendar Back	1884	—	£600.00
50	A.F.C. Nicknames	1933	£7.00	£350.00
50	Air-Raid Precautions	1939	£1.25	£62.50
60	Animal Pictures	1899	£34.00	—
50	Arms & Armour	1924	£2.80	£140.00
25	Beauties "CHOAB"	1900	£225.00	—
50	Beauties, Gravure (Cavalier)	1898	£80.00	—
50	(Golden Butterfly)	1898	£80.00	—
MF50	Beauties (Chess Cigarettes) (Set 1)	1927	£1.40	£70.00
MF50	(No Brand) (Set 1)	1927	£1.75	—
MF50	Beauties (Chess Cigarettes) (Set 2)	1927	£1.80	£90.00
50	British Birds & Their Eggs	1938	£2.80	£140.00
50	Broadcasting	1935	£2.75	—
19	Cabinet 1900	1900	£90.00	—
25	Cathedrals & Churches	1909	£3.40	£85.00
50	Celebrated Old Inns	1925	£3.20	£160.00
50	Champions Of 1936	1936	£3.50	—
25	Common Objects Of The Sea-Shore	1924	£2.40	£60.00
25	Company Drill	1915	£3.50	£87.50
50	Coronation Procession	1937	£3.00	—
P8	Counter Display Cards - Beauties	1890	£400.00	—
X6	Diamond Jubilee	1897	£600.00	—
50	Dogs	1936	£2.40	£120.00
50	Football Caricatures	1935	£3.60	£180.00
50	Football Club Captains	1936	£3.60	£180.00
25	Greetings Of The World	1907	£2.80	£70.00
25	Historical London	1926	£2.80	£70.00
50	How To Swim	1935	£1.25	£62.50
50	Interesting Buildings	1905	£6.50	£325.00
25	International Caps And Badges	1924	£4.60	£115.00
25	Life In Pond & Stream	1925	£3.20	£80.00
40	Medals	1900	£25.00	—
25	Military Portraits	1917	£5.00	£125.00
50	Modern Railways	1936	£2.60	£130.00
25	Modern Statesmen (Butterfly Cigarettes)	1906	£4.60	£115.00
25	(Pioneer Cigarettes)	1906	£4.60	£115.00

Qty		Date	Odds	Sets
20	Music Hall Artistes	1898	£70.00	£1,400.00
50	Ocean Greyhounds	1938	£1.70	£85.00
M1	Oracle Butterfly (Several Printings)	1898	–	£85.00
25	Panama Canal	1914	£6.00	£150.00
12	Pretty Girl Series "RASH"	1900	£60.00	£650.00
50	Prominent Cricketers Of 1938	1938	£4.00	£200.00
50	Prominent Racehorses Of 1933	1934	£2.60	£130.00
G1	Riddle Folder	1893	–	£650.00
50	Sea Adventure	1939	£0.75	£37.50
25	Ships, Flags & Cap Badges, A Series	1926	£4.50	£112.50
25	Ships, Flags & Cap Badges, 2nd Series	1927	£5.00	£125.00
50	Shots From The Films	1936	£3.60	£180.00
X6	Story Of A Boy Who Robs A Stork's Nest	1890	£600.00	–
25	The Prince Of Wales Empire Tour	1924	£2.40	£60.00
50	Trick Billiards	1934	£6.00	–
25	Turnpikes	1927	£2.50	£62.50
P8	Uniforms & Armies Of Countries	1899	£650.00	–
25	V.C. Heroes	1901	£60.00	£1,500.00
20	Yachts (Black Back)	1898	£70.00	–
20	(White Back)	1898	£75.00	–
50	Zoo Studies	1937	£1.00	£50.00

R. & J. HILL LTD.

Qty		Date	Odds	Sets
25	Actresses-Belle Of New York (39mm Wide)	1899	£25.00	£625.00
25	(41mm Wide)	1899	£26.00	£650.00
20	Actresses-Chocolate (Hill Cigarettes)	1917	£18.00	–
20	(Hill Tobaccos)	1917	£19.00	–
20	(Plain Back)	1917	£18.00	–
30	Actresses-Continental (Whisky Back)	1906	£21.00	–
30	(Seven Wonders)	1906	£17.50	£525.00
30	(Plain Back)	1906	£18.00	–
26	Actresses "FROGA"	1900	£62.50	–
16	Actresses "HAGG" (High Class Cigarettes)	1900	£35.00	–
16	(Stockrider)	1900	£35.00	–
20	Animal Series (Crowfoot Cigarettes)	1909	£26.00	–
20	(Hill's)	1909	£27.50	–
20	(Anonymous, Cigarettes Back)	1909	£27.50	–
20	(Anonymous, Space At Base)	1909	£27.50	–
20	(Anonymous, Plain Back)	1909	£27.50	–
F25	Artistas Teatrais Portuguesos	1924	£35.00	–
25	Aviation Series (Hill Name)	1934	£3.50	£87.50
25	(Gold Flake Honeydew)	1934	£3.50	£87.50
?17	Battleships (Printed Back)	1914	£350.00	–
?17	(Plain Back)	1914	£45.00	–
25	Battleships & Crests	1901	£22.00	£550.00
12	Boer War Generals - Campaigners	1901	£35.00	£420.00
20	Breeds Of Dogs (Archer's M.F.H.)	1914	£24.00	–
20	(Badminton)	1914	£24.00	–
20	(Spinet Tobacco)	1914	£24.00	–
20	(Verbena Mixture)	1914	£24.00	–
L30	Britain's Stately Homes (Silk)	1917	£3.75	£112.50
?48	British Navy Series	1902	£26.50	–
L40	Canvas Masterpieces, Series 1 (Spinet)	1916	£2.25	£90.00
L40	(Badminton)	1916	£1.25	£50.00

Qty		Date	Odds	Sets
L40	Canvas Masterpieces, Series 2 (Silk)	1922	£2.50	£100.00
X10	Canvas Masterpieces, Series 2 (Silk)	1916	£2.00	—
50	Caricatures Of Famous Cricketers	1926	£3.20	£160.00
L50	Caricatures Of Famous Cricketers	1926	£2.30	£115.00
?	Celebrated Pictures	1905	£750.00	—
50	Celebrities Of Sport (Hill Name)	1939	£2.30	£115.00
50	(Gold Flake)	1939	£4.00	—
P4/5	Chinese Pottery & Porcelain (Silk)	1915	£0.50	£2.00
P5	(Complete Set)	1915	—	£40.00
X11	Chinese Pottery & Porcelain 2 (Silk)	1915	£6.00	—
10	Chinese Series	1912	£80.00	—
35	Cinema Celebrities (Spinet House)	1936	£1.10	£38.50
35	(Anonymous)	1936	£1.10	£38.50
30	Colonial Troops (Leading Lines)	1901	£24.00	£690.00
30	(Perfection Vide Dress)	1901	£24.00	£690.00
50	(Sweet American)	1901	£23.00	£1,150.00
40	Crystal Palace Souvenir Cards (Matt)	1937	£2.75	£110.00
40	(Varnished)	1937	£2.00	£80.00
48	Decorations And Medals (Hill Back)	1940	£1.60	£80.00
48	(Gold Flake)	1940	£3.00	—
F48	Famous Cinema Celebrities (Spinet - 2 Printings)	1931	£4.50	—
F48	(No Brand)	1931	£4.00	£192.00
LF48	Famous Cinema Celebrities, Series A (Kadi)	1931	£4.20	—
LF48	(No Brand)	1931	£4.20	—
F50	Famous Cinema Celebs, Series C (Devon)	1932	£6.80	—
F50	(Toucan)	1932	£6.80	—
F50	(No Brand)	1932	£3.75	—
LF50	Famous Cinema Celebs, Series D (Kadi)	1932	£3.50	—
LF50	(No Brand)	1932	£4.50	—
28	Famous Cricketers Series (Blue Back)	1912	£65.00	—
28	(Red Back)	1912	£70.00	—
40	Famous Cricketers	1923	£5.25	£210.00
50	Famous Cricketers, Inc. S. African Team	1925	£5.50	£275.00
L50	Famous Cricketers, Inc. S. African Team	1925	£5.75	£287.50
50	Famous Dog Breeds	1952	£8.50	—
L30	Famous Engravings, Series XI"	1910	£4.15	£125.00
40	Famous Film Stars (English Text)	1938	£1.15	£46.00
40	(Arabic Text)	1938	£1.10	£44.00
20	Famous Footballers Series	1912	£26.00	£520.00
50	Famous Footballers (Brown)	1923	£3.80	£190.00
50	Famous Footballers (Coloured, Archer)	1939	£2.80	£140.00
50	(Coloured, With Address)	1939	£2.60	£130.00
25	Famous Footballers, Additional (51-75)	1939	£3.00	£75.00
25	Famous Pictures (Fine Art Cigarettes)	1913	£3.50	£87.50
25	(Cigarette Series)	1913	£3.60	£90.00
50	Famous Ships (Matt)	1940	£1.70	£85.00
50	(Varnished)	1940	£1.10	£55.00
48	Film Stars And Celebrity Dancers	1935	£1.60	£75.00
30	Flags & Flags With Soldiers	1901	£25.00	—
24	Flags, Arms & Types Of Nations"	1910	£13.00	£312.00
20	Football Captain Series (Large Print)	1906	£65.00	—
20	(Small Print)	1906	£50.00	—
20	Fragments From France (Coloured)	1916	£25.00	£500.00
10	(Buff)	1916	£27.50	—
10	(Black & White)	1916	£100.00	—

R. & J. HILL LTD.– cont.

Qty		Date	Odds	Sets
L23	Great War Leaders, Series 10 (Silk)	1917	£6.00	£140.00
50	Historic Places From Dickens' Classics	1926	£0.75	£37.50
L50	Historic Places From Dickens' Classics (2 Printings)	1926	£0.60	£30.00
50	Holiday Resorts (Brown Back)	1925	£1.50	—
50	(Green Back)	1925	£0.65	£32.50
L50	Holiday Resorts (Brown Back)	1925	£1.50	—
L50	(Green Back)	1925	£0.80	£40.00
20	Inventors & Their Inventions (1-20)	1907	£4.50	£90.00
20	Inventors & Their Inventions (21-40)	1908	£7.50	£150.00
15	Japanese Series (Black & White)	1904	£50.00	£750.00
15	(Black & White, Lind Back)	1904	£225.00	—
15	(Coloured, Blue Panel)	1904	£250.00	—
15	(Coloured, Red Panel)	1904	£65.00	—
20	Lighthouse Series (No Frame Line)	1903	£36.00	£720.00
30	(With Frame Line)	1903	£35.00	£1,050.00
50	Magical Puzzles	1938	£2.20	£110.00
50	Modern Beauties	1939	£1.00	£50.00
30	Music Hall Celebrities-Past & Present	1930	£2.50	£75.00
L30	Music Hall Celebrities-Past & Present	1930	£2.75	£82.50
20	National Flag Series (Printed Back)	1914	£8.50	£170.00
20	(Plain Back)	1914	£7.00	£140.00
30	Nature Pictures	1930	£1.00	£30.00
30	Nautical Songs	1937	£1.25	£37.50
M25	Naval Series (Unnumbered)	1901	£45.00	—
20	Naval Series (Numbered 21-40)	1911	£13.00	£260.00
10	Naval Series (Numbered 41-50)	1911	£55.00	—
30	Our Empire Series	1929	£0.35	£10.50
L30	Our Empire Series	1929	£0.50	£15.00
M30	Popular Footballers Series A	1935	£3.30	£100.00
M20	Popular Footballers Series B	1935	£3.60	£72.00
20	Prince Of Wales Series	1911	£12.00	£240.00
50	Public Schools And Colleges	1923	£0.70	£35.00
L50	Public Schools And Colleges	1923	£0.70	£35.00
75	Public Schools And Colleges	1923	£0.80	£60.00
L75	Public Schools And Colleges	1923	£1.00	£75.00
50	Puzzle Series	1937	£1.50	£75.00
42	Real Photographs Set 1 (Space At Back)	1930	£2.50	—
F42	(Space At Back)	1930	£2.50	—
42	(London Idol)	1930	£2.20	£92.50
F42	(London Idol)	1930	£2.40	—
F42	Real Photographs Set 2	1930	£3.00	—
20	Rhymes	1904	£27.50	£550.00
F50	Scenes From The Films	1934	£3.50	—
40	Scenes From The Films	1938	£1.00	£40.00
35	Scientific Inventions and Discoveries (Black/White)	1929	£1.10	£40.00
35	(Coloured)	1929	£1.30	£45.00
20	(Plain Back)	1934	£1.35	£27.00
L35	Scientific Inventions and Discoveries (Coloured)	1929	£1.30	£45.00
F50	Sports	1934	£5.00	£250.00
F50	Sports Series (as above)	1934	£12.50	—
F50	Sports Series (as above, no title)	1934	£15.00	—
30	Statuary Set 1 (Matt Front)	1898	£60.00	—
30	(Varnished)	1898	£11.50	—
30	Statuary Set 2	1899	£8.00	£240.00
26	Statuary Set 3 (Black Panel)	1898	£25.00	—

**The 1924 Cabinet
Godfrey Phillips**

**History Of Aviation
Nabisco Foods**

**Famous Cricketers
Barratt & Co**

**Conquest Of Space
Weetabix**

Cycles & Motorcycles
Priory Tea

Empire Games & Test Teams
Hoadley's Chocolates

Olympics
Goodies

Adventures Of Pinky & Perky
Gaycon Products

R. & J. HILL LTD.– cont.

Qty		Date	Odds	Sets
26	Statuary Set 3 (Grey Panel)	1898	£50.00	—
26	(White Panel)	1898	£27.50	—
30	The All Blacks	1924	£7.00	£210.00
50	The Railway Centenary, A Series	1925	£1.30	£65.00
L50	The Railway Centenary (Brown Back)	1925	£1.30	£65.00
L50	(Grey Back)	1925	£4.00	—
25	The Railway Centenary, 2nd Series	1925	£1.60	£40.00
L25	The Railway Centenary, 2nd Series	1925	£2.00	£50.00
25	The River Thames (1-25)	1924	£1.70	£42.50
25	The River Thames (26-50)	1924	£1.40	£35.00
L50	The River Thames (Green Back)	1924	£1.50	£75.00
100	Transfers	1935	£6.50	—
20	Types Of The British Army (Badminton)	1914	£30.00	—
20	(Verbena)	1914	£30.00	—
LF48	Views Of Interest, 1st Series (Spinet)	1938	£0.25	£12.00
LF48	(Sunripe)	1938	£0.25	£12.00
LF48	Views Of Interest, 2nd Series	1938	£0.25	£12.00
LF48	Views Of Interest, 3rd Series	1939	£0.25	£12.00
LF48	Views Of Interest, 4th Series	1939	£0.35	£17.00
LF48	Views Of Interest, 5th Series	1939	£0.35	£17.00
LF48	Views Of Interest-Canada	1940	£0.30	£15.00
LF48	Views Of Interest-India	1940	£3.00	£144.00
50	Views Of London	1925	£0.80	£40.00
L50	Views Of London	1925	£0.80	£40.00
L50	Views Of River Thames (Green & Black)	1924	£1.60	£80.00
25	War Series	1915	£13.00	£325.00
50	Who's Who In British Films	1927	£1.70	£85.00
L50	Who's Who In British Films	1927	£1.80	£90.00
84	Wireless Telephony	1923	£1.60	£135.00
L20	Wireless Telephony Broadcasting Series	1923	£2.50	£2.75
25	World's Masterpieces, Second Series	1914	£2.00	£50.00
50	Zoological Series	1924	£0.80	£40.00
L50	Zoological Series	1924	£0.90	£45.00

L.HIRST & SON

T25	Soldiers & Their Uniforms (Cut-outs)	1914	£275.00	—

J.W. HOBSON

18	Motor Cycle Series	1914	£110.00	—

HOCKINGS BAZAAR, PORTHCAWL

30	Army Pictures, Cartoons, etc	1916	£135.00	—

J. & T. HODGE

?5	Britain's Naval Crests	1896	£750.00	—
16	British Royal Family	1901	£300.00	—
?11	Scottish Views (Size 74 X 39Mm)	1898	£200.00	—
?14	(Size 80 X 45Mm)	1898	£225.00	—

HOOK OF HOLLAND CIGARETTES

?5	Footballers	1900	£650.00	—

HUDDEN & CO.

Qty		Date	Odds	Sets
26	Actresses "FROGA"	1900	£65.00	—
25	Beauties "CHOAB"	1901	£60.00	—
20	Beauties, Crown Seal	1898	£140.00	—
24	Beauties "HUMPS" (Blue Back)	1899	£75.00	—
24	(Orange Back - 2 Printings)	1899	£55.00	—
24	(Type Set Back)	1899	£400.00	—
12	Comic Phrases	1900	£110.00	—
25	Famous Boxers	1927	£35.00	—
25	Flags Of All Nations	1904	£26.00	£650.00
48	Japanese Playing Cards (Dandy Dot)	1900	£200.00	—
48	(Hudden's Cigarettes)	1900	£90.00	—
18	Pretty Girl Series "RASH"	1900	£90.00	—
50	Public Schools And Colleges	1924	£2.20	£110.00
25	Soldiers Of The Century	1903	£55.00	£1,375.00
25	Sports And Pastimes	1926	£65.00	—
25	Star Girls	1900	£110.00	—
25	Types Of Smokers	1903	£55.00	—

HUDSON'S

Qty		Date	Odds	Sets
?26	Actresses "ANGOOD"	1898	£650.00	—
25	Beauties "BOCCA"	1900	£550.00	—

HUNTER

Qty		Date	Odds	Sets
?11	Footballers	1906	£2,000.00	—

JAMES ILLINGWORTH LTD.

Qty		Date	Odds	Sets
MF48	Beautiful Scotland	1939	£2.00	£100.00
M25	Cavalry	1924	£5.50	£137.50
MF48	Coastwise	1938	£1.00	£50.00
25	'Comicartoons' of Sport	1927	£7.00	£175.00
MF48	Flying	1938	£2.00	£100.00
25	Motor Car Bonnets	1925	£7.50	£187.50
25	Old Hostels	1926	£6.00	£150.00
MF48	Our Countryside	1938	£2.00	—
MF24	Shots From The Films	1937	£5.00	—
25	Views From The English Lakes	1894	£250.00	—

IMPERIAL TOBACCO CO. LTD.

Qty		Date	Odds	Sets
50	British Birds	1909	£5.50	£275.00
X1	Coronation Folder	1902	—	£100.00
T12	Russ Abbot Advertising Cards	1993	—	£12.00

INGRAMS (Eastleigh) (Tobacconist)

Qty		Date	Odds	Sets
30	Army Pictures, Cartoons, etc.	1916	£140.00	—

INTERNATIONAL TOBACCO CO. LTD.

Qty		Date	Odds	Sets
28	Domino Cards	1938	£0.20	£6.00
D50	Famous Buildings & Monuments, Series A			
	(International Tobacco Co. Ltd)	1934	£1.20	£60.00
	(International Tobacco (Overseas) Ltd.)	1934	£1.60	—
D50	Famous Buildings & Monuments, Series B	1934	£2.00	£100.00
100	Film Favourites (Black Back)	1937	£2.65	—
100	(Brown Back)	1937	£2.00	£200.00

Qty		Date	Odds	Sets
D100	Gentlemen! The King! (Black Back)	1938	£0.20	£20.00
D100	Gentlemen! The King! (Blue Back)	1938	£0.60	—
50	International Code Of Signals	1934	£1.20	£60.00
48	Screen Lovers (Summit)	Unissued	£3.50	£170.00

PETER JACKSON

Qty		Date	Odds	Sets
F28	Beautiful Scotland	1939	£1.35	£40.00
MF48	Beautiful Scotland	1939	£1.00	£48.00
F28	Coastwise	1938	£1.35	£40.00
MF48	Coastwise	1938	£1.25	£60.00
F28	Famous Film Stars	1935	£3.75	£105.00
F27	Famous Films	1934	£3.75	£100.00
F28	Film Scenes	1936	£3.50	£100.00
LF28	Film Scenes (Different)	1936	£4.50	£126.00
F28	Flying	1938	£3.25	£90.00
MF48	Flying	1938	£3.50	—
D100	Gentlemen! The King!			
	(Overprinted on Black International)	1938	£1.00	—
	(Overprinted on Blue International)	1938	£1.00	—
	(Reprinted Black With Jackson Name)	1938	£1.00	—
	(Reprinted Blue With Jackson Name)	1938	£2.00	—
F28	Life In The Navy	1937	£2.00	£56.00
LF28	Life In The Navy (Different)	1937	£2.50	£70.00
F28	Our Countryside	1938	£1.00	£28.00
MF48	Our Countryside	1938	£1.25	£60.00
F28	Shots From The Films	1937	£3.25	£90.00
MF24	Shots From The Films	1937	£3.75	£90.00
D250	Speed Through The Ages (Mixed Sizes)	1937	£0.30	£75.00
F28	Stars In Famous Films	1934	£3.75	£105.00
D150	The Pageant Of Kingship (P.Jackson Ltd)	1937	£0.50	—
D150	(P.Jackson Overseas Ltd)	1937	£0.30	£45.00

JACOBI BROS. & CO. LTD.

Qty		Date	Odds	Sets
?32	Boer War Celebrities "JASAS"	1901	£225.00	—

JAMES & CO. (B'HAM) LTD.

Qty		Date	Odds	Sets
M20	Arms Of Countries	1915	£160.00	—

JAMES'S

Qty		Date	Odds	Sets
?11	Pretty Girl Series "BAGG"	1898	£375.00	—

JERSEY TOBACCO CO.LTD.(Channel Isles)

Qty		Date	Odds	Sets
K53	Miniature Playing Cards	1933	£1.00	—

SOCIETE JOB (J Bardou & Co)

Qty		Date	Odds	Sets
25	British Lighthouses	1925	£8.00	£200.00
M48	Cinema Stars (Numbered)	1926	£7.00	—
M48	Cinema Stars (Unnumbered)	1926	£1.00	£75.00
48	Cinema Stars (Numbered)	1926	£3.00	—
48	Cinema Stars (Unnumbered)	1926	£3.25	—
25	Dogs	1911	£27.00	£675.00
25	Liners	1912	£35.00	—
53	Miniature Playing Cards	1926	£6.50	—

SOCIETE JOB (J Bardou & Co) – cont.

Qty		Date	Odds	Sets
25	Orders Of Chivalry	1924	£3.80	£95.00
25	Orders Of Chivalry, 2nd Series"	1927	£3.80	£95.00
3	Orders Of Chivalry (Unnumbered)	1927	£8.00	£24.00
25	Racehorses	1909	£27.00	£675.00
	GERMAN ISSUES			
X70	Sport In Zehn Bildern	1930	£2.50	—

J.B. JOHNSON & CO.

Qty		Date	Odds	Sets
25	National Flags And Flowers - Girls	1901	£350.00	—

JOHNSTON'S

Qty		Date	Odds	Sets
?3	Carlisle Views	1910	£650.00	—

JONES BROS.

Qty		Date	Odds	Sets
10/13	Spurs Footballers	1911	£14.00	£140.00
4/6	Spurs Footballers	1912	£14.00	£56.00

A.I. JONES & CO. LTD.

Qty		Date	Odds	Sets
M1	Advertisement Card	1901	—	£750.00
12	Nautical Terms	1905	£47.50	£570.00

ALEX JONES & CO.

Qty		Date	Odds	Sets
?23	Actresses "ANGOOD" (Brown Front)	1898	£275.00	—
?23	(Green Front)	1898	£400.00	—
1	Diamond Jubilee 1897	1897	—	£150.00

A.S. JONES

Qty		Date	Odds	Sets
30	Army Pictures,Cartoons,etc."	1916	£135.00	—

T.E. JONES & CO.

Qty		Date	Odds	Sets
?12	Conundrums	1900	£225.00	—
50	Flags Of All Nations	1899	£80.00	—
16	Well-Known Proverbs	1900	£225.00	—
?52	Welsh Rugby Players	1900	£250.00	—

C.H. JORDEN LTD.

Qty		Date	Odds	Sets
F12	Celebrities Of The Great War	1915	£90.00	—

J. & E. KENNEDY

Qty		Date	Odds	Sets
25	Beauties "FECKSA"	1902	£50.00	—

RICHARD KENNEDY

Qty		Date	Odds	Sets
P25	Army & Navy Cartoons	1906	£750.00	—
50	War Portraits	1916	£130.00	—

KINNEAR LTD.

Qty		Date	Odds	Sets
13	Actresses	1899	£120.00	—
M1	A Gentleman In Kharki	1900	—	£80.00
15	Australian Cricket Team	1897	£240.00	—
?17	Cricketers	1898	£500.00	—
X1	Cricket Fixture Folder	1903	—	£1,500.00

KINNEAR LTD. – cont.

Qty		Date	Odds	Sets
25	Footballers & Club Colours	1898	£220.00	–
12	Jockeys, Set 1	1898	£62.50	£750.00
1	Jockeys, Tod Sloan	1898	–	£110.00
?4	Jockeys (Different), (Large Caption)	1898	£125.00	–
25	(Small Caption)	1898	£110.00	–
2	Prominent Personages	1902	£750.00	–
13	Royalty	1897	£45.00	£585.00
L1	The Four Generations	1900	–	£500.00
K?32	Views	1898	£400.00	–

KINNEAR, WHITWHAM & CO LTD

18	Motor Cycle Series	1914	£130.00	–

B. KRIEGSFELD & CO.

1	Advertisement Card	1900	–	£1,500.00
?63	Beauties "KEWA" (Matt Front)	1898	£85.00	–
?6	Semi Glossy Front	1898	£160.00	–
?10	Celebrities (Horizontal Back)	1901	£200.00	–
?10	(Vertical Back)	1901	£200.00	–
50	Flags Of All Nations	1899	£65.00	–
50	Phrases & Advertisements	1900	£85.00	–

A. KUIT LTD.

K?12	Arms Of Cambridge Colleges	1914	£115.00	–
K?12	Arms Of Companies	1914	£120.00	–
F30	British Beauties (Oval)	1914	£50.00	–
F?46	Crosmedo Bijou Cards	1915	£135.00	–
25	Principal Streets Of British Cities	1915	£100.00	–
F50	Types Of Beauty	1914	£100.00	–

L. & Y. TOBACCO MFG. CO.

26	Actresses "FROGA"	1900	£500.00	–

LAMBERT & BUTLER

10	Actresses & Their Autographs (Narrow, Cigarettes)	1898	£135.00	–
10	(Wide, Tobaccos)	1898	£150.00	–
20	Actresses "BLARM"	1900	£34.00	–
50	Admirals (Mixed Backs)	1900	–	£850.00
50	(Bird's Eye)	1900	£17.00	–
50	(Flaked Gold Leaf Honeydew)	1900	£17.00	–
50	(May Blossom)	1900	£17.00	–
50	(Viking)	1900	£17.00	–
1	Advertisement Card	1898	–	£450.00
50	Aeroplane Markings	1937	£2.00	£100.00
25	A History Of Aviation (Brown Front)	1933	£2.80	£70.00
25	(Green Front)	1932	£2.20	£55.00
40	Arms Of Kings & Queens Of England	1906	£4.50	£180.00
25	Aviation	1915	£3.60	£90.00
26	Beauties "HOL" (Mixed Backs)	1899	–	£845.00
26	(Flaked Gold Leaf)	1899	£32.50	–
26	Log Cabin)	1899	£32.50	–
26	(May Blossom)	1899	£32.50	–
26	(Viking Navy Cut)	1899	£32.50	–
50	Birds & Eggs	1906	£3.00	£150.00

Qty		Date	Odds	Sets
25	Boer War & Boxer Rebellion-Sketches	1901	£32.50	—
20	Boer War Generals "CLAM" (Black Back)	1901	£35.00	—
20	(Brown Back)	1901	£35.00	—
10	Boer War Generals "FLAC"	1901	£40.00	—
25	British Trees & Their Uses	1927	£2.20	£55.00
1	Colonel R.S.S. Baden-Powell, The King Of Scouts	1901	—	£450.00
25	Common Fallacies	1928	£2.00	£50.00
50	Conundrums (Blue Back)	1901	£20.00	—
50	(Green Back)	1901	£16.50	£825.00
12	Coronation Robes	1902	£17.50	£210.00
25	Dance Band Leaders	1936	£4.00	£100.00
28	Dominoes (Packets)	1955	£4.50	—
50	Empire Air Routes	1936	£2.30	£115.00
25	Famous British Airmen & Airwomen	1935	£1.80	£45.00
25	Fauna Of Rhodesia	1929	£0.90	£22.50
50	Find Your Way! (Drury Lane In Address)	1932	£1.40	£70.00
50	(Without Drury Lane)	1932	£1.50	£75.00
50	(Red Overprint)	1932	£1.50	£75.00
1	Find Your Way Joker Card	1932	—	£12.50
50	Footballers 1930-1	1931	£4.30	£215.00
25	Garden Life	1930	£0.80	£20.00
25	Hints & Tips For Motorists	1929	£4.00	£100.00
50	Horsemanship	1938	£2.50	£125.00
25	How Motor Cars Work	1931	£2.50	£62.50
50	Interesting Customs & Traditions Of The Navy, Army & Air Force	1939	£1.20	£60.00
25	Interesting Musical Instruments	1929	£2.80	£70.00
50	Interesting Sidelights On The Work Of The G.P.O.	1939	£1.10	£55.00
20	International Yachts, America v England Since 1871	1902	£65.00	£1,300.00
25	Japanese Series	1904	£7.50	£187.50
4	Jockeys (No Frame)	1902	£55.00	£220.00
10	Jockeys (With Frame, Different)	1902	£55.00	—
50	Keep Fit	1937	£0.90	£45.00
25	London Characters	1934	£2.20	£55.00
25	Motor Car Radiators	1928	£5.50	£137.50
25	Motor Cars, A Series (Green Back)	1922	£2.60	£65.00
25	Motor Cars, 2nd Series (26-50)	1923	£2.60	£65.00
50	Motor Cars, 3rd Series	1926	£4.00	£200.00
25	Motor Cars (Grey Back)	1934	£3.60	£90.00
50	Motor Cycles	1923	£3.60	£180.00
50	Motor Index Marks	1926	£2.80	£140.00
25	Motors	1908	£26.00	£650.00
25	Naval Portraits (Series Of 25)	1914	£3.50	£87.50
50	(Series Of 50)	1915	£3.50	£175.00
25	Pirates & Highwaymen	1926	£2.00	£50.00
25	Rhodesian Series	1928	£1.20	£30.00
X1	The Mayblossom Calendar 1900	1899	—	£750.00
50	The Thames From Lechlade To London			
	(Large Numerals)	1907	£7.00	—
	(Small Numerals)	1907	£6.50	£325.00
25	Third Rhodesian Series	1930	£0.50	£12.50
4	Types Of The British Army & Navy			
	(Black Specialities Back)	1897	£65.00	—
	(Brown Specialities Back)	1897	£65.00	£260.00
	(Viking Cigarettes)	1897	£70.00	—

LAMBERT & BUTLER - cont.

Qty		Date	Odds	Sets
PF?	Warships	1910	£65.00	—
25	Waverley Series	1904	£13.00	£325.00
25	Winter Sports	1914	£4.50	£112.50
25	Wireless Telegraphy	1909	£5.00	£125.00
25	Wonders Of Nature	1924	£0.50	£12.50
25	World's Locomotives (Series Of 25)	1912	£4.00	£100.00
50	(Series Of 50)	1912	£5.50	£275.00
25	World's Locomotives (Additional)	1913	£4.50	£112.50

OVERSEAS ISSUES

Qty		Date	Odds	Sets
50	Actors & Actresses "WALP"	1908	£3.50	—
250	Actresses "ALWICS" (With Firm's Name)	1905	£3.50	—
250	(Scout Cigarettes)	1905	£4.50	—
250	(Black Front)	1905	£7.00	—
250	Mauve Front,4 Backs)	1905	£27.50	—
250	(Red Portrait)	1905	£15.00	—
50	Beauties "LAWHA" (Scout Cigarettes)	1908	£3.75	—
50	(No Brand, Black, 2 Editions)	1908	£3.75	—
50	(No Brand, Unicoloured)	1908	£20.00	—
83	Danske Byvaabner	1926	£15.00	—
26	Etchings (Dogs)	1928	£27.50	—
L26	Etchings (Dogs)	1928	£32.50	—
25	Flag Girls Of All Nations	1910	£13.00	£325.00
F50	Homeland Events	1928	£2.50	—
?1	Indian Women (Blue Front)	1910	£100.00	—
?1	(Red Front)	1910	£100.00	—
25	London Characters	1934	£17.50	—
F50	London Zoo	1927	£1.25	£62.50
50	Merchant Ships Of The World	1924	£2.50	£125.00
30	Music Hall Celebrities	1906	£6.50	—
F50	Popular Film Stars (Title In 1 Line)	1925	£1.50	£75.00
F50	(Title In 2 Lines)	1925	£1.50	£75.00
F50	(Varsity Cigarettes)	1926	£2.60	£130.00
100	Royalty Notabilities & Events 1900-2	1902	£14.00	—
100	Russo Japanese Series	1905	£6.50	£650.00
F50	The Royal Family At Home And Abroad	1927	£1.40	£70.00
F50	The World Of Sport	1927	£2.00	£100.00
F50	Types Of Modern Beauty	1927	£1.25	£62.50
F50	Who's Who In Sport (1926)	1926	£1.80	£200.00
50	Zoological Studies	1928	£8.00	—

LAMBKIN BROS.

Qty		Date	Odds	Sets
36	Country Scenes (Series 1-6)	1924	£6.50	—
L36	Country Scenes (Series 7-12)	1926	£7.50	—
L?9	Irish Views (Plain Back)	1925	£35.00	—
L?5	Lily Of Killarney Views	1925	£200.00	—

LAMPORT & HOLT

Qty		Date	Odds	Sets
L1	T.S.S. Vandyke And Voltaire (2 Printings)	1930	—	£5.00

ED. LAURENS. LTD.

Qty		Date	Odds	Sets
M55	British Cavalry Uniforms (P/C Inset)	1975	—	£60.00

C. & J. LAW

Qty		Date	Odds	Sets
25	Types Of British Soldiers	1914	£30.00	£750.00
50	War Portraits	1915	£130.00	—

R.J. LEA LTD.

Qty		Date	Odds	Sets
1	Advertisement Card	1913	—	£1,000.00
M12	Butterflies & Moths (Silk)	1924	£4.75	£57.00
X12	Butterflies & Moths (Silk, Different)	1924	£4.50	£54.00
P6	Butterflies & Moths (Silk, Different)	1924	£5.00	£30.00
12	Chairman Puzzles	1910	£275.00	—
70	Cigarette Transfers (Locomotives)	1916	£8.00	£560.00
25	Civilians Of Countries Fighting With The Allies	1914	£13.00	£325.00
F48	Coronation Souvenir (Glossy, Lea Back)	1937	£0.65	£32.00
F48	(Glossy, Successors)	1937	£0.50	£24.00
48	(Matt, Lea Back)	1937	£1.25	£60.00
48	(Matt, Successors)	1937	£0.65	£32.00
MF48	Coronation Souvenir	1937	£0.65	£32.00
25	Dogs (1-25)	1923	£4.50	£112.50
25	Dogs (26-50)	1923	£6.50	—
25	English Birds (Glossy)	1922	£3.20	£80.00
25	(Matt)	1922	£6.50	—
F54	Famous Film Stars	1939	£1.30	£70.00
F48	Famous Racehorses Of 1926	1927	£3.00	£144.00
MF48	Famous Racehorses Of 1926	1927	£7.50	—
F48	Famous Views (Glossy)	1936	£0.30	£15.00
48	(Matt)	1936	£1.00	£48.00
MF48	Famous Views	1936	£0.60	£30.00
F36	Film Stars, 1st Series	1934	£3.20	£115.00
F36	Film Stars, 2nd Series	1934	£3.00	£108.00
25	Fish	1926	£2.40	£60.00
50	Flowers To Grow-The Best Perennials	1913	£3.60	£180.00
F48	Girls From The Shows (Glossy)	1935	£2.25	£108.00
48	(Matt)	1935	£2.50	£120.00
50	Miniatures (No Border)	1912	£2.70	£135.00
50	(Gold Border)	1912	£2.60	£130.00
50	Miniatures (51-100)	1912	£2.60	£130.00
46/50	Modern Miniatures	1913	£1.75	£80.00
12	More Lea's Smokers (Green Border)	1906	£80.00	—
12	(Red Frame)	1906	£125.00	—
P24	Old English Pottery & Porcelain	1908	£5.00	£144.00
50	Old English Pottery & Porcelain	1912	£1.70	£85.00
50	Old Pottery & Porcelain, 2nd (Chairman)	1912	£1.50	£75.00
50	(Recorder)	1912	£6.00	—
50	Old Pottery & Porcelain, 3rd (Chairman)	1912	£1.40	£70.00
50	(Recorder)	1912	£6.00	—
50	Old Pottery & Porcelain, 4th Series"	1913	£1.40	£70.00
50	Old Pottery & Porcelain, 5th Series"	1913	£1.40	£70.00
54	Old Pottery (Silk)	1914	£0.90	£50.00
72	Old Pottery (Silk, Different)	1914	£1.00	£80.00
F54	Radio Stars (Glossy)	1935	£2.25	£121.50
54	Radio Stars (Matt)	1935	£3.00	£162.00
M100	Regimental Crests & Badges (Silk)	1923	£1.75	—
50	Roses	1924	£1.70	£85.00
50	Ships Of The World	1925	£2.00	£100.00
25	The Evolution Of The Royal Navy	1925	£2.40	£60.00

R.J. LEA LTD. – cont.

Qty		Date	Odds	Sets
25	War Pictures	1915	£4.00	£100.00
25	War Portraits	1915	£5.00	£125.00
F48	Wonders Of The World (Glossy)	1938	£0.50	£24.00
48	(Matt)	1938	£1.50	—
MF48	Wonders Of The World	1938	£0.65	£32.00

ALFRED L. LEAVER

M12	Manikin Cards	1915	£150.00	—

J. LEES

21	Northampton Town Football Club	1912	£120.00	—

LEON DE CUBA CIGARS

30	Colonial Troops	1902	£165.00	—

A. LEWIS & CO. (Westminster) LTD.

52	Horoscopes	1938	£1.00	£52.00

H.C. LLOYD & SON LTD.

28	Academy Gems (Green Front, Multibacks)	1902	£45.00	—
28	(Mauve Front, Multibacks)	1902	£45.00	—
28	(Orange Front, Multibacks)	1902	£45.00	—
26	Actresses & Boer War Celebrities	1901	£45.00	—
M?6	Devon Footballers (With Frame Line)	1902	£225.00	—
M42	Devon Footballers & Boer War Celebrities (2 Printings)	1902	£50.00	—
25	Star Girls (Different Printings)	1899	£400.00	—
L36	War Pictures	1914	£325.00	—

RICHARD LLOYD & SONS

?23	Actresses, Celebrities & Yachts	1900	£100.00	—
25	Atlantic Records	1936	£2.80	£70.00
25	Boer War Celebrities	1899	£40.00	—
F27	Cinema Stars (1-27)	1935	£7.00	£190.00
F27	Cinema Stars (28-54)	1935	£3.00	£81.00
F27	Cinema Stars, 3rd Series (55-81)	1936	£6.00	£162.00
25	Cinema Stars (Matt)	1937	£2.20	£55.00
25	Famous Cricketers Puzzle Series	1930	£7.00	£175.00
96	National Types, Costumes & Flags	1900	£35.00	—
25	Old English Inns	1923	£1.80	£45.00
25	Old Inns, Series 2	1924	£3.00	£75.00
50	Old Inns	1924	£1.50	£75.00
10	Scenes From San Toy	1905	£10.00	£100.00
7	The Seven Ages Of Man	1900	£1,500.00	—
25	Tricks & Puzzles	1935	£2.00	£50.00
25	Types Of Horses	1926	£4.00	£100.00
25	Zoo Series	1926	£1.00	£25.00

A. LOWNIE (Tobacconist)

30	Army Pictures, Cartoons, etc.	1916	£140.00	—

LUSBY LTD.

25	Scenes From Circus Life	1902	£125.00	—

HUGH MCCALL

Qty		Date	Odds	Sets
1	RAF Recruiting Card	1924	£400.00	—

D. & J. MACDONALD

10	Actresses "MUTA"	1901	£125.00	—
L?13	Cricket & Football Teams (Tontine)	1902	£450.00	—
L?24	(Winning Team)	1902	£450.00	—
25	Cricketers	1902	£500.00	—
L1	Yorkshire County Team	1900	—	£1,500.00

MACKENZIE & CO.

F50	Music Hall Artistes	1902	£23.00	£1,150.00
50	The Zoo	1910	£28.00	—
50	Victorian Art Pictures	1910	£24.00	—

WM. MCKINNELL (or M'Kinnell)

12	The European War Series	1915	£60.00	—
50	War Portraits	1916	£125.00	—

MACNAUGHTON JENKINS & CO. LTD.

M50	Castles Of Ireland-Ancient & Modern	1924	£3.75	£187.50
50	Various Uses Of Rubber	1924	£2.60	£150.00

A. MCTAVISH (Tobacconist)

30	Army Pictures, Cartoons, etc.	1916	£135.00	—

MCWATTIE & SONS

30	Army Pictures, Cartoons, etc.	1916	£140.00	—

THE MANXLAND TOBACCO CO

?6	Views Of The Isle Of Man (Matt)	1900	£500.00	—
?6	(Varnished)	1900	£500.00	—

MARCOVITCH & CO.

F18	Beauties (Plain Back)	1932	£1.00	£18.00
6	The Story In Red And White	1955	£3.50	—
L7	The Story In Red And White	1955	£2.50	£17.50

MARCUS'S

?17	Cricketers	1897	£550.00	—
25	Footballers & Club Colours	1898	£220.00	—
L1	The Four Generations	1900	—	£350.00

MARKHAM

M?28	Views Of Bridgwater	1906	£90.00	—

MARSUMA CO.

50	Famous Golfers & Their Strokes	1914	£50.00	£2,500.00

C. MARTIN (Tobacconist)

30	Army Pictures, Cartoons, etc.	1916	£140.00	—

MARTINS LTD.

Qty		Date	Odds	Sets
1	Arf A Mo Kaiser!..	1915	—	£75.00
D?14	Carlyle Series(Different Printings)	1923	£125.00	—
P?781	Leading Artistes	1916	£6.00	—
25	V.C. Heroes..	1916	£27.50	—

MASCOT SPECIAL VIRGINIA CIGARETTES

?20	British Views	1925	£65.00	—

R. MASON & CO.

30	Colonial Troops..	1902	£55.00	—
40	Naval & Military Phrases (No Border)...............	1904	£47.50	—
40	(White Border)	1904	£47.50	—

JUSTUS VAN MAURIK

X12	Dutch Scenes	1915	£175.00	—

MAY QUEEN VIRGINIA CIGARETTES

M10/12	Interesting Pictures................................Unissued		£0.50	£5.00

MENTORS LTD.

32	Views Of Ireland..	1912	£12.00	£384.00

J. MILLHOFF & CO. LTD.

F54	Antique Pottery	1927	£0.90	£50.00
MF56	Antique Pottery	1927	£0.80	£45.00
30	Art Treasures	1927	£1.00	£30.00
L50	Art Treasures	1926	£0.70	£35.00
L25	Art Treasures, 2nd Series (51-75)	1928	£1.00	£25.00
25	British Orders Of Chivalry & Valour.................	1939	£2.00	£50.00
M20	De Reszke Rilette Pictures	1925	£3.00	—
M25	De Reszke Rilette Pictures	1925	£3.00	—
M30	De Reszke Rilette Pictures	1925	£3.00	—
M42	De Reszke Rilette Pictures	1925	£3.00	£95.00
M43	De Reszke Rilette Pictures	1925	£3.00	—
M56	De Reszke Rilette Pictures	1925	£3.00	—
M74	De Reszke Rilette Pictures	1925	£3.00	—
L25	England Historic & Picturesque (1-25).............	1928	£0.80	£20.00
L25	England Historic & Picturesque 2nd................	1928	£0.80	£20.00
F27	Famous Golfers	1928	£13.50	£475.00
F27	Famous Test Cricketers..................................	1928	£6.00	£160.00
MF27	Famous Test Cricketers..................................	1928	£5.25	£140.00
P24	Film Stars..	1934	£8.50	—
M25	Gallery Pictures..	1929	£1.00	£25.00
50	Geographia Map Series (Sect.).......................	1931	£1.75	£87.50
F36	In The Public Eye	1930	£1.60	£57.50
1	Jigsaw Advertisement Card (4 Types)	1933	—	£12.00
25	Men Of Genius...	1924	£5.00	£125.00
L25	Picturesque Old England	1931	£1.20	£30.00
F27	Real Photographs, A Series (Glossy)	1931	£0.40	£11.00
F27	(Matt)....................	1931	£0.75	£20.00
F27	Real Photographs, 2nd Series.........................	1931	£0.75	£20.00
F27	Real Photographs, 3rd Series..........................	1932	£0.40	£11.00
F27	Real Photographs, 4th Series"	1932	£0.60	£16.50

J. MILLHOFF & CO. LTD. – cont.

Qty		Date	Odds	Sets
F27	Real Photographs, 5th Series	1933	£1.00	£27.00
F27	Real Photographs, 6th Series	1933	£1.00	£27.00
25	Reproductions Of Celebrated Oil Paintings	1928	£1.50	£37.50
L25	Roses	1927	£2.60	£65.00
MF?16	Theatre Advertisement Cards (Multi-Backed)	1905	£175.00	—
XF?5	Theatre Advertisement Cards (Multi-Backed)	1905	£275.00	—
F54	The Homeland Series	1933	£0.30	£16.00
MF56	The Homeland Series	1933	£0.25	£14.00
50	Things To Make	1935	£0.75	£37.50
50	What The Stars Say	1934	£0.90	£45.00
F36	Zoological Studies	1929	£0.20	£7.50

DUTCH ISSUES

Qty		Date	Odds	Sets
F76	Dutch Footballers	1929	£25.00	—
L40	Film Series 1	1932	£6.50	—
L60	Film Series 1 (2 Printings)	1932	£6.50	—
L60	Film Series 2 (Coloured, 2 Addresses)	1935	£6.50	—
L25	Film Series 3 (Red-Brown)	1930	£6.50	—
MF105	Film Series 4	1933	£5.00	—
MF?249	Film Series 4 (Inscribed "Series Of 206")	1934	£5.00	—
MF105	Film Series "SERIE 6"	1936	£5.00	—

MIRANDA LTD.

Qty		Date	Odds	Sets
20	Dogs	1925	£8.50	—
25	Sports And Pastimes	1925	£7.00	£200.00

STEPHEN MITCHELL & SON

Qty		Date	Odds	Sets
51	Actors & Actresses "FROGA" (Coloured)	1899	£24.00	—
26	Actors & Actresses "FROGA B" (Brown)	1899	£24.00	—
25	Actors & Actresses "FROGA C"(Brown)	1899	£24.00	—
50	Actors & Actresses "FROGA D" (Brown)	1899	£24.00	£1,200.00
50	A Gallery Of 1934	1935	£2.80	£160.00
50	A Gallery Of 1935	1936	£2.00	£100.00
50	Air-Raid Precautions	1938	£1.00	£50.00
30	A Model Army	1932	£1.25	£37.50
25	Angling	1928	£6.50	£162.50
50	Arms & Armour	1916	£3.70	£185.00
25	Army Ribbons & Buttons	1916	£4.00	£100.00
50	A Road Map Of Scotland (Small Numeral)	1933	£3.50	—
50	(Large Numeral)	1933	£3.50	—
50	(Red Overprint)	1933	£4.50	—
1	A Road Map Of Scotland (Substitute)	1933	—	£15.00
25	Boxer Rebellion-Sketches	1901	£30.00	—
25	British Warships (1-25)	1915	£7.00	£175.00
25	British Warships, 2nd Series (26-50)	1915	£6.50	£162.50
50	Clan Tartans, A Series	1927	£2.00	£100.00
25	Clan Tartans, 2nd Series	1927	£1.20	£30.00
25	Empire Exhibition, Scotland 1938	1938	£1.20	£30.00
25	Famous Crosses	1923	£0.60	£15.00
50	Famous Scots	1933	£2.00	£100.00
50	First Aid	1938	£1.20	£60.00
P3	Glasgow International Exhibition 1901	1901	£85.00	—
50	Humorous Drawings	1924	£2.60	£130.00
50	Interesting Buildings	1905	£8.50	£425.00
40	London Ceremonials	1928	£1.40	£56.00

STEPHEN MITCHELL & SON – cont.

Qty		Date	Odds	Sets
25	Medals	1916	£4.50	£112.50
25	Money	1913	£4.50	£112.50
25	Old Sporting Prints	1930	£1.60	£40.00
50	Our Empire	1937	£0.50	£25.00
25	Regimental Crests & Collar Badges	1900	£14.00	£350.00
70	River & Coastal Steamers	1925	£4.00	£280.00
50	Scotland's Story	1929	£2.75	£137.50
25	Scottish Clan Series	1903	£12.00	£350.00
50	Scottish Footballers	1934	£3.20	£160.00
50	Scottish Football Snaps	1935	£2.80	£140.00
25	Seals	1911	£4.50	£112.50
25	Sports	1907	£14.00	£400.00
25	Stars Of Screen & History	1939	£2.80	£70.00
25	Statues & Monuments	1914	£4.40	£110.00
50	The World Of Tomorrow	1936	£2.00	£100.00
25	Village Models	1925	£2.40	£60.00
L25	Village Models	1925	£5.50	–
25	Village Models, 2nd Series	1925	£2.40	£60.00
25	2nd (Not Inscribed 2nd)	1925	£4.50	–
L25	Village Models, 2nd Series"	1925	£5.50	£137.50
50	Wonderful Century	1937	£0.90	£45.00

MOORGATE TOBACCO CO. LTD.

D30	The New Elizabethan Age (Matt)	1953	£3.50	–
D30	(Varnished)	1953	£2.00	£60.00

B. MORRIS & SONS LTD.

30	Actresses (Black & White)	1898	£1.70	£75.00
26	Actresses "FROGA A" (Borneo Queen)	1899	£32.50	–
26	(Gold Seals)	1899	£32.50	–
26	(Morris's Cigarettes)	1899	£32.50	–
26	(Tommy Atkins)	1899	£75.00	–
L?4	Actresses "FROGA B"	1899	£1,500.00	–
1	Advertisement Card	1900	–	£2,000.00
6	Agriculture In The Orient	1910	£6.50	£39.00
50	Animals At The Zoo (Blue Back)	1924	£0.70	£35.00
50	(Grey Back)	1924	£0.90	£45.00
6	Architectural Monuments	1910	£6.50	£39.00
35	At The London Zoo Aquarium	1928	£0.45	£15.00
25	Australian Cricketers	1925	£3.60	£90.00
M24	Battleship Crests (Silk)	1915	£36.50	–
50	Beauties "CHOAB" (Gold Flake Honeydew)	1900	£50.00	–
50	(Golden Virginia)	1900	£50.00	–
50	(Levant Favorites)	1900	£50.00	–
50	(Reina Regenta)	1900	£50.00	–
?53	Beauties Collotype(Multi-Backed)	1897	£175.00	–
21	Beauties "MOM" (Borneo Queen)	1899	£32.50	–
21	(Gold Seals)	1899	£32.50	–
21	(Morris Cigarettes)	1899	£32.50	–
21	(Tommy Atkins)	1899	£75.00	–
20	Boer War 1900	1900	£35.00	£700.00
25	Boer War Celebrities "PAM"	1901	£32.00	–
25	Captain Blood	1937	£1.20	£30.00
L25	English & Foreign Birds (Silk)	1915	£5.00	£125.00
L25	English Flowers (Silk, Panel Cigs)	1915	£3.80	£95.00

B. MORRIS & SONS LTD. – cont.

Qty		Date	Odds	Sets
L25	English Flowers ("Cruel" Silk)	1915	£8.00	–
L25	(Silk, No Brand)	1915	£6.25	–
L50	English Flowers (Silk)	1915	£4.20	£210.00
50	Film Star Series	1923	£3.40	£168.00
25	Golf Strokes Series	1923	£6.00	£150.00
12	Horoscopes	1936	£0.75	£9.00
25	How Films Are Made	1934	£1.80	£45.00
50	How To Sketch	1929	£1.25	£62.50
20	London Views (American Gold)	1904	£32.50	–
20	(Borneo Queen)	1904	£32.50	–
20	(Gold Flake)	1904	£32.50	–
20	(Reina Regenta)	1904	£32.50	–
25	Marvels Of The Universe Series	1912	£3.50	£87.50
25	Measurement Of Time	1924	£2.00	£50.00
25	Motor Series	1922	£4.50	£112.50
50	National & Colonial Arms	1917	£6.00	£300.00
25	Racing Greyhounds	1939	£2.20	£55.00
L25	Regimental Colours (Silk)	1916	£3.75	–
G4	Regimental Colours (Silk)	1916	£70.00	–
6	Schools In Foreign Countries	1910	£6.50	£39.00
24	Shadowgraphs	1925	£2.65	£65.00
6	Strange Vessels	1910	£7.00	£42.00
6	The Ice Breaker	1910	£7.00	£42.00
25	The Queen's Dolls House	1925	£3.00	£75.00
13	Treasure Island	1924	£1.25	£16.00
50	Victory Signs Series	1928	£0.75	£37.50
25	War Celebrities	1916	£6.00	£150.00
25	War Pictures	1916	£8.00	£200.00
25	Wax Art Series	1931	£0.70	£17.50
25	Whipsnade Zoo	1932	£0.60	£15.00
25	Wireless Series	1923	£4.60	£115.00

PHILIP MORRIS & CO. LTD.

Qty		Date	Odds	Sets
50	British Views	1924	£2.50	£125.00
L50	British Views	1924	£3.50	£175.00
T108	Classic Collection	1985	£1.25	–
M72	Motormania	1986	£1.35	–

P. MOUAT & CO.

Qty		Date	Odds	Sets
30	Colonial Troops	1902	£300.00	–

MOUSTAFA LTD.

Qty		Date	Odds	Sets
F50	Camera Studies (Printed Back)	1923	£3.50	–
F50	(Plain Back)	1923	£3.20	£160.00
25	Cinema Stars	1924	£5.50	–
40	Leo Chambers Dogs Heads	1924	£3.25	£130.00
25	Pictures Of World Interest	1923	£3.40	£85.00
F25	Real Photos	1925	£0.50	£12.50
X20	Wrestling Holds	1930	£35.00	–

MUNRO

Qty		Date	Odds	Sets
30	Colonial Troops	1902	£500.00	–

B. MURATTI SONS & CO. LTD.

Qty		Date	Odds	Sets
P?24	Actresses, Collotype"	1899	£125.00	—
26	Actresses "FROGA" (Cigarette Connoisseur)	1899	£27.50	£715.00
26	(Zinnia)	1899	£35.00	—
P26	Actresses "FROGA A" (Horizontal Back)	1899	£140.00	—
P?20	Actresses "FROGA C" (Vertical Back)	1899	£160.00	—
X?36	Advertisement Cards	1900	£375.00	—
F24	Australian Racehorses	1931	£1.00	£24.00
50	Beauties "CHOAB" (Black Back)	1900	£45.00	—
50	(Green Back)	1900	£60.00	—
P50	Beauties "CHOAB" (Printed Back)	1900	£135.00	—
P25	(Rubber Stamped Back)	1899	£160.00	—
P25	(Plain Back)	1899	£140.00	—
P?3	Beauties "MOM"	1900	£275.00	—
M?66	Beautiful Women	1900	£90.00	—
20	Boer War Generals "CLAM"	1900	£37.50	—
X?	Book Postcard Series	1902	£250.00	—
M15	Caricatures (4 Brands)	1903	£32.00	£480.00
M15	(Vassos)	1903	£70.00	—
M15	(Vassos Blanked Out)	1903	£60.00	—
M15	(Zinnia, Black)	1903	£32.00	£480.00
M15	(Zinnia, Brown)	1903	£35.00	—
M35	Crowned Heads	1914	£14.00	£575.00
53	Japanese Series (Printed Back)	1904	£17.00	£925.00
53	(Plain Back)	1904	£15.00	—
XF?340	Midget Post Card Series (Glossy)	1902	£8.50	—
X?107	(Matt)	1902	£8.00	—
X?127	Queens Postcard Series	1902	£11.00	—
19	Russo Japanese Series	1904	£15.00	£285.00
25	Star Girls	1899	£240.00	—
50	Views Of Jersey (Printed Back)	1913	£18.00	—
50	(Plain Back)	1913	£17.50	—
25	War Series I	1916	£23.00	—
25	War Series II (2 Printings)	1917	£14.00	£350.00

SILK ISSUES

Qty		Date	Odds	Sets
L40	Canvas Masterpieces Series M (Large Globe)	1916	£5.50	—
L40	(Small Globe)	1916	£2.50	£100.00
P16	Canvas Masterpieces Series P	1916	£12.50	—
M24	Flags, Series A (26-49)	1914	£3.75	£90.00
P3	Flags, Series A (1-3)	1914	£10.00	—
L1	Flags, Series B (No.19)	1914	—	£12.50
M25	Flags, Series C (20-44)	1914	£3.75	£95.00
P18	Flags, Series C (1-18)	1914	£10.00	—
P3	Flags, Series D (45-47)	1914	£10.00	—
M24/25	Flags, Series E (48-72, Green Back)	1914	£3.75	£90.00
M24/25	(48-72, Grey Back)	1914	£4.00	£100.00
P6	Flags, Series F (73-78)	1914	£9.00	—
P18	Great War Leaders, Series P	1916	£15.00	—
M25	Regimental Badges, Series A	1915	£4.50	£112.50
L48	Regimental Badges, Series B	1915	£6.00	£300.00
L15	Regimental Badges, Series B (Diff, 4-18)	1915	£6.00	£90.00
L16	Regimental Badges, Series G (79-94)	1915	£8.00	—
L25	Regimental Colours, Series CB	1915	£10.00	—
M72	Regimental Colours, Series RB	1915	£6.00	£425.00

CONTINENTAL ISSUES

Qty		Date	Odds	Sets
X215/216	Brennpunkte Des Deutschen Sports 1	1935	£0.80	£172.00

B. MURATTI SONS & CO. LTD – cont.

Qty		Date	Odds	Sets
X288	Brennpunkte Des Deutschen Sports 2	1936	£1.00	–
X216	Brennpunkte Des Deutschen Sports 3	1936	£0.80	–
?30	Cinema Stars Serie N0.1	1932	£5.00	–
?30	Cinema Stars Serie N0.2	1932	£5.00	–

MURRAY, SONS & CO.

Qty		Date	Odds	Sets
20	Actresses "BLARM" (Pineapple Cigs)	1902	£90.00	–
20	(Special Crown Cigs)	1902	£90.00	–
F22	Bathing Beauties	1929	£6.00	£130.00
40	Bathing Belles	1939	£0.50	£20.00
15	Chess And Draughts Problems	1910	£85.00	–
F22	Cinema Scenes	1929	£6.50	£145.00
20	Cricketers (Series H, Black Front)	1912	£75.00	–
20	(Series H, Brown Front)	1912	£200.00	–
25	Crossword Puzzles	1923	£350.00	–
F26	Dancers	1929	£5.50	£165.00
F25	Dancing Girls (Belfast, Ireland)	1929	£3.50	£87.50
F25	(London & Belfast)	1929	£3.50	£87.50
F26	("Series Of 26")	1930	£3.20	£85.00
25	Famous Works Of Art	1910	£25.00	–
M16	Flags (Silk)	1910	£22.00	–
X3	Flags & Arms (Silk)	1910	£65.00	–
34	Footballers, Series H"	1912	£50.00	–
104	Footballers, Series J"	1913	£50.00	–
29	Football Colours (Shaped, Maple Cigarettes)	1905	£75.00	–
29	(Shaped, Murray Cigarettes)	1905	£70.00	–
25	Football Rules	1911	£30.00	£750.00
25	High Class Works Of Art	1909	£26.00	–
20	Holidays By The L.M.S.	1927	£10.00	£200.00
20	Inventors Series	1924	£5.00	£100.00
25	Irish Scenery (Hall Mark Cigarettes)	1905	£22.50	–
25	(Pine Apple Cigarettes)	1905	£22.50	–
25	(Special Crown Cigs)	1905	£22.50	–
25	(Straight Cut Cigs)	1905	£22.50	–
25	(Yachtsman Cigarettes)	1905	£22.50	–
31	Orders Of Chivalry (Silk)	1925	£17.50	–
25	Polo Pictures	1910	£28.00	£700.00
M50	Prominent Politicians (With "In two strengths")	1909	£2.60	£130.00
M50	(Without "In two strengths")	1909	£17.00	–
50	Puzzle Series	1929	£7.50	–
M25	Regimental Badges (Silk)	1910	£17.50	–
50	Stage And Film Stars	1926	£4.20	£210.00
25	Steam Ships	1939	£1.60	£40.00
50	The Story Of Ships	1940	£0.60	£30.00
25	Types Of Aeroplanes	1929	£2.00	£50.00
20	Types Of Dogs	1924	£6.50	£130.00
35	War Series K	1915	£27.50	£950.00
25	War Series L	1916	£2.50	£80.00

H.J. NATHAN

Qty		Date	Odds	Sets
40	Comical Military & Naval Pictures (No Border)	1904	£60.00	–
	(White Border)	1904	£60.00	–

JAMES NELSON

Qty		Date	Odds	Sets
?23	Beauties "FENA"	1899	£1,000.00	–

Moon Fleet
Walls

Puppies
The Molassine Co

Famous Cricketers
Clevedon Confectionery

Flags
Wilbur-Suchard Chocolate Co

Motor Cars (Black & White)
Kellogg's

With Captain Scott At The
South Pole
Fry's

Optical Illusions
Goodwin's

British Royalty Series
Lovell's

NETTLETON AND MITCHELL

Qty		Date	Odds	Sets
30	Army Pictures, Cartoons, etc.	1916	£200.00	—

EDWD. J. NEWBEGIN

F50	Actors & Actresses	1901	£55.00	—
10	Actresses "HAGG"	1900	£185.00	—
20	Cricketers Series	1902	£500.00	—
1	Mabel Love Advert Card (3 Colours)	1900	—	£1,000.00
19	Russo Japanese Series	1904	£160.00	—
16	Well-Known Proverbs	1900	£140.00	—
25	Well-Known Songs	1900	£150.00	—

W.H. NEWMAN LTD.

18	Motor Cycle Series	1914	£110.00	—

THE NEW MOSLEM CIGARETTE CO. LTD.

30	Proverbs	1903	£115.00	—

THOS. NICHOLLS & CO.

50	Orders Of Chivalry	1916	£7.50	£375.00

THE NILMA TOBACCO COY.

40	Home & Colonial Regiments	1903	£125.00	—
30	Proverbs	1903	£110.00	—

M.E. NOTARAS LTD.

M24	Chinese Scenes	1925	£1.25	£30.00
F36	National Types Of Beauty	1925	£0.85	£31.50

A. NOTON

M12	Manikin Cards	1915	£135.00	—

OGDENS LTD.

25	A.B.C. Of Sport	1927	£3.20	£80.00
50	Actors, Natural & Character Studies	1938	£1.00	£50.00
25	Actresses ("No Glycerine", Black Front)	1895	£90.00	—
25	("No Glycerine", Brown Front)	1895	£90.00	—
?104	Actresses, Collotype (Mauve Stamped Back)	1894	£65.00	—
?104	(Red Stamped Back)	1894	£130.00	—
?99	Actresses, Collotype (Printed Back)	1894	£65.00	—
50	Actresses, Green Gravure	1898	£12.00	£600.00
?1	Actresses, Green, Green Border	1898	£1,000.00	—
50	Actresses, Tabs Type, Red Tint	1902	£35.00	—
?205	Actresses, Woodburytype	1894	£37.50	—
F?589	Actresses, Guinea Gold Type	1900	£3.25	—
50	A.F.C. Nicknames	1933	£4.80	£240.00
50	Air-Raid Precautions	1938	£0.80	£40.00
50	Applied Electricity	1928	£1.20	£60.00
192	Army Crests And Mottoes	1902	£5.50	£1,050.00
36	Australian Test Cricketers	1928	£3.75	£135.00
28	Beauties "BOCCA"	1899	£27.50	£770.00
50	Beauties "CHOAB"	1899	£30.00	—
26	Beauties "HOL" (Blue Printed Back)	1899	£22.50	£585.00

OGDENS LTD. – cont.

Qty		Date	Odds	Sets
26	Beauties "HOL" Rubber Stamped Back)	1899	£275.00	—
66	Beauties, Green Net Back (Black & White)	1901	£15.00	£1,000.00
99	(Coloured)	1901	£27.50	—
52	Beauties, P/C Inset	1899	£32.00	£1,650.00"
26	Beauties (No Insets, Subjects As Above)	1899	£37.50	—
52	Beauties & Military, P/C Inset	1898	£32.00	£1,650.00
F?83	Beauty Series (Unnumbered)	1900	£70.00	—
F50	Beauty Series (Numbered)	1900	£3.00	£150.00
50	Billiards By Tom Newman	1928	£2.40	£120.00
50	Birds' Eggs	1908	£1.60	£80.00
50	Bird's Eggs (Cut-Outs)	1923	£1.20	£60.00
F?142	Boer War & General Interest	1901	£3.50	—
LF?69	Boer War & General Interest	1901	£45.00	—
50	Boxers	1915	£7.25	£360.00
25	Boxing	1914	£5.25	£130.00
50	Boy Scouts (Blue Back)	1911	£3.20	£160.00
50	(Green Back)	1911	£4.50	£225.00
50	Boy Scouts, 2nd Series (Blue Back)	1912	£3.20	£160.00
50	(Green Back)	1912	£4.50	£225.00
50	Boy Scouts, 3rd Series (Blue Back)	1912	£3.50	£175.00
50	(Green Back)	1912	£4.50	£225.00
50	Boy Scouts, 4th Series	1913	£3.20	£160.00
25	Boy Scouts, 5th Series	1914	£3.20	£80.00
50	Boy Scouts (Different)	1929	£2.80	£140.00
50	British Birds	1905	£1.60	£80.00
50	British Birds, Second Series	1909	£2.00	£100.00
50	British Birds (Cut-Outs)	1923	£0.80	£40.00
50	British Birds & Their Eggs	1939	£2.60	£130.00
50	British Costumes From 100 B.C.To 1904	1905	£5.60	£280.00
50	Broadcasting	1935	£1.75	£87.50
50	By The Roadside	1932	£1.00	£50.00
44	Captains Of Association Football Clubs & Colours	1926	£3.25	£143.00
50	Cathedrals & Abbeys	1936	£1.10	£55.00
50	Champions Of 1936	1937	£2.00	£100.00
50	Children Of All Nations	1924	£0.80	£40.00
50	Club Badges	1915	£4.80	£240.00
50	Colour In Nature	1932	£0.80	£40.00
?27	Comic Pictures	1897	£350.00	—
50	Construction Of Railway Trains	1930	£2.40	£120.00
50	Coronation Procession (Sect.)	1937	£1.60	£80.00
12	Cricket & Football-Women (Gold Medal)	1896	£400.00	—
12	(Cox Back, Black Or Brown)	1896	£400.00	—
12	(Otto De Rose)	1896	£500.00	—
50	Cricketers & Sportsmen	1899	£90.00	—
50	Cricket 1926	1926	£2.80	£140.00
25	Derby Entrants 1926	1926	£2.60	£65.00
50	Derby Entrants 1928	1928	£2.40	£120.00
50	Derby Entrants 1929	1929	£2.40	£120.00
50	Dogs	1936	£2.40	£120.00
55	Dominoes	1909	£1.40	£77.00
112	Dominoes-Actress & Beauty Backs			
28	Actresses, Corners Mitred	1900	£26.50	—
28	Actresses, Corners Not Mitred	1900	£25.00	£700.00
56	Beauties, Corners Not Mitred	1900	£26.50	—

Qty		Date	Odds	Sets
P10	English Actresses	1890	£750.00	–
25	Famous Dirt-Track Riders	1929	£5.00	£125.00
50	Famous Footballers	1908	£4.25	£212.50
50	Famous Rugby Players	1926	£2.50	£125.00
50	Flags & Funnels Of Leading Steamship Lines	1906	£4.00	£200.00
50	Football Caricatures	1935	£3.00	£150.00
43	Football Club Badges (Shaped)	1910	£7.50	
50	Football Club Captains	1936	£2.70	£135.00
51	Football Club Colours	1906	£3.80	£195.00
50	Foreign Birds	1924	£0.80	£40.00
50	Fowls Pigeons & Dogs	1904	£3.20	£160.00
25	Greyhound Racing, 1st Series	1927	£4.40	£110.00
25	Greyhound Racing, 2nd Series	1928	£4.40	£110.00
1	History Of The Union Jack (Folder)	1900	–	£225.00
50	How To Swim	1935	£1.25	£62.50
50	Infantry Training	1915	£2.60	£130.00
50	Jockeys, And Owners' Colours	1927	£2.50	£125.00
50	Jockeys, 1930"	1930	£2.50	£125.00
50	Leaders Of Men	1924	£1.80	£90.00
MF3	Liners (Guinea Gold Type)	1901	£180.00	–
P6	Liners(6 Brands)	1902	£160.00	–
25	Marvels Of Motion	1928	£2.40	£60,00
K52	Miniature Playing Cards (Actresses)	1900	£5.00	–
K102	Miniature Playing Cards (Beauty Backs)	1900	£5.00	–
K52	Miniature Playing Cards (Coolie No Border)	1904	£2.50	£130.00
K52	(Coolie White Border)	1904	£4.00	–
K52	Miniature Playing Cards (Tabs)	1909	£2.60	£135.00
50	Modern British Pottery	1925	£1.00	£50.00
50	Modern Railways	1936	£2.30	£115.00
50	Modern War Weapons	1915	£3.30	£165.00
25	Modes Of Conveyance	1927	£2.40	£60.00
50	Motor Races 1931	1931	£2.70	£137.00
50	Ocean Greyhounds	1938	£1.20	£60.00
25	Optical Illusions	1923	£3.20	£80.00
50	Orders Of Chivalry	1907	£3.50	£175.00
25	Owners Racing Colours & Jockeys (Green Back)	1914	£4.20	£105.00
50	Owners Racing Colours & Jockeys (Blue Back)	1906	£3.20	£160.00
25	Picturesque People Of The Empire	1927	£1.20	£30.00
50	Picturesque Villages	1936	£1.50	£75.00
25	Poultry (1-25) (Ogdens On Front)	1915	£5.40	£135.00
25	(1-25) (No Ogdens On Front)	1915	£5.40	£135.00
25	Poultry, 2nd Series (26-50)	1916	£5.40	£135.00
25	Poultry Alphabet	1924	£4.40	£110.00
25	Poultry Rearing & Management, 1st Series	1922	£3.00	£75.00
25	Poultry Rearing & Management, 2nd Series	1923	£3.00	£75.00
50	Prominent Cricketers Of 1938	1938	£2.50	£125.00
50	Prominent Racehorses Of 1933	1934	£2.00	£100.00
50	Pugilists & Wrestlers, 1st Series	1908	£5.50	£275.00
25	Pugilists & Wrestlers, Second Series	1909	£6.00	£150.00
50	Pugilists In Action	1928	£3.80	£190.00
50	Racehorses	1907	£3.70	£185.00
50	Racing Pigeons	1931	£4.00	£200.00
25	Records Of The World	1908	£2.80	£70.00
50	Royal Mail	1909	£4.25	£212.50

Qty		Date	Odds	Sets
50	Sea Adventure	1939	£0.90	£45.00
50	Sectional Cycling Map	1910	£2.75	£137.50
50	Shakespeare Series (Numbered)	1905	£12.00	£600.00
50	(Unnumbered)	1905	£12.50	£625.00
50	Shots From The Films	1936	£2.20	£110.00
25	Sights Of London	1923	£1.50	£37.50
50	Smugglers And Smuggling	1932	£2.40	£120.00
50	Soldiers Of The King (Grey Caption)	1909	£5.00	£250.00
25	(Brown Caption)	1909	£6.50	£162.50
P30	Sporting & Other Girls	1898	£650.00	—
50	Steeplechase Celebrities	1931	£2.00	£100.00
50	Steeplechase Trainers &Owners Colours	1927	£2.00	£100.00
50	Swimming Diving And Life-Saving	1931	£1.50	£75.00
25	Swiss Views (1-25)	1910	£2.60	£65.00
25	Swiss Views (26-50)	1910	£4.80	£120.00
50	The Blue Riband Of The Atlantic	1929	£2.50	£125.00
50	The Story Of Sand	1935	£1.00	£50.00
25	Trainers And Owners Colours, 1st Series	1925	£2.50	£62.50
25	Trainers And Owners Colours, 2nd Series	1926	£3.20	£80.00
50	Trick Billiards	1934	£1.70	£85.00
50	Turf Personalities	1929	£2.40	£120.00
48	Victoria Cross Heroes	1901	£16.00	£760.00
25	Whaling	1927	£2.80	£70.00
50	Yachts & Motor Boats	1930	£2.60	£130.00
50	Zoo Studies	1937	£0.60	£30.00

GUINEA GOLD PHOTOGRAPHIC ISSUES

LF1	Actresses Base C	1899	—	£50.00
F376	Actresses Base D	1900	£1.50	—
MF55	Actresses Base D (Medium Size)	1900	£14.00	—
LF270	Actresses Base D	1900	£1.75	—
F40	Actresses Base E	1900	£3.75	£150.00
F639	Actresses Base I	1899	£1.25	—
LF?26	Actresses Base I (3/4 White Frame)	1899	£6.00	—
LF?26	Actresses And Actors Base I	1899	£40.00	—
F30	Actresses Base J	1899	£4.00	£120.00
F238	Actresses Base K	1899	£3.00	—
F216	Actresses Base L	1899	£2.40	—
F60	Actresses, Base M, 3/4 White Frame	1900	£2.50	£150.00
F113	Actresses & Miscellaneous Base I	1900	£1.20	£135.00
F2918	Actresses & Miscellaneous Base M	1900	£1.25	—
LF406	Actresses & Miscellaneous Base M	1900	£1.75	—
F58	Boer War & Actresses Base F	1901	£1.00	£60.00
F193	Boer War & Miscellaneous Base D	1901	£1.00	—
LF158	Boer War & Miscellaneous Base D	1900	£1.35	—
F?323	Continental Actresses Base B	1899	£3.00	—
LF?77	Continental Actresses Base B	1899	£18.00	—
F11	Cricketers Base I	1901	£13.50	£150.00
F50	Cricketers Base M (Set 1)	1899	£20.00	—
F27	Cricketers Base M (Set 2)	1899	£30.00	—
F57	Cyclists Base M	1899	£6.00	£340.00
F59	Denumbered Group Base D	1900	£2.75	£160.00
LF51	Denumbered Group Base D	1900	£4.00	£200.00
F176	Footballers Base M	1899	£22.50	—
F320	General Interest (White Panel)Bases D/I	1900	£1.20	£385.00
F200	General Interest Numbered 1-200	1901	£0.60	£120.00

OGDENS LTD. – cont.

Qty		Date	Odds	Sets
F300	General Interest Numbered 201-500	1901	£1.50	–
F395/398	General Interest Numbered 501-898	1901	£1.10	£435.00
F180/200	General Interest Numbered 899-1098	1901	£1.75	£315.00
F50	General Interest Numbered 1099-1148	1901	£1.50	£75.00
F18	Golf Base I	1901	£24.00	–
F14	London Street Scenes Base I	1901	£3.50	£49.00
F400	New Series 1	1902	£1.25	£500.00
F400	New Series B	1902	£1.50	£600.00
F300	New Series C	1902	£1.20	£360.00
F46	Pantomime & Theatre Artistes Base D	1899	£4.00	£184.00
LF45	Pantomime & Theatre Artistes Base D	1899	£6.00	£270.00
F50	Pantomime & Theatre Artistes Base M	1899	£6.50	–
F60/62	Politicians,Base D	1900	£1.25	£75.00
F3	Royalty Base M	1899	£3.00	£9.00
F32	Turner Paintings Base I	1901	£2.00	£64.00
F10	Views & Scenes Abroad Base I	1901	£1.75	£17.50
TABS TYPE ISSUES				
75	Actresses (Numbered 126-200)	1900	£13.50	–
200	Actresses (Plain Back)	1900	£2.75	–
200	Actresses & Foreign Views	1900	£2.25	–
1	General De Wet	1901	–	£4.50
1	General Interest (Unnumbered)	1901	–	£6.50
?40	General Interest (No Labour Clause)	1900	£25.00	–
150	General Interest A Series	1901	£1.00	–
200	General Interest B Series	1901	£0.85	–
200	General Interest C Series (1-200)	1902	£0.85	–
100	General Interest C Series (201-300)	1902	£2.25	–
50	General Interest C Series (301-350)	1902	£1.20	£60.00
200	General Interest D Series	1902	£0.80	£225.00
120	General Interest E Series	1902	£1.20	–
320	General Interest F Series (1-320)	1902	£1.40	–
99	General Interest F Series (321-420)	1902	£2.75	–
120	General Interest (1-120)	1902	£1.20	–
196	General Interest (Item 95)	1902	£0.85	£170.00
100	General Interest (Item 96)	1902	£1.00	£100.00
100	General Interest (Item 97-1)	1902	£1.35	£135.00
21	General Interest (Item 97-2, Cricket)	1902	£7.50	£157.50
25	General Interest (Item 97-2, Football)	1902	£6.00	£150.00
15	General Interest (Item 97-2, Golf)	1902	£22.00	£330.00
139	General Interest (Item 97-2, Various)	1902	£0.90	£125.00
?111	General Interest (Oblong Back)	1902	£16.00	–
17	Heroes Of The Ring	1901	£7.50	–
1	H.M. The Queen	1901	–	£5.00
2	H.R.H. The Prince Of Wales	1901	£3.75	£7.50
14	Imperial Interest	1901	£0.85	£12.00
106	Imperial Or International Interest	1901	£0.75	£80.00
3	International Interest	1901	£1.65	£5.00
14	International Interest Or A Prominent British Officer	1901	£0.75	£10.00
71	Leading Artistes Of The Day (Name In Black)	1901	£1.35	£95.00
?35	(Name In Black, No Labour Clause)	1901	£20.00	–
25	Leading Artistes Of The Day			
	(Name In White, Printed Back)	1901	£14.00	–
	(Name In White, Plain Back)	1901	£14.00	–
	(No Name)	1901	£14.00	–

OGDENS LTD. – cont.

Qty		Date	Odds	Sets
?91	Leading Artistes Of The Day			
	Leading Artistes Of The Day (Non Descriptive, Printed Back)	1901	£11.50	—
	Leading Artistes Of The Day (Non Descriptive, Plain Back) .	1901	£11.50	—
22	Leading Athletes	1901	£2.75	£60.00
15	Leading Favourites Of The Turf	1901	£4.50	£67.50
54	Leading Generals At The War	1901	£1.00	—
25	Leading Generals At The War (Different)	1901	£1.00	—
25	(No"Tabs")	1901	£2.00	—
47	Leading Generals At The War (Non Descriptive)	1901	£1.00	
25	Leading Generals At The War			
	(Lucky Star)	1901	£6.00	—
	("Guinea Gold" Rubber Stamped)	1901	£10.00	—
2	Members Of Parliament	1901	£3.50	£7.00
11	Notable Coursing Dogs	1901	£7.50	—
12	Our Leading Cricketers	1901	£15.00	£180.00
17	Our Leading Footballers	1901	£9.00	—
37	Prominent British Officers	1901	£0.80	£30.00
50	Stage Artistes & Celebrities	1900	£2.75	£137.50
1	The Yacht "Columbia"	1901	—	£6.50
1	The Yacht "Shamrock"	1901	—	£6.50
	AUSTRALIAN ISSUES TABS TYPE			
1	Christian De Wet	1901	—	£10.00
1	Corporal G.E. Nurse,V.C.	1901	—	£10.00
14	English Cricketer Series	1901	£60.00	£840.00
400	General Interest (Numbered)	1901	£3.00	—
100	General Interest (Unnumbered)	1901	£6.00	—
1	Imperial Interest	1901	—	£10.00
?29	Imperial Or International Interest	1901	£7.50	—
?6	International Interest	1901	£7.50	—
1	Lady Sarah Wilson	1901	—	£10.00
?41	Leading Generals At The War	1901	£7.50	—
?13	Prominent British Officers	1901	£7.50	—
	OTHER OVERSEAS ISSUES			
51	Actresses, Black & White (Polo)	1906	£3.25	—
?30	Actresses, Black & White			
	(Polo, Small, Pictures, Numbered)	1906	£20.00	—
?3	Actresses, Black & White			
	(Polo, Small, Pictures, Unnumbered)	1906	£20.00	—
30	Actresses, Brown (Polo, 3 Printings)	1908	£2.80	£84.00
17	Animals (Polo)	1916	£11.50	—
60	Animals (Ruler)	1912	£3.25	£195.00
60	(Tabs, With Captions)	1912	£3.25	£195.00
50	Animals (Tabs, No Captions)	1912	£3.25	£62.50
50	Aviation Series (Tabs, Ogden At Base)	1912	£7.00	—
50	(Tabs, "Ogden England")	1912	£8.00	—
45	Beauties-Picture Hats (Polo)	1911	£6.00	—
50	Best Dogs Of Their Breed (Polo, Blue)			
	(With Eastern Characters)	1916	£8.00	—
	(Without Eastern Characters)	1916	£8.50	—
50	(Polo, Pink)	1916	£9.00	—
52	Birds Of Brilliant Plumage			
	(With Frame Line, 2 Printings)	1914	£3.40	£175.00
	(No Frame Line)	1914	£3.20	£166.00
25	British Trees &Their Uses (Guinea Gold)	1927	£2.00	£50.00

OGDENS LTD. – cont.

Qty		Date	Odds	Sets
25	Burmese Women (Polo, Apple Green Border)	1919	£6.00	£150.00
25	(Polo, Emerald Green)	1919	£6.00	£150.00
25	China's Ancient Warriors (Ruler)	1913	£6.00	–
25	Famous Railway Trains (Guinea Gold)	1928	£2.60	£65.00
20	Flowers (Polo Packet 49mm Long)			
	(No Eastern Characters)	1915	£6.00	–
	(With Eastern Characters)	1915	£6.00	–
20	(Polo Packet 46mm Long)	1915	£6.00	–
30	Music Hall Celebrities (Polo)	1911	£6.00	£180.00
50	(Tabs)	1911	£6.00	–
52	Playing Cards (Polo)	1922	£12.50	–
50	Riders Of The World (Polo, Reg.No.1294)	1911	£3.60	£180.00
50	(Polo, No "Reg.No")	1911	£3.60	£180.00
50	(Polo, Cigarettes Uneven)	1911	£4.00	£200.00
50	Russo Japanese Series	1904	£20.00	–
36	Ships & Their Pennants (Polo)	1911	£6.50	–
32	Transport Of The World (Polo)	1917	£6.00	–

THE ORLANDO CIGARETTE & CIGAR CO.

Qty		Date	Odds	Sets
40	Home & Colonial Regiments	1901	£600.00	–

W.T. OSBORNE & CO.

Qty		Date	Odds	Sets
40	Naval & Military Phrases (No Border)	1904	£45.00	–
40	(White Border)	1904	£45.00	–

OSBORNE TOBACCO CO.LTD.

Qty		Date	Odds	Sets
50	Modern Aircraft (Blue Front)	1952	£0.75	£37.50
50	(Brown Front)	1952	£1.40	£70.00

PALMER & CO

Qty		Date	Odds	Sets
M12	Manikin Cards	1915	£125.00	–

J.A. PATTREIOUEX LTD.
EARLY PHOTOGRAPHIC ISSUES

Qty		Date	Odds	Sets
F96	Animals (CA1-96)	1926	£1.50	–
LF50	Animals & Scenes (Unnumbered)	1924	£1.50	–
LF50	Animals & Scenes (1-50)	1925	£1.40	–
F192	Animals & Scenes (250-441, Titled, 2 Printings)	1925	£1.20	–
F192	(250-441, Junior Member)	1925	£1.20	–
F96	(346-441, 3 Brands)	1925	£1.20	–
F96	Animals & Scenes (CC1-96)	1926	£1.30	–
LF50	Animals & Scenes (I1-50, 2 Printings)	1927	£1.50	–
F96	Animals & Scenes (JS1-96A)	1928	£1.10	–
LF96	Animal Studies (A42-137)	1925	£1.25	–
LF50	Animal Studies (A151-200)	1925	£1.25	–
LF30	Beauties (JM1-30)	1928	£3.50	–
LF50	British & Egyptian Scenes (CM1-50A)	1927	£1.25	–
LF50	British Empire Exhibition (JM1-50B)	1928	£2.00	£100.00
XF100	Cathedrals,Abbeys & Castles (SJ1-100)	1928	£2.75	–
LF30	Child Studies (JM No.1-30)	1928	£4.25	–
F96	Famous Cricketers (C1-96, Plain Back)	1926	£50.00	–
F96	(C1-96, Printed Back)	1926	£50.00	–
F191	Famous Footballers (F1-191)	1922	£12.00	–
LF50	Famous Statues (JCM1-50C)	1928	£2.00	£100.00
F96	Footballers (FA1-96)	1922	£8.00	–

Qty		Date	Odds	Sets
F96	Footballers (FB1-96)	1923	£8.00	—
F96	Footballers (FC1-96)	1923	£8.00	—
LF50	Football Teams (F192-241)	1922	£50.00	—
F96	Natives & Scenes (1-96B)	1926	£1.20	£115.00
F36	(1-36B) (As Above)	1926	£1.50	—
F96	Natives & Scenes (Numbered CB1-CB96)	1926	£1.20	—
F96	(Numbered 1-96)	1926	£1.20	—
F96	(JS1-96)(As Above)	1926	£1.15	£110.00
F96	Overseas Scenes (1-96C)	1926	£1.20	£115.00
LF50	Overseas Scenes (CM1-50B)	1926	£1.35	—
LF50	(JM1-50) (As Above)	1928	£1.20	£60.00
LF50	Overseas Scenes (CM101-150S)	1927	£1.20	£60.00
LF50	(S101-150) (As Above)	1929	£1.20	£60.00
F96	Overseas Scenes (1-96D)	1927	£1.75	—
LF50	Overseas Scenes (1-50E)	1928	£1.20	£60.00
LF50	Overseas Scenes (1-50F)	1928	£1.20	£60.00
LF50	Overseas Scenes (JM1-50A)	1928	£1.20	£60.00
LF50	Scenes (201-250)	1925	£1.30	£65.00
LF50	Scenes (G1-50)	1927	£1.60	£80.00
LF50	Scenes (1-50H, Grey Back)	1927	£1.20	£60.00
LF50	(1-50H, Brown Back)	1927	£1.50	—
LF50	Scenes (JCM1-50D, With Firm's Name)	1927	£1.20	£60.00
LF50	(JCM1-50D, Junior Member No.10, 2 Sizes)	1927	£1.30	—
LF100	Scenes (S1-100)	1928	£1.30	—
LF4	Scenes (V1-4)	1928	£5.00	—
	OTHER ISSUES			
F28	Beautiful Scotland	1939	£1.20	£35.00
MF48	Beautiful Scotland	1939	£0.25	£12.00
MF48	Britain From The Air	1939	£0.25	£12.00
50	British Empire Exhibition Series	1929	£2.70	£135.00
MF48	British Railways	1938	£0.85	£42.00
50	Builders Of The British Empire	1929	£3.20	£160.00
50	Celebrities In Sport	1930	£3.60	£280.00
F28	Coastwise	1939	£1.30	£36.00
MF48	Coastwise	1939	£0.25	£12.00
75	Cricketers Series	1926	£11.00	£825.00
50	Dirt Track Riders	1929	£10.00	£500.00
F54	Dirt Track Riders (Descriptive)	1930	£11.00	£600.00
F54	(Non Descriptive)	1930	£27.50	—
PF54	Dirt Track Riders (Premium Issue)	1930	£160.00	—
MF48	Dogs	1939	£0.65	£32.50
30	Drawing Made Easy	1930	£2.40	£72.00
F28	Flying	1938	£2.00	£55.00
MF48	Flying	1938	£0.40	£20.00
F78	Footballers In Action	1934	£3.70	£290.00
100	Footballers Series (Brown Caption)	1927	£9.00	—
50	(Blue Caption)	1927	£8.50	£425.00
MF48	Holiday Haunts By The Sea	1938	£0.30	£15.00
X24	Jackpot Jigsaws	1969	£1.25	—
25	King Lud Problems	1936	£17.50	—
26	Maritime Flags	1931	£9.00	£234.00
F28	Our Countryside	1938	£1.60	£45.00
MF48	Our Countryside	1938	£0.25	£12.00
25	Photo's Of Football Stars	1929	£32.50	—
50	Railway Posters By Famous Artists	1930	£8.00	£400.00

J.A. PATTREIOUEX LTD. – cont.

Qty		Date	Odds	Sets
F54	Real Photographs Of London	1936	£2.40	£130.00
F28	Shots From The Films	1938	£2.80	£80.00
MF48	Sights Of Britain	1936	£0.50	£24.00
MF48	Sights Of Britain, 2nd Series (2 Printings)	1936	£0.25	£12.00
MF48	Sights Of Britain, 3rd Series	1937	£0.50	£24.00
MF48	Sights Of London, First Series	1935	£1.25	£60.00
MF12	Sights Of London-Supplementary Series	1935	£0.75	£9.00
F54	Sporting Celebrities	1935	£4.25	–
MF96	Sporting Events And Stars	1935	£1.25	£220.00
50	Sports Trophies	1931	£3.00	£150.00
MF48	The Bridges Of Britain	1938	£0.25	£12.00
52	The English & Welsh Counties	1928	£2.00	£100.00
MF48	The Navy (2 Printings)	1937	£0.70	£35.00
M24	Treasure Isle	1968	£1.25	–
F51	Views	1933	£1.20	£60.00
F54	Views Of Britain	1937	£1.60	£85.00
MF48	Winter Scenes	1937	£0.35	£17.00

W. PEPPERDY

Qty		Date	Odds	Sets
30	Army Pictures, Cartoons, etc.	1916	£135.00	–

M. PEZARO & SON

Qty		Date	Odds	Sets
25	Armies Of The World (Cake Walk)	1900	£140.00	–
25	(Nestor)	1900	£135.00	–
?18	Song Titles Illustrated	1900	£325.00	–

GODFREY PHILLIPS LTD.

Qty		Date	Odds	Sets
50	Actresses (Oval)	1916	£7.00	£350.00
50	(Oval, Anonymous)	1916	£5.50	£275.00
25	Actresses, C Series (Ball Of Beauty)	1900	£85.00	–
25	(Carriage)	1900	£30.00	£750.00
25	(Derby)	1900	£85.00	–
25	(Horseshoe)	1900	£32.50	–
25	(Teapot)	1900	£90.00	–
25	(Volunteer)	1900	£80.00	–
2	Advertisement Cards	1934	£12.00	£24.00
50	Aircraft	1938	£2.20	£110.00
54	Aircraft Series No.1 (Matt)	1938	£0.50	£27.00
54	(Varnished)	1938	£3.00	£162.00
54	(Millhoff Back)	1938	£3.00	£162.00
40	Animal Series	1903	£6.50	£260.00
M30	Animal Studies	1936	£0.25	£7.50
50	Annuals	1939	£0.25	£12.50
L25	Arms Of The English Sees	1924	£4.40	£110.00
48	A Selection Of BDV Wonderful Gifts	1930	£1.20	£60.00
48	A Selection Of BDV Wonderful Gifts	1931	£1.10	£53.00
48	A Selection Of BDV Wonderful Gifts	1932	£1.10	£53.00
24	Beauties "HUMPS" (Phillips Front)	1898	£85.00	–
24	("Plums" Front)	1898	£600.00	–
30	Beauties, Nymphs	1896	£90.00	–
?60	Beauties, PLUMS (Black & White Front)	1897	£175.00	–
50	(Green Front)	1897	£70.00	–
50	(Plum Front)	1897	£70.00	–
25	Beauties (Numbered B801-B825)	1902	£12.50	£312.50

Qty		Date	Odds	Sets
30	Beauties, Oval (Plain Back)	1914	£2.50	£75.00
44	Beauties Of To-Day	1937	£1.60	£70.00
50	Beauties Of To-Day	1938	£1.20	£60.00
36	Beauties Of To-Day, 2nd Series	1940	£1.20	£44.00
F54	Beauties Of To-Day	1939	£1.40	£76.00
LF36	Beauties Of To-Day	1938	£3.00	£108.00
LF36	Beauties Of To-Day (Different Subjects)	1938	£6.00	—
XF36	Beauties Of To-Day (Unnumbered)	1937	£1.60	£57.50
XF36	Beauties Of To-Day, 2nd Series	1938	£1.25	£45.00
XF36	Beauties Of To-Day, 3rd Series	1938	£1.00	£36.00
XF36	Beauties Of To-Day, 4th Series	1938	£1.00	£36.00
XF36	Beauties Of To-Day, 5th Series	1938	£1.00	£36.00
XF36	Beauties Of To-Day, 6th Series	1939	£1.00	£36.00
XF36	Beauties Of To-Day, 7th Series	1939	£1.00	£36.00
XF36	(B.D.V. Back)	1939	£0.60	£21.50
36	Beauties Of The World	1931	£1.60	£57.50
36	Beauties Of The World Series No.2	1933	£1.50	£54.00
50	Beautiful Women (I F Series)	1908	£11.00	£550.00
50	(W.I. Series)	1908	£11.00	£550.00
L50	Beautiful Women	1908	£24.00	£1,200.00
P30	Beauty Spots Of The Homeland	1938	£0.30	£9.00
50	Bird Painting	1938	£0.80	£40.00
25	Boxer Rebellion	1904	£32.00	—
50	British Beauties (Photogravure)	1916	£8.00	£400.00
K76	British Beauties	1916	£3.20	£240.00
F54	British Beauties, 1-54	1914	£2.60	£140.00
F54	(Plain Back, Glossy)	1914	£3.50	—
54	(Plain Back, Brown)	1914	£3.50	—
F54	British Beauties, 55-108 (Glossy)	1915	£2.40	£130.00
54	(Matt)	1915	£2.75	—
54	(Plain Back, Sepia)	1915	£3.25	—
50	British Birds And Their Eggs	1936	£1.10	£55.00
30	British Butterflies, No.1 Issue	1911	£4.75	£145.00
25	British Butterflies	1927	£1.20	£30.00
25	(Transfers)	1936	£1.00	£25.00
25	British Orders Of Chivalry & Valour	1939	£3.00	£75.00
25	British Warships	1915	£9.00	£225.00
L25	British Warships	1915	£40.00	—
F80	British Warships	1916	£16.50	—
50	Busts Of Famous People (Brown Back)	1907	£50.00	—
50	(Green Back)	1907	£7.50	£375.00
50	(Pale Green)	1907	£30.00	—
M36	Characters Come To Life	1938	£1.25	£45.00
?25	Children's Stories(Booklets)	1924	£35.00	—
25	Chinese Series (English Text)	1910	£8.00	£200.00
25	(Volunteer Cigarettes)	1910	£10.00	£250.00
G?6	Chinese Series	1910	£300.00	—
M25	Cinema Stars (Circular)	1924	£3.40	£85.00
F52	Cinema Stars	1923	£3.00	£150.00
30	Cinema Stars (Brown)	1924	£3.00	£90.00
30	Cinema Stars (Black & White)	1925	£1.60	£48.00
32	Cinema Stars (Black & White)	1930	£1.60	£52.00
32	Cinema Stars (Brown, Hand Coloured)	1934	£1.75	£56.00
30	Cinema Stars (Plain Back)	1935	£1.00	£30.00
50	Colonial Troops	1902	£27.50	—

Qty		Date	Odds	Sets
50	Coronation Of Their Majesties	1937	£0.35	£17.50
M36	Coronation Of Their Majesties	1937	£0.30	£11.00
P24	Coronation Of Their Majesties (Postcard)	1937	£1.50	£36.00
P24	Non-Postcard)	1937	£4.50	–
KF198	Cricketers (Pinnace)	1924	£8.00	–
F192	Cricketers (Brown Back)	1924	£8.50	–
LF25	Cricketers (Brown Back)	1924	£23.00	£575.00
LF?157	(Pinnace)	1924	£40.00	–
PF?180	Cricketers (Premium Issue)	1924	£40.00	–
1	Cricket Fixture Card	1936	–	£6.00
25	Derby Winners & Jockeys	1923	£4.00	£100.00
30	Eggs, Nests & Birds (Numbered)	1912	£6.00	£180.00
30	(Unnumbered)	1912	£6.50	£195.00
25	Empire Industries	1927	£1.20	£30.00
49/50	Evolution Of The British Navy	1930	£1.00	£49.00
25	Famous Boys	1924	£2.80	£70.00
32	Famous Cricketers	1926	£5.50	£175.00
25	Famous Crowns	1938	£0.50	£12.50
50	Famous Footballers	1936	£2.20	£110.00
M36	Famous Love Scenes	1939	£0.75	£27.00
50	Famous Minors	1936	£0.30	£15.00
P26	Famous Paintings	1936	£1.30	£34.00
25	Feathered Friends	1928	£1.60	£40.00
50	Film Favourites	1934	£0.75	£37.50
50	Film Stars	1934	£0.75	£37.50
P24	Film Stars (Series Of Cards, Postcard)	1934	£1.20	£30.00
P24	("Series Of Cards", Non-Postcard)	1934	£3.00	£72.00
P24	Film Stars (Series Of 24Cards, Postcard	1934	£3.00	£72.00
P24	("Series Of 24 Cards", Non-Postcard)	1934	£4.50	–
P24	Film Stars, 2nd (25-48, Postcard Backs)	1934	£3.00	£72.00
P24	(25-48, Non-Postcard)	1934	£5.00	–
50	First Aid	1923	£1.60	£80.00
25	First Aid Series	1914	£7.00	£175.00
25	Fish	1924	£2.80	£70.00
M30	Flower Studies	1937	£0.30	£9.00
P30	Flower Studies	1937	£0.60	£18.00
KF112	Footballers (Brown Oval Back)	1920	£4.00	–
KF400	(Black Oval Back)	1920	£1.75	–
KF?388	(Double Frame Line Back)	1921	£2.25	–
KF?827	(1-940, Address "Photo")	1921	£1.35	–
KF?63	(941-1109, Address "Photo")	1922	£2.25	–
KF?836	(1-940, Address "Pinnace")	1922	£1.35	–
KF?1514	(941-2462, Address"Pinnace")	1923	£2.25	–
LF?400	Footballers (Oval Design Back)	1920	£3.50	–
LF?1100	(Oblong Frame "Photo"Back)	1921	£10.00	–
LF?2462	("Pinnace" Back)	1922	£3.50	–
PF2462	Footballers(Premium Issue)	1922	£9.00	–
GF?24	Football Teams (Premium Issue)	1921	£500.00	–
P1	Franco British Exhibition	1908	–	£30.00
P30	Garden Studies	1938	£0.30	£9.00
13	General Interest	1896	£45.00	£700.00
90	Guinea Gold Series (Numbered, Glossy)	1902	£5.00	£450.00
90	(Numbered, Matt)	1902	£5.00	£450.00
100	Guinea Gold Series	1902	£6.50	£650.00
161	Guinea Gold Series (Different)	1902	£5.00	£800.00

Qty		Date	Odds	Sets
100	Guinea Gold Series (Brown)	1902	£9.00	–
25	Home Pets	1924	£2.00	£50.00
25	How To Build A Two Valve Set	1929	£2.80	£70.00
25	How To Do It Series	1913	£8.00	£200.00
25	How To Make A Valve Amplifier	1924	£3.20	£80.00
25	How To Make Your Own Wireless Set	1923	£2.80	£70.00
25	Indian Series	1908	£14.00	£350.00
54	In The Public Eye	1935	£0.60	£32.50
50	International Caps	1936	£2.00	£100.00
35/37	Kings & Queens Of England	1925	£2.00	£70.00
25	Lawn Tennis	1930	£3.00	£3.20
K52	Miniature Playing Cards (Red Back)	1906	£130.00	–
K53	Miniature Playing Cards (Blue Design)	1934	£0.60	–
K53	(Buff, 3 Types)	1932	£0.50	£26.50
K53	(White)	1933	£0.60	–
K53	(Yellow)	1933	£0.60	–
25	Model Railways	1927	£3.20	£80.00
30	Morse Signalling	1916	£11.00	£330.00
50	Motor Cars At A Glance	1924	£4.00	£200.00
20	Novelty Series	1924	£12.00	£240.00
25	Old Favourites	1924	£1.80	£45.00
M36	Old Masters	1939	£0.25	£9.00
36	Olympic Champions, Amsterdam 1928	1928	£2.75	£100.00
25	Optical Illusions	1927	£2.60	£65.00
36	Our Dogs	1939	£1.60	£60.00
M30	Our Dogs	1939	£0.65	£19.50
P30	Our Dogs	1939	£3.50	£105.00
M48	Our Favourites	1935	£0.25	£12.00
P30	Our Glorious Empire	1939	£0.50	£15.00
M30	Our Puppies	1936	£1.80	£54.00
P30	Our Puppies	1936	£1.80	£54.00
25	Personalities Of To-Day	1932	£2.20	£55.00
25	Popular Superstitions	1930	£1.50	£37.50
25	Prizes For Needlework	1925	£2.00	£50.00
25	Railway Engines	1934	£3.40	£85.00
KF27	Real Photo Series (War Leaders)	1916	£7.50	£200.00
1	Real Stamp Card	1928	–	£2.25
25	Red Indians	1927	£3.50	£87.50
20	Russo Japanese War Series	1905	£350.00	–
25	School Badges	1927	£1.20	£30.00
48	Screen Stars A (Embossed)	1936	£1.10	£55.00
48	(Not Embossed)	1936	£1.70	£85.00
48	Screen Stars B (Different)	1936	£1.10	£55.00
30	Semaphore Signalling	1916	£11.00	£330.00
25	Ships And Their Flags	1924	£3.00	£75.00
M36	Ships That Have Made History	1938	£0.80	£37.50
M48	Shots From The Films	1934	£0.80	£39.00
50	Soccer Stars	1936	£2.20	£110.00
36	Soldiers Of The King (Adhesive)	1939	£1.50	£54.00
36	(Non-Adhesive)	1939	£0.70	£25.00
P12	Special Jubilee Series	1935	£2.00	£24.00
M20	Special Jubilee Year Series	1935	£0.40	£8.00
30	Speed Champions	1930	£2.00	£60.00
36	Sporting Champions	1929	£2.75	£100.00
25	Sporting Series	1910	£20.00	–

Qty		Date		
25	Sports	1923	£4.2	
50	Sportsmen-Spot The Winner (Normal)	1937	£1.60	
50	(Back Inverted)	1937	£1.20	
35	Stage And Cinema Beauties A	1933	£1.20	
35	Stage And Cinema Beauties B (Different)	1933	£1.10	
50	Stage And Cinema Beauties (Different)	1935	£1.20	£6
54	Stars Of The Screen	1934	£1.20	£65.
48	Stars Of The Screen (Embossed)	1936	£1.00	£48.00
48	(Not Embossed)	1936	£0.80	£40.00
X16	Stars Of The Screen (Strips Of 3)	1936	£3.00	£48.00
25	Statues & Monuments (Brown Back)	1907	£80.00	–
25	(Green, "Patent")	1907	£9.00	£225.00
25	(Green, "Provisional Patent")	1907	£9.00	£225.00
25	Territorial Series (Motors Back)	1908	£26.00	£650.00
25	The 1924 Cabinet	1924	£2.00	£50.00
48	The "Old Country	1935	£0.60	£30.00
50	This Mechanized Age First (Adhesive)	1936	£0.30	£15.00
50	(Non-Adhesive)	1936	£0.40	£20.00
50	This Mechanized Age Second Series	1937	£0.25	£12.50
25	Types Of British & Colonial Troops	1899	£45.00	–
25	Types Of British Soldiers (M651-M675)	1900	£26.00	£650.00
F63	War Photos	1916	£8.50	£535.00
XS30	Zoo Studies-Come To Life Series	1939	£1.40	£42.00
X1	Zoo Studies Viewer	1939	–	£7.50

BDV PACKAGE ISSUES

Qty		Date		
17	Boxers	1932	£7.00	–
?55	Cricketers	1932	£8.00	–
?68	Film Stars	1932	£2.50	–
136	Footballers	1932	£6.50	–
19	Jockeys	1932	£4.50	–
21	Speedway Riders	1932	£8.50	–
?28	Sportsmen	1932	£4.50	–

"SPORTS" PACKAGE ISSUES

Qty		Date		
50	All Sports, 1st	1948	£5.00	–
25	All Sports, 2nd	1949	£5.00	–
25	All Sports, 3rd (Card Or Paper)	1953	£5.00	–
25	All Sports, 4th	1954	£5.00	–
25	Cricketers, 1st	1948	£9.00	–
25	Cricketers, 2nd (Card Or Paper)	1951	£9.00	–
25	Footballers, 1st	1948	£8.50	–
50	Footballers, 2nd (Card Or Paper)	1950	£8.50	–
25	Footballers, 3rd (Card Or Paper)	1951	£8.50	–
25	Jockeys (Card Or Paper)	1952	£5.00	–
25	Radio Stars	1949	£3.50	–
25	Rugby & Association Footballers	1952	£7.00	–

OVERSEAS ISSUES

Qty		Date		
50	Animal Studies	1930	£1.40	£70.00
50	Annuals	1939	£1.60	£80.00
X32	Australian Birds (Cartons)	1968	–	£16.00
X24	Australian Scenes (Cartons)	1965	–	£16.00
50	Australian Sporting Celebrities	1932	£3.20	£160.00
X32	Australian Wild Flowers (Cartons)	1967	–	£17.50
50	Film Stars	1934	£2.00	£100.00
E16	Gemstones (Cartons)	1970	–	£12.00
50	Stars Of British Films (B.D.V.)	1934	£1.75	£87.50

DFREY PHILLIPS LTD. – cont.

		Date	Odds	Sets
	Reszke)	1934	£1.75	£87.50
	ys)	1934	£2.00	–
	Brand)	1934	£1.80	£90.00
		1932	£3.50	£135.00
		1932	£3.50	£135.00
		1932	£3.50	£135.00
		1968	–	£12.00
		1933	£4.50	£225.00
		1933	£4.50	–
	rvo Brand)	1933	£4.50	–
	ootballers	1933	£6.00	–
	ctorian League & AssociationFootballers	1934	£6.00	–
ꜧUU	Who's Who In Australian Sport	1933	£3.75	£375.00
SILK ISSUES				
M1	Allies Flags	1915	–	£9.00
G2	Allies Flags (Anon)	1915	£9.00	–
G2	(B.D.V)	1915	£9.00	–
M62	Arms Of Countries & Territories	1912	£3.80	£235.00
M32	Beauties-Modern Paintings	1910	£12.50	£400.00
P32	Beauties-Modern Paintings	1910	£42.50	–
M100	Birds	1921	£2.65	–
M12	Birds Of The Tropics	1913	£10.00	£120.00
L12	Birds Of The Tropics	1913	£12.50	–
P12	Birds Of The Tropics	1913	£17.50	–
X24	British Admirals	1916	£6.50	–
D50	British Butterflies & Moths	1922	£6.00	–
M108	British Naval Crests (Anon, Blue Nos)	1915	£2.00	–
M9	(Anon, Brown Nos)	1915	£7.50	–
M108	(B.D.V.)	1915	£2.00	–
M23	Butterflies	1911	£10.00	£230.00
M47	Ceramic Art (70 X 43mm)	1925	£1.10	£52.00
M47	(70 X 48mm)	1925	£0.90	£43.00
L47	Ceramic Art	1925	£1.75	–
M65	Clan Tartans (68 X 44mm)	1922	£1.25	–
M65	(71 X 48mm) (B.D.V)	1922	£1.10	£71.50
M49	(71 X 48mm) (Anon)	1922	£1.20	£60.00
L56	Clan Tartans	1922	£3.00	–
P12	Clan Tartans	1922	£5.50	£66.00
M108	Colonial Army Badges	1913	£2.75	–
M17	County Cricket Badges (Anon)	1921	£17.50	–
M17	(BDV)	1921	£15.00	£255.00
M108	Crests & Badges Of The British Army			
	(Anon, Numbered)	1914	£1.25	£130.00
	(Anon, Unnumbered)	1914	£1.40	£150.00
	(B.D.V.)	1914	£1.25	£130.00
L105	Crests & Badges Of The British Army (Anon)	1914	£1.50	–
L108	(BDV)	1914	£1.75	–
M143	Flags, Set 4-1 (Short)	1913	£1.00	–
M119	Flags, Set 4-2 (Short, Renumbered)	1913	£1.00	£120.00
M114	Flags, Set 4-3 (Short, Renumbered)	1913	£1.00	£115.00
L142	Flags, Set 4 (Long)	1913	£1.60	£227.50
M24	Flags, Set 5 (With Caption)	1913	£0.90	£21.50
M12	Flags, Set 5 (No Caption)	1913	£1.25	£15.00
P8	Flags, Set 5	1913	£13.00	–
M18	Flags, Set 6	1913	£0.90	£16.00

70

Qty		Date	Odds	Sets
M20	Flags, Set 7	1913	£0.90	–
M50	Flags, 5th Series	1914	£1.75	£87.50
M120	Flags, 7th Series	1914	£0.90	£108.00
L120	Flags, 10th Series	1915	£1.00	£120.00
M120	Flags, 12h Series	1915	£0.90	£108.00
L65	Flags, 15th Series	1916	£1.25	–
L64	Flags, 16th Series	1916	£1.25	–
M120/132	Flags, 20h Series (B.D.V.Brown)	1917	£0.90	£108.00
M?48	(B.D.V.Orange)	1917	£2.50	–
M120/126	Flags, 25th Series	1917	£0.90	£108.00
L62	Flags, 25th Series	1917	£3.00	–
M112	Flags, 26th Series (In Brown)	1918	£0.90	£100.00
M?55	(In Blue)	1918	£4.00	–
M70	Flags, 28th Series	1918	£0.90	£63.00
P17	Flags, Set 13	1914	£2.25	£38.00
G23	Flags, Set 13 (Anon)	1914	£2.25	£52.00
G27	(BDV)	1914	£2.25	£60.00
M21	Football Colours (Anon)	1914	£7.50	–
M86	(BDV)	1920	£6.25	–
P78	Football Colours	1920	£6.50	–
M126	G.P. Territorial Badges	1913	£2.20	£275.00
L25	Great War Leaders (Sepia)	1915	£6.50	£162.50
M3	Great War Leaders & Celebrities (Anon)	1916	£6.50	£19.50
M4	(BDV)	1916	£6.50	
L3	Great War Leaders & Celebrities (Anon)	1916	£6.50	£19.50
L2	(BDV)	1916	£6.50	£13.00
P4	Great War Leaders & Celebrities (Anon)	1916	£6.50	
P18	(BDV)	1916	£6.00	–
G29	Great War Leaders & Celebrities (Anon)	1916	£6.00	–
G45	(BDV)	1916	£6.50	–
P1	Great War Leaders (BDV In Blue)	1916	–	£15.00
M52	Great War Leaders & Warships	1914	£6.50	–
M25	Heraldic Series (69 X 43mm)	1924	£1.30	£32.50
M25	(68 X 47mm)	1924	£1.30	£32.50
L25	Heraldic Series	1924	£2.75	–
P12	Heraldic Series	1924	£5.50	£66.00
M26	House Flags	1915	£9.00	£234.00
M10	Irish Patriots	1919	£12.00	£120.00
X10	Irish Patriots	1919	£13.00	–
P10	Irish Patriots	1919	£16.50	–
M1	Irish Republican Stamp	1925	–	£2.00
M1	Let "Em All Come	1920	–	£10.00
X?	Miniature Rugs	1924	£6.50	–
M54	Naval Badges Of Rank & Military Headdress	1917	£6.00	£324.00
G1	Nelson's Signal At Trafalgar	1921	–	£125.00
G40	Old Masters, Set 1	1911	£32.50	£1,300.00
P20	Old Masters, Set 2 (Anon)	1912	£4.00	£80.00
P20	(BDV At Top)	1912	£3.80	£76.00
P20	(BDV At Bottom)	1912	£7.00	–
M85	Old Masters, Set 3 (Anon)	1912	£2.50	–
M40	(BDV)	1912	£3.00	£120.00
M120	Old Masters, Set 4	1913	£2.25	–
M20	Old Masters, Set 5 (Anon, Unnumbered)	1922	£3.00	–
M20	(Anon, 101-120)	1922	£1.75	£35.00
M60	(BDV 1-60)	1922	£1.25	£75.00

GODFREY PHILLIPS LTD. – cont.

Qty		Date	Odds	Sets
M20	Old Masters, Set 5 (BDV 101-120)..	1922	£1.75	£35.00
M50	Old Masters, Set 6	1924	£1.30	£65.00
M50	Old Masters, Set 7 (301-350)..	1916	£2.50	£125.00
M50	Orders Of Chivalry (Anon)...	1920	£2.40	£120.00
M24	Orders Of Chivalry (BDV, 1-24)..	1914	£1.80	£44.00
M24	(GP401-424)..	1914	£2.00	£48.00
M25	Pilot & Signal Flags (Anon)..	1921	£4.00	£100.00
M25	(BDV)..	1921	£3.00	£75.00
L72	Regimental Colours	1914	£4.00	–
M50	Regimental Colours, Series 12	1918	£2.20	£110.00
M120	Regimental Colours & Crests (BDV)...................................	1915	£1.75	–
M120	(Anon)....................................	1915	£1.75	–
M40	(Anon, *With Vignettes*)	1915	£1.60	–
G120	Regimental Colours & Crests (Anon)	1915	£6.50	–
G120	(BDV)....................................	1915	£6.50	–
M10	Religious Pictures	1911	£17.50	–
X10	Religious Pictures	1911	£20.00	–
P10	Religious Pictures	1911	£25.00	–
M75	Town & City Arms	1918	£2.00	£225.00
L75	Town & City Arms	1918	£3.00	–
M25	Victoria Cross Heroes I	1915	£12.00	–
M25	Victoria Cross Heroes II (With Flags)	1915	£12.50	–
M90	War Pictures	1915	£5.75	£525.00

JOHN PLAYER & SONS

Qty		Date	Odds	Sets
25	Actors & Actresses	1898	£25.00	£625.00
50	Actresses	1897	£25.00	£1,250.00
6/7	Advertisement Cards (Navy Cut Back)	1894	£300.00	–
4/5	(Testimonial Back)........................	1894	£300.00	–
1	Advertisement Card-Sailor	1929	–	£5.00
L1	Advertisement Card-Sailor	1929	–	£18.00
L1	Advertisement Card-Wants List...	1936	–	£1.00
P6	Advertisement Postcards	1906	£100.00	–
50	Aeroplanes (Eire)..	1935	£1.60	£80.00
50	Aeroplanes (Civil)..	1935	£1.00	£50.00
50	Aircraft Of The Royal Air Force	1938	£1.00	£50.00
X10	Allied Cavalry	1914	£10.00	£100.00
L24	A Nature Calendar	1930	£5.00	£120.00
50	Animals Of The Countryside	1939	£0.20	£10.00
50	(Eire)...	1939	£0.85	£42.50
L25	Aquarium Studies	1932	£1.80	£45.00
L25	Architectural Beauties..	1927	£2.20	£55.00
50	Arms & Armour (Blue Back)	1909	£2.40	£120.00
50	Army Corps & Divisional Signs (1-50, 2 Printings)...............	1924	£0.40	£20.00
100	Army Corps & Div. Signs 2nd (51-150)	1925	£0.65	£65.00
25	Army Life	1910	£2.00	£50.00
X12	Artillery In Action	1917	£5.00	£60.00
50	A Sectional Map Of Ireland	1932	£2.50	£125.00
50	Association Cup Winners..	1930	£2.00	£100.00
50	Aviary And Cage Birds...	1933	£0.80	£40.00
50	(Transfers)	1933	£0.30	£15.00
L25	Aviary & Cage Birds...	1935	£3.50	£87.50
50	Badges & Flags Of British Regiments.................................			
	(Green Back)	1903	£1.80	£90.00
	(Brown Back, Numbered)	1904	£2.00	£100.00
	(Brown Back, Unnumbered)	1904	£2.40	£120.00

CODE NAMES

When cigarette cards first became popular in this country the most prolific subjects were actresses and militaria—since virtually all cigarette smokers were men! In the golden age around the turn of the century many manufacturers including many of the largest issued some of the same sets as their competitors. In order to distinguish the many similar series a coding system has been developed for series of Actresses and Boer War subjects that in general do not have a series title of their own. This is based on the first letter (or letters) of the names of some of the leading issuers of the particular set.

Thus Beauties PAC were issued by Pritchard & Burton, Adkin and Cope, and Beauties HOL by Harris, Ogden & Lambert & Butler. Actresses HAGG were issued by Hill, Anonymous, Gabriel and Glass (as well as Baker and Bell), while Boer War Celebrities CLAM, is taken from Churchman, Lambert & Butler, Anonymous and Muratti. The most popular of this set must surely have been Actresses FROGA which includes four sets all similar in appearance and was issued by more than 25 different companies, including Dunn's Hats in Britain, and tobacco issuers in Canada and India.

It is fortunate that so many of the series had an anonymous version, allowing the frequent use of the letter 'A', and hence some sort of pronounceable acronyms.

As a general rule in British issues Actress series are those in which the subject's name is printed, while the unidentified ladies are known as Beauties.

BRAND ISSUES

A brand issue is a card which bears the name of the cigarette with which it was inserted, but not the name of the issuing firm. This does not normally present a problem to compilers of catalogues and other lists, since most brand names have been registered, so that they cannot be used by a competitor—just as "Nostalgia" is a registered brand name for plastic albums!

Whenever possible we have listed brand issues under the name of the firm. This often enables us to bring together alternative printings of the same set, such as Hill Aviation and Decorations & Medals, each of which was issued either with the Hill name at the base or just advertising Gold Flake Honeydew. Similarly, under B. Morris there will be found four printings of Beauties CHOAB, 2 of which do not mention the firm's name.

One difficulty that occurs is that one Company may take over another, and inherit brand names. Hence Honest Long Cut was used by Duke and then the American Tobacco Co., which also took over brands such as Kinney's Sweet Caporal and Lorillard's Red Cross.

The most difficult problem however concerns groups of Companies which may use the same brand name under a different firm in different countries. Thus the Phillips Group used "Greys" as a U.K.T.C. brand in Britain, but as a Phillips brand in Australia. Similarly, Flag Cigarettes was used by Wills in Asia and U.T.C. in South Africa.

In the Catalogue on Pages 18-20 there appears an Index of brands with the name of the issuing firm (or firms), and the catalogue section in which they are listed. Names will only appear in the index when the firm's name does NOT appear AS WELL AS the brand on the card. When the issuer of the brand is not known, such as Field Favorite Cigarettes, the brand will not appear in the Index, and the set will be listed in the normal alphabetic order in the catalogue.

In a similar way to cigarette cards, there may also be brand issues of chocolates, periodicals etc. These have their own index at the beginning of section 3 of the Catalogue.

JOHN PLAYER & SONS – cont.

Qty		Date	Odds	Sets
50	Birds & Their Young..	1937	£0.25	£12.50
50	(Eire) (Adhesive)	1937	£1.00	£50.00
50	(Eire) (Non-Adhesive)	1937	£1.00	£50.00
25	(Non-Adhesive) ....Unissued		£0.30	£7.50
25	(2nd (Non-Adhesive) ....Unissued		£0.20	£5.00
K1	Bookmark (Calendar Back)......................................	1902	–	£250.00
PF10	Bookmarks (Authors)	1902	£65.00	£650.00
25	Boxing (Eire)..	1934	£6.00	£150.00
50	Boy Scout & Girl Guide..	1933	£0.40	£20.00
50	((Transfers)	1933	£0.25	£12.50
L25	British Butterflies..	1934	£4.40	£110.00
50	British Empire Series	1904	£1.25	£62.50
25	British Live Stock...	1915	£2.60	£65.00
X25	British Live Stock (Blue Back)..............................	1923	£4.00	£100.00
X25	(Brown Back)	1916	£4.00	£100.00
L25	British Naval Craft..	1939	£1.20	£30.00
X20	British Pedigree Stock	1925	£4.25	£85.00
L25	British Regalia..	1937	£1.20	£30.00
50	Butterflies..	1932	£1.20	£60.00
50	((Transfers)	1932	£0.30	£15.00
50	Butterflies & Moths	1904	£1.80	£90.00
25	Bygone Beauties..	1914	£1.20	£30.00
X10	Bygone Beauties..	1916	£4.50	£45.00
G?2	Cabinet Size Pictures (Brown Front,Printed Back)	1899	£90.00	–
G?10	(Brown Front,Plain Back)	1899	£90.00	–
G?30	(Green Front,Printed Back)	1899	£80.00	–
G?30	(Green Front,Plain Back).......................................	1899	£90.00	–
20	Castles, Abbeys Etc (No Border)	1895	£27.50	£550.00
20	(White Border)......................	1895	£26.00	£520.00
L24	Cats	1936	£7.00	£168.00
50	Celebrated Bridges..	1903	£2.60	£130.00
50	Celebrated Gateways	1909	£1.50	£75.00
25	Ceremonial And Court Dress................................	1911	£1.80	£45.00
L25	Championship Golf Courses.................................	1936	£8.50	£212.50
25	Characters From Dickens, A Series (1-25)	1912	£2.00	£50.00
25	Characters From Dickens, 2nd Series (26-50)......	1912	£2.00	£50.00
50	Characters From Dickens (Re-Issue)	1923	£1.40	£70.00
X10	Characters From Dickens	1914	£5.50	£55.00
L25	Characters From Fiction	1933	£3.80	£100.00
25	Characters From Thackeray	1913	£1.40	£35.00
50	Cities Of The World..	1900	£3.80	£190.00
L20	Clocks-Old & New	1928	£5.00	£100.00
25	Colonial & Indian Army Badges	1917	£1.30	£32.50
50	Coronation Series-Ceremonial Dress	1937	£0.20	£10.00
25	Counties And Their Industries (Numbered)...........	1915	£2.50	£62.50
25	(Unnumbered)......	1914	£2.60	£65.00
50	Countries Arms & Flags (Thick Card)...................	1905	£0.90	£45.00
50	(Thin Card)...................	1912	£1.00	£50.00
50	Country Seats And Arms (1-50)............................	1909	£0.80	£40.00
50	Country Seats And Arms, 2nd (51-100)................	1910	£0.80	£40.00
50	Country Seats And Arms, 3rd (101-150)...............	1910	£0.80	£40.00
L25	Country Sports...	1930	£6.00	£150.00
50	Cricketers 1930..	1930	£1.60	£80.00
50	Cricketers 1934..	1934	£1.40	£70.00

JOHN PLAYER & SONS – cont.

Qty		Date	Odds	Sets
50	Cricketers 1938	1938	£1.20	£60.00
50	Cricketers, Caricatures By "RIP"	1926	£2.00	£100.00
25	Cries Of London, A Series	1913	£2.00	£50.00
X10	Cries Of London, A Series	1912	£4.75	£47.50
X10	Cries Of London, 2nd Series	1914	£3.50	£35.00
25	Cries Of London, 2nd Series (Blue Back)	1916	£0.80	£20.00
25	(Black Back)	1916	£7.50	–
50	Curious Beaks	1929	£0.80	£40.00
50	Cycling	1939	£0.90	£45.00
50	((Eire) (Adhesive)	1939	£1.60	£80.00
50	((Eire) (Non-Adhesive)	1939	£1.60	£80.00
50	Dandies	1932	£0.35	£17.50
L25	Dandies	1932	£2.00	£50.00
50	Decorations & Medals	Unissued	£2.20	£110.00
50	Derby And Grand National Winners	1933	£1.70	£85.00
50	(Transfers)	1933	£0.40	£20.00
50	Dogs (Scenic Background)	1925	£1.00	£50.00
X12	Dogs (Scenic Background)	1924	£3.30	£40.00
50	Dogs, By Wardle (Full Length)	1931	£0.80	£40.00
50	(Transfers)	1931	£0.30	£15.00
L25	Dogs, By Wardle (Full Length)	1933	£2.60	£65.00
50	Dogs, By Wardle (Heads)	1929	£1.00	£50.00
L20	Dogs, By Wardle, A Series (Heads)	1926	£2.75	£55.00
L20	Dogs, By Wardle, 2nd Series (Heads)	1928	£2.75	£55.00
25	Dogs, By Wardle, A Series (Eire)(Heads)	1927	£2.00	£50.00
25	Dogs, By Wardle, 2nd Series(Eire)(Heads)	1929	£2.00	£50.00
50	Dogs Heads By Biegel (Unissued)	Unissued	£1.20	£60.00
L25	Dogs (Heads)(Unissued)	Unissued	£1.80	£45.00
50	Dogs' Heads (Silver Background, Eire)	1940	£3.20	£160.00
50	Drum Banners & Cap Badges(2 Printings)	1924	£0.80	£40.00
25	Egyptian Kings & Queens And Classical Deities	1912	£2.00	£50.00
X10	Egyptian Sketches	1915	£3.75	£37.50
25	England's Military Heroes (Narrow)	1898	£32.00	£800.00
25	(Wide)	1898	£40.00	£1,000.00
25	(Narrow, Plain Back)	1898	£27.50	£685.00
25	(Wide, Plain Back)	1898	£37.50	–
25	England's Naval Heroes			
25	(Non-Descriptive, Narrow)	1897	£26.00	£650.00
25	(Non-Descriptive, Wide)	1897	£36.00	£900.00
25	England's Naval Heroes			
25	(Descriptive, Narrow)	1898	£27.50	£685.00
25	(Descriptive, Wide)	1898	£38.00	£950.00
25	Everyday Phrases (By Tom Browne)	1900	£17.00	£425.00
L25	Fables Of Aesop	1927	£2.50	£62.50
20	Famous Authors & Poets (Narrow)	1900	£20.00	£400.00
20	(Wide)	1900	£30.00	£600.00
L25	Famous Beauties	1937	£1.80	£45.00
50	Famous Irish-Bred Horses	1936	£3.80	£190.00
50	Famous Irish Greyhounds	1935	£5.50	£275.00
X10	Famous Paintings	1913	£3.50	£35.00
50	Film Stars	1934	£1.20	£60.00
50	Film Stars, Second Series	1934	£1.00	£50.00
50	(Eire)	1934	£1.70	£85.00
50	Film Stars, Third Series	1938	£0.80	£40.00
L25	Film Stars	1934	£3.20	£80.00

Qty		Date	Odds	Sets
L25	Film Stars (Eire)	1934	£7.00	£175.00
50	Fire-Fighting Appliances	1930	£1.60	£80.00
50	Fishes Of The World	1903	£2.00	£100.00
50	Flags Of The League Of Nations	1928	£0.40	£20.00
50	Football Caricatures By "MAC"	1927	£1.25	£62.50
50	Footballers, Caricatures By "RIP"	1926	£1.30	£65.00
50	Footballers 1928	1928	£2.00	£100.00
25	Footballers 1928-9, 2nd Series	1929	£1.60	£40.00
50	Fresh-Water Fishes (Pink Back)	1933	£1.30	£65.00
50	(White Back)	1934	£1.60	£80.00
L25	Fresh-Water Fishes	1935	£2.80	£70.00
L25	Eire, Non-Adhesive)	1935	£5.00	£125.00
25	From Plantation To Smoker	1926	£0.25	£6.25
50	Gallery Of Beauty Series	1896	£23.00	£1,150.00
5	Alternative Subjects	1896	£65.00	–
50	Game Birds And Wild Fowl	1927	£1.50	£75.00
L25	Game Birds & Wild Fowl	1928	£5.40	£135.00
25	Gems Of British Scenery	1917	£1.00	£25.00
50	Gilbert And Sullivan, A Series	1925	£1.20	£60.00
X25	Gilbert & Sullivan, A Series	1926	£3.40	£85.00
50	Gilbert And Sullivan, 2nd Series	1927	£1.10	£55.00
L25	Gilbert & Sullivan, 2nd Series	1928	£4.00	£100.00
L25	Golf	1939	£7.75	£192.50
25	Hidden Beauties	1929	£0.20	£5.00
25	Highland Clans	1907	£4.40	£110.00
50	Hints On Association Football	1934	£0.90	£45.00
X10	Historic Ships	1910	£5.50	£55.00
50	History Of Naval Dress	1930	£1.00	£50.00
L25	History Of Naval Dress	1929	£2.20	£55.00
50	International Air Liners	1936	£0.40	£20.00
50	(Eire)	1936	£0.90	–
25	Irish Place Names A Series	1927	£3.20	£80.00
25	Irish Place Names 2nd Series	1929	£3.00	£75.00
1	Joker Card (Eire)	1935	–	£4.00
M5	Jubilee Issue	1960	£1.20	£6.00
50	Kings & Queens Of England	1935	£1.50	£75.00
L50	Kings & Queens Of England	1935	£2.80	£140.00
50	Life On Board A Man Of War-1805 &1905	1905	£2.00	£100.00
25	Live Stock	1925	£4.00	£100.00
50	Military Head-Dress	1931	£1.20	£60.00
50	Military Series	1900	£22.00	£1,100.00
50	Military Uniforms Of The British Empire Overseas	1938	£0.80	£40.00
25	Miniatures	1923	£0.40	£10.00
50	Modern Naval Craft	1939	£0.60	£30.00
50	(Eire)	1939	£1.00	£50.00
50	Motor Cars, A Series	1936	£1.50	£75.00
50	Motor Cars, A Series (Eire)	1936	£2.30	£115.00
50	Motor Cars, Second Series	1937	£1.00	£50.00
L20	Mount Everest	1925	£5.00	£100.00
25	Napoleon	1916	£2.20	£55.00
50	National Flags And Arms	1936	£0.40	£20.00
50	(Eire)	1936	£0.75	£37.50
50	Natural History	1924	£0.25	£12.50
X12	Natural History	1924	£1.00	£12.00
X12	Natural History,2nd Series	1924	£1.00	£12.00

Qty		Date	Odds	Sets
50	Nature Series	1909	£1.30	£65.00
X10	Nature Series (Birds)	1908	£9.00	£90.00
X10	Nature Series (Mammals)	1913	£6.00	£60.00
50	Old England's Defenders	1898	£22.00	£1,100.00
L25	Old Hunting Prints	1938	£3.00	£75.00
L25	Old Naval Prints	1936	£2.50	£62.50
X25	Old Sporting Prints	1924	£4.60	£115.00
L25	Picturesque Bridges	1929	£2.80	£70.00
L25	Picturesque Cottages	1929	£3.60	£90.00
L25	Picturesque London	1931	£5.00	£125.00
25	Players Past & Present	1916	£1.00	£25.00
25	Polar Exploration, A Series	1915	£2.60	£65.00
25	Polar Exploration,2nd Series	1916	£2.20	£55.00
L25	Portals Of The Past	1930	£2.20	£55.00
50	Poultry	1931	£1.75	£87.50
50	Transfers)	1931	£0.40	£20.00
25	Products Of The World	1908	£0.70	£17.50
50	Products Of The World (Different)	1928	£0.20	£10.00
25	Racehorses	1926	£5.50	£137.50
40	Racing Caricatures	1925	£0.80	£32.00
L25	Racing Yachts	1938	£3.80	£95.00
50	R.A.F. Badges (No Motto)	1937	£0.60	£30.00
50	(With Motto)	1937	£0.65	£32.50
50	Regimental Colours & Cap Badges (Regulars)	1907	£1.20	£60.00
50	Regimental Colours & Cap Badges			
	(Territorials, Blue Back)	1910	£1.20	£60.00
50	(Territorials, Brown Back)	1910	£1.00	£50.00
50	Regimental Standards And Cap Badges	1930	£0.65	£32.50
50	Regimental Uniforms (Blue Back)	1912	£2.00	£100.00
50	(Brown Back)	1914	£2.20	£110.00
X10	Regimental Uniforms (Different)	1914	£8.00	£80.00
50	Regimental Uniforms, 2nd Series (51-100)	1913	£1.20	£60.00
50	Riders Of The World	1905	£1.60	£80.00
P30	Rulers & Views	1902	£110.00	—
50	Sea Fishes	1935	£0.30	£15.00
50	(Eire)	1935	£0.80	—
50	Screen Celebrities (Eire)	1938	£2.00	£100.00
25	Shakespearean Series	1917	£1.80	£45.00
L20	Ship-Models	1926	£2.75	£55.00
50	Shipping (Unissued)	Unissued	—	£70.00
25	Ships' Figure-Heads (2 Printings)	1912	£2.60	£65.00
L25	Ships' Figure-Heads	1931	£2.00	£50.00
L8	Snap Cards	1930	£7.00	—
50	Speedway Riders	1937	£1.75	£87.50
S?148	Stereoscopic Series	1904	£125.00	—
50	Straight Line Caricatures	1926	£0.60	£30.00
25	Struggle For Existence (2 Printings)	1923	£0.20	£5.00
50	Tennis	1936	£1.00	£50.00
116	The Corsair Game (Eire)	1965	£1.00	—
L25	The Nation's Shrines	1929	£2.20	£55.00
X1	The Royal Family	1937	—	£2.40
P6	The Royal Family	1901	£45.00	£260.00
25	Those Pearls Of Heaven	1916	£1.20	£30.00
66	Transvaal Series	1902	£5.00	—

JOHN PLAYER & SONS – cont.

Qty		Date	Odds	Sets
L25	Treasures Of Britain	1931	£1.80	£45.00
25	Treasures Of Ireland	1930	£1.80	£45.00
L25	Types Of Horses	1939	£4.00	£100.00
50	Uniforms Of The Territorial Army	1939	£0.90	£45.00
50	Useful Plants & Fruits	1902	£2.40	£120.00
25	Victoria Cross	1914	£2.80	£70.00
90	War Decorations & Medals	1927	£0.75	£67.50
50	Wild Animals' Heads	1931	£0.60	£30.00
25	(Transfers)	1931	£1.60	£40.00
50	(Transfers, "Series of 50")	1927	£0.40	£20.00
L25	Wild Animals (Heads), A Series	1932	£1.80	£45.00
L25	Wild Animals (Heads), 2nd Series	1932	£1.80	£45.00
45	Wild Animals Of World (Narrow) (No Ltd)	1901	£5.00	–
45	(Narrow) (With Ltd)	1901	£5.00	–
45	(Narrow) ("Branch")	1901	£6.50	–
50	Wild Animals Of World (Wide) (No Ltd)	1901	£2.40	£120.00
50	(Wide) (With Ltd)	1901	£2.30	£115.00
50	(Wide) ("Branch")	1901	£4.50	–
50	Wild Birds	1932	£0.50	£25.00
50	(Transfers)	1932	£0.30	£15.00
L25	Wild Birds	1934	£2.80	£70.00
L25	Wildfowl	1937	£3.20	£80.00
50	Wonders Of The Deep	1904	£2.00	£100.00
25	Wonders Of The World (Blue Back)	1916	£0.70	£17.50
25	(Grey Back, Eire)	1926	£1.20	£30.00
X10	Wooden Walls	1908	£5.75	£57.50
25	Wrestling & Ju-Jitsu (Blue Back)	1913	£2.40	£60.00
25	(Grey Back, Eire)	1925	£1.60	£40.00
26	Your Initials (Transfers)	1932	£0.50	£13.00
L25	Zoo Babies	1938	£0.60	£15.00
	OVERSEAS ISSUES			
50	Aeroplane Series	1926	£2.40	£120.00
50	Aircraft Of The Royal Air Force	1938	£1.50	£75.00
50	Animals Of The Countryside	1939	£0.60	£30.00
50	Arms & Armour (Grey Back)	1926	£3.00	£150.00
F50	Beauties	1925	£1.60	£80.00
MF50	Beauties (Coloured)	1925	£1.80	£90.00
F50	Beauties, 2nd Series"	1925	£1.70	£85.00
50	Birds & Their Young	1937	£0.60	£30.00
52	Birds Of Brilliant Plumage	1927	£3.40	–
25	"Bonzo" Dogs	1923	£5.00	£125.00
50	Boy Scouts	1924	£3.50	£175.00
L25	British Live Stock	1924	£7.50	£187.50
50	Butterflies (Girls)	1928	£6.00	£300.00
50	Coronation Series-Ceremonial Dress	1937	£1.00	–
50	Cricketers 1938	1938	£2.00	£100.00
50	Cycling	1939	£1.50	£75.00
25	Dogs (Heads)	1927	£1.50	£37.50
32	Drum Horses	1911	£8.50	–
L25	Famous Beauties	1937	£2.50	£62.50
50	Film Stars, Third Series	1938	£1.60	–
25	Flag Girls Of All Nations	1908	£8.00	–
L25	Golf	1939	£7.00	£175.00
50	Household Hints	1928	£1.00	£50.00
50	International Air Liners	1936	£1.20	£60.00

Qty		Date	Odds	Sets
50	Lawn Tennis	1928	£4.50	£225.00
50	Leaders Of Men	1925	£2.40	£120.00
50	Military Uniforms Of The British Empire Overseas			
	(Adhesive)	1938	£1.40	£70.00
	(Non-Adhesive)	1938	£1.50	£75.00
50	Modern Naval Craft	1939	£1.00	£50.00
50	Motor Cars A Series	1936	£2.00	£100.00
50	Motor Cars Second Series	1937	£1.80	£90.00
50	National Flags And Arms	1936	£0.65	£32.50
L25	Old Hunting Prints	1938	£4.50	£112.50
M15/22	Old Masters (Package Issue)	1966	£1.20	£18.00
P2	Old Masters (Package Issue)	1966	£2.50	£5.00
L25	Old Naval Prints	1936	£4.00	£100.00
48	Pictures Of The East	1931	£2.40	£115.00
25	Picturesque People Of The Empire	1938	£2.20	£55.00
M53	Playing Cards	1929	£1.40	–
50	Pugilists In Action	1928	£4.50	£225.00
L25	Racing Yachts	1938	£5.00	–
50	R.A.F. Badges	1937	£1.00	£50.00
50	Railway Working	1927	£2.20	£110.00
50	Sea Fishes	1935	£0.70	£35.00
50	Ships Flags & Cap Badges	1930	£2.20	£110.00
50	Signalling Series	1926	£1.80	£85.00
F50	The Royal Family At Home And Abroad	1927	£2.75	–
L25	Types Of Horses	1939	£4.60	£115.00
25	Whaling	1930	£3.00	£75.00
L25	Zoo Babies	1937	£1.80	£45.00
	MODERN ISSUES (DONCELLA)			
T32	Britain's Endangered Wildlife	1984	£0.30	£10.00
T30	Britain'sNocturnal Wildlife	1987	£1.00	£30.00
T30	Britain's Wild Flowers	1986	£0.50	£15.00
T32	British Butterflies	1984	£0.65	£20.00
T30	British Mammals	1983	£0.50	£15.00
T32	Country Houses And Castles	1981	£0.20	£5.00
T24	Golden Age Of Flying	1977	£0.30	£7.00
T1	Golden Age Of Flying Completion Offer	1978	–	£4.00
T24	Golden Age Of Motoring	1975	£0.30	£7.00
T24	Golden Age Of Motoring Completion Offer	1976	£4.00	£95.00
T24	Golden Age Of Sail	1978	£0.30	£7.00
T1	Golden Age Of Sail Completion Offer	1979	–	£4.00
T24	Golden Age Of Steam	1976	£0.35	£8.50
T1	Golden Age Of Steam Completion Offer	1977	–	£4.00
T24	History Of The V.C.	1980	£0.80	£20.00
T1	History Of The V.C. Completion Offer	1980	–	£4.00
T24	Napoleonic Uniforms	1980	£0.30	£7.50
T1	Napoleonic Uniforms Completion Offer	1980	–	£6.00
T30	The Living Ocean	1985	£0.50	£15.00
	MODERN ISSUES (GRANDEE)			
T30	African Wildlife	1990	£0.40	£12.00
T32	Britain's Endangered Wildlife	1984	£0.25	£8.00
T30	Britain's Nocturnal Wildlife	1987	£0.25	£7.50
T30	Britain's Wayside Wildlife	1988	£0.25	£7.50
T30	Britain's Wild Flowers	1986	£0.25	£7.50
T32	British Birds	1980	£0.50	£16.00
T32	British Butterflies	1983	£0.40	£13.00

JOHN PLAYER & SONS – cont.

Qty		Date	Odds	Sets
T30	British Mammals (Imperial Tobacco Ltd)	1982	£0.20	£6.00
T30	(Imperial Group plc)	1983	£0.20	£6.00
T28	Famous M.G. Marques	1981	£0.85	£25.00
T7	Limericks	1977	£10.00	–
T30	The Living Ocean	1985	£0.25	£7.50
T25	Top Dogs	1979	£1.00	£25.00
T6	World Of Gardening	1976	£10.00	£60.00
	MODERN ISSUES (TOM THUMB)			
L30	Britain's Maritime History	1989	£0.40	£12.00
L32	Exploration Of Space	1982	£0.30	£9.00
L30	History Of Britain's Railways	1987	£0.60	£18.00
L30	History Of British Aviation	1988	£0.70	£21.00
L30	History Of Motor Racing (Imperial Tobacco Ltd.)	1986	£1.00	£30.00
L30	(Imperial Group plc.)	1986	£1.50	£45.00
L32	Myths & Legends	1981	£0.85	£27.50
T4	Record Breakers	1976	£2.50	–
L32	Wonders Of The Ancient World	1984	£0.50	£16.00
L30	Wonders Of The Modern World	1985	£0.30	£9.00
	MODERN ISSUES (OTHER)			
44	Black Jack	1984	£1.25	–
M44	Black Jack	1984	£0.60	–
T44	Black Jack	1984	£0.50	–
T8	Panama Puzzles	1976	£6.50	–
T?	Player Clues (Headings In Red)	1987	£0.60	–
T?	Player Clues (Headings In Blue)	1987	£0.60	–
T?63	Player Games (Green)	1983	£0.50	–
T?29	Player Games (Yellow)	1983	£0.75	–
T?62	Player Games (Orange)	1984	£0.50	–
T?106	Player Games (Silver)	1984	£0.50	–
T?	Player Games (Yellow)	1984	£0.75	–
T?127	Player Quiz (Green)	1985	£0.65	–
T?	Player Quiz (Blue)	1986	£0.65	–
T?	Player Quiz (Red)	1986	£0.65	–
T6	Play Ladbroke Spot-Ball	1975	£7.00	–
T6	Play Panama Spot Six	1977	£7.00	–
T4	Recordbreakers	1976	£6.00	–
T50	Super Cars (39 x 90mm)	1987	£0.65	–
T50	(47 X 90mm)	1987	£0.65	–
60	Super Deal	1984	£1.25	–
M60	Super Deal	1984	£0.65	–
T60	Super Deal (35 X 90mm)	1984	£1.25	–
T60	(47 X 90mm)	1984	£0.65	–
T108	Super Year 88 (35 X 90mm)	1988	£1.25	–
T108	(47 X 90mm)	1988	£0.65	–
M4	Vanguard Limericks	1981	£1.50	–
156	World Tour	1986	£1.25	–
M156	World Tour	1986	£0.65	–
T156	World Tour (35 X 90mm)	1986	£1.25	–
T156	(47 X 90mm)	1986	£0.65	–

JAMES PLAYFAIR & CO.

Qty		Date	Odds	Sets
25	How To Keep Fit	1912	£34.00	£850.00

PREMIER TOBACCO MFRS. LTD.

Qty		Date	Odds	Sets
48	Eminent Stage & Screen Personalities	1936	£2.00	£100.00
K52	Miniature Playing Cards	1935	£8.00	—
50	Stage & Screen Personalities (Brown)	1936	£2.40	—
100	Stage & Screen Personalities (Grey)	1936	£1.60	£160.00

PRITCHARD & BURTON

Qty		Date	Odds	Sets
51	Actors & Actresses "FROGA" (Blue Back)	1899	£22.50	—
51	(Grey Back)	1899	£75.00	—
15	Beauties "PAC"	1899	£65.00	£975.00
20	Boer War Cartoons	1900	£120.00	
30	Flags & Flags With Soldiers (Draped)	1902	£17.50	£525.00
15	(Different Back)	1902	£22.50	
15	Flags & Flags With Soldiers (Undraped)	1902	£20.00	—
25	Holiday Resorts & Views	1902	£20.00	£500.00
40	Home & Colonial Regiments	1901	£55.00	—
25	Royalty Series	1902	£24.00	£600.00
25	South African Series	1901	£23.00	£575.00
25	Star Girls	1900	£225.00	—

G. PRUDHOE

Qty		Date	Odds	Sets
30	Army Pictures, Cartoons, etc.	1916	£130.00	—

Q.V. CIGARS

Qty		Date	Odds	Sets
M?7	Barnum & Bailey's Circus Performers	1900	£350.00	—

JAS. QUINTON LTD.

Qty		Date	Odds	Sets
26	Actresses "FROGA"	1899	£200.00	—

RAY & CO. LTD.

Qty		Date	Odds	Sets
K7	Flags Of The Allies (Shaped)	1916	£65.00	—
25	War Series (1-25)	1915	£16.00	—
75	War Series (26-100)	1915	£12.50	—
24	War Series (101-124)	1916	£25.00	—

RAYMOND REVUEBAR

Qty		Date	Odds	Sets
MF25	Striptease Artistes (2 Printings)	1960	£16.00	—

RECORD CIGARETTE & TOBACCO CO.

Qty		Date	Odds	Sets
X34	The Talkie Cigarette Card (Record Cigarette Co)	1934	£37.50	—
X34	(Record Tobacco Co.)	1934	£55.00	—

REDFORD & CO.

Qty		Date	Odds	Sets
20	Actresses "BLARM"	1900	£75.00	—
25	Armies Of The World	1901	£60.00	—
25	Beauties "GRACC"	1899	£135.00	—
30	Colonial Troops	1902	£55.00	—
24	Nautical Expressions	1900	£75.00	—
40	Naval & Military Phrases	1904	£65.00	—
25	Picture Series	1906	£65.00	—
25	Sports & Pastimes	1906	£85.00	—
50	Stage Artistes Of The Day	1908	£22.00	£1,100.00

RELIANCE TOBACCO MFG. CO.

Qty		Date	Odds	Sets
24	British Birds	1934	£5.00	£120.00
35	Famous Stars	1934	£5.00	£175.00

A.S. RICHARDSON

M12	Manikin Cards (2 Printings)	1915	£125.00	—

RICHMOND CAVENDISH CO. LTD.

26	Actresses "FROGA"	1900	£32.50	£850.00
28	Actresses "PILPI I"	1902	£15.00	£420.00
F50	Actresses "PILPI II"	1903	£11.00	£550.00
?179	Actresses, Gravure (Back Top-Bottom)	1904	£7.50	—
50	Actresses, Gravure (Back Bottom-Top)	1904	£8.50	£425.00
14	Beauties "AMBS" (12 Backs)	1899	£50.00	—
52	Beauties P/C Inset	1897	£50.00	—
28	Chinese Actors & Actresses	1923	£3.75	£105.00
F50	Cinema Stars	1927	£3.60	£180.00
40	Medals	1900	£22.00	£880.00
20	Music Hall Artistes	1901	£47.50	£950.00
12	Pretty Girl Series "RASH"	1899	£45.00	£540.00
20	Yachts (Black Back)	1900	£62.50	—
20	(White Back)	1900	£65.00	—

RIDGWAY'S MANCHESTER

M?	Play Up Sporting Shields	1900	£80.00	—

RITMEESTER CIGARS (Cigar Brands)

24	Austrian Cavalry Serie D	1975	£1.25	—
X28	Austrian Cavalry Serie D	1975	£1.25	£35.00
24	English Cavalry Serie A	1973	£1.00	£24.00
X28	English Cavalry Serie A	1973	£1.50	—
24	French Cavalry Serie B	1973	£1.00	£24.00
X28	French Cavalry Serie B	1973	£1.00	—
24	German Cavalry Serie C	1975	£1.25	—
X28	German Cavalry Serie C	1975	£0.75	£21.00
24	Military Bandsmen Serie K	1978	—	£20.00

ROBERTS & SONS

26	Actresses "FROGA"	1899	£70.00	—
25	Armies Of The World (Plain Back)	1900	£45.00	—
25	(Printed Back)	1900	£50.00	—
M50	Beautiful Women	1898	£275.00	—
50	Beauties "CHOAB" (Black Back)	1900	£70.00	—
50	(Blue Back)	1900	£75.00	—
50	Colonial Troops	1902	£40.00	£2,000.00
M28	Dominoes	1905	£60.00	—
K52	Miniature Playing Cards (Blue)	1905	£65.00	—
K52	(Pink)	1905	£65.00	—
K52	(Yellow)	1905	£65.00	—
24	Nautical Expressions (Navy Cut Cigs)	1902	£65.00	—
24	(No Brand)	1902	£65.00	—
70	Stories Without Words	1904	£60.00	—
25	Types Of British & Colonial Troops	1900	£50.00	—

ROBINSON & BARNSDALE LTD.

Qty		Date	Odds	Sets
24	Actresses, Colin Campbell	1898	£140.00	—
?31	Actresses, Cupola"	1898	£240.00	—
1	Advertisement Card,Colin Campbell	1897	—	£125.00
?26	Beauties, Collotype (Black Back, "NANA")	1895	£250.00	—
?26	(Red Back, "NANA")	1895	£250.00	—
?26	Beauties, Collotype (Our Golden Beauties)	1895	£250.00	—
M?16	Beauties,Highest Honors ("Viginia")	1895	£350.00	—
M?16	("Virginia" Label)	1895	£350.00	—
?3	Beauties - "KEWA II"	1900	£350.00	—

E. ROBINSON & SONS LTD

Qty		Date	Odds	Sets
10	Beauties(10 Brands)	1897	£60.00	—
?49	Derbyshire And The Peak	1903	£225.00	—
25	Egyptian Studies	1914	£26.00	—
25	King Lud Problems	1934	£22.50	—
6	Medals & Decorations Of Great Britain			
	(Red Terra Cotta Back)	1902	£250.00	—
	(General Favourite Onyx Back)	1902	£500.00	—
40	Nature Studies	1914	£24.00	—
25	Regimental Mascots	1916	£67.50	—
25	Types Of British Soldiers (General Favourite Onyx)	1914	£400.00	—
25	Wild Flowers	1915	£21.00	—

ROMAN STAR CIGARS

Qty		Date	Odds	Sets
26	Actresses "FROGA"	1899	£175.00	—
25	Beauties "BOCCA"	1899	£175.00	—

ROTHMANS LTD.

Qty		Date	Odds	Sets
40	Beauties Of The Cinema	1939	£1.85	£74.00
L24	Beauties Of The Cinema (Circular, Matt)	1939	£4.50	£108.00
L24	(Varnished)	1939	£4.50	£108.00
P25	Canterbury Bankstown District Rugby League Football Club			
	"New Zealand"	1980	£10.00	—
24	Cinema Stars	1925	£1.50	£36.00
L25	Cinema Stars	1925	£1.20	£30.00
P30	Country Living Cards	1974	—	£13.50
28	Dominoes	1986	£3.00	—
M50	Football International Stars	1984	£0.50	£25.00
15	Know Africa	1970	£2.50	£37.50
15/16	Know Your Language	1970	£2.50	£37.50
36	Landmarks In Empire History	1936	£1.20	£43.00
?	Lucky Charms (Metal)	1930	£4.00	—
50	Modern Inventions	1935	£1.20	£60.00
LF54	New Zealand	1933	£0.85	£45.00
24	Prominent Screen Favourites	1934	£1.35	£32.50
F50	Punch Jokes	1935	£0.65	£32.50
M?	Puzzle Card Series	1930	£30.00	—
5	Rare And Historic Banknotes	1970	£4.00	£20.00
L8	Wiggle-Woggle Picture Cards	1933	£35.00	—

WM. RUDDELL LTD.

Qty		Date	Odds	Sets
?	Couplet Cards	1924	£30.00	—
25	Grand Opera Series	1924	£7.20	£180.00
25	Rod & Gun	1924	£7.20	£180.00
50	Songs That Will Live For Ever	1924	£4.00	£200.00

RUTHERFORDS

Qty		Date	Odds	Sets
?6	Footballers	1900	£2,000.00	—

I. RUTTER & CO.

Qty		Date	Odds	Sets
15	Actresses (Printed Back)................................	1900	£60.00	—
15	Actresses (Rubber Stamped Back)................	1900	£100.00	—
15	(Plain Back)	1900	£27.50	—
1	Advertisement Card	1899	—	£1,250.00
7	Boer War Celebrities (Printed Back)	1901	£60.00	£420.00
7	(Plain Back)	1901	£30.00	—
54	Comic Phrases	1905	£20.00	£1,080.00
20	Cricketers Series..	1902	£325.00	—
30	Flags & Flags With Soldiers	1901	£26.50	£795.00
24	Girls, Flags & Arms Of Countries	1900	£35.00	£840.00
25	Proverbs (Green Seal)	1904	£42.50	—
25	(Red Seal)	1904	£42.50	—
25	Shadowgraphs...	1903	£42.50	—

S.D.V. TOBACCO CO. LTD.

Qty		Date	Odds	Sets
16	British Royal Family	1901	£600.00	—

SACCONE & SPEED

Qty		Date	Odds	Sets
F55	Beauties...	1912	£12.50	—
F55	(Red Overprint)...	1912	£6.00	—
?119	Picture Competition	1912	£15.00	—

ST. PETERSBURG CIGARETTE CO. LTD.

Qty		Date	Odds	Sets
?12	Footballers	1900	£1,500.00	—

SALMON & GLUCKSTEIN LTD.

Qty		Date	Odds	Sets
X1	Advertisement Card (Snake Charmer)	1897	—	£500.00
15	Billiard Terms (Large Numerals)...........................	1905	£80.00	—
15	(Small Numerals).........................	1905	£75.00	£1,125.00
12	British Queens	1902	£45.00	£540.00
X30	Castles, Abbeys & Houses (Brown Back).............	1906	£17.50	£525.00
X30	(Red Back).............	1906	£27.50	—
32	Characters From Dickens	1903	£30.00	—
25	Coronation Series, 1911	1911	£12.50	£312.50
L25	Famous Pictures (Brown).....................................	1912	£11.00	£275.00
L25	Famous Pictures (Green,Different)........................	1912	£9.00	£225.00
6	Her Most Gracious Majesty Queen Victoria	1897	£50.00	£300.00
40	Heroes Of The Transvaal War..............................	1901	£13.00	£800.00
25	Magical Series	1923	£7.00	£175.00
48	Methods Of Conveying The Mails	1900	£27.50	£1,320.00
30	Music Hall Stage Characters	1902	£55.00	£1,650.00
25	Occupations	1898	£500.00	—
20	Owners & Jockeys Series....................................	1900	£85.00	£1,700.00
L50	Pottery Types (Silk, Nd Front & Back)	1916	£4.50	£225.00
L50	(Silk, Nd Backs Only).................	1916	£4.25	£200.00
6	Pretty Girl Series "RASH"	1900	£65.00	£390.00
22	Shakespearian Series (Frame On Back)	1902	£30.00	£660.00
22	(No Frame On Back)........................	1902	£40.00	—
25	Star Girls (Brown Back).......................................	1899	£125.00	—
25	(Red Back)	1899	£120.00	—

SALMON & GLUCKSTEIN LTD. – cont.

Qty		Date	Odds	Sets
50	The Great White City..	1908	£14.00	£700.00
25	Traditions Of The Army&Navy (Large No.)	1917	£17.00	£425.00
25	(Small No.)	1917	£15.00	£375.00
25	Wireless Explained..	1923	£5.60	£140.00

W. SANDORIDES & CO. LTD.

Qty		Date	Odds	Sets
25	Aquarium Studies From The London Zoo			
25	(Large Numerals)..	1925	£3.40	£85.00
25	(Small Numerals)..	1925	£3.20	£80.00
L25	Aquarium Studies From The London Zoo	1925	£3.60	£90.00
25	Cinema Celebrities..	1924	£2.60	£65.00
X25	Cinema Celebrities..	1924	£4.00	–
25	Cinema Stars (With Firm's Name)...............................	1924	£6.00	–
25	(Big Gun)	1924	£8.00	–
25	(Lucana)...................................	1924	£6.00	–
X25	Cinema Stars (Big Gun)	1924	£2.60	£65.00
X25	(Lucana 66).................................	1924	£8.00	–
50	Famous Racecourses	1926	£4.50	£225.00
L50	Famous Racecourses	1926	£5.00	£250.00
50	Famous Racehorses (Lucana Cigarettes).........................	1923	£3.20	£160.00
50	(Big Gun Label)	1923	£12.50	–
12	London Views (4 Types)..	1936	£5.00	–
25	Sports & Pastimes	1924	£12.50	–

SANSOM'S CIGAR STORES

Qty		Date	Odds	Sets
?13	London Views	1905	£650.00	–

NICOLAS SARONY & CO.

Qty		Date	Odds	Sets
25	A Day On The Airway...	1928	£1.20	£30.00
L25	A Day On The Airway...	1928	£1.20	£30.00
50	Around The Mediterranean.......................................	1926	£1.00	£50.00
L50	Around The Mediterranean.......................................	1926	£1.20	£60.00
?7	Boer War Scenes	1901	£750.00	–
M100	Celebrities And Their Autographs (2 Printings)...................	1923	£0.75	£75.00
L100	Celebrities And Their Autographs (2 Printings)...................	1923	£0.80	£80.00
50	Cinema Stars	1933	£1.40	£70.00
P38	Cinema Stars	1930	£9.00	–
P42	Cinema Stars, Second Series.....................................	1930	£5.50	£230.00
P50	Cinema Stars, Third Series..	1930	£5.50	£275.00
P42	Cinema Stars, Fourth Series......................................	1930	£5.50	£230.00
P25	Cinema Stars, Fifth Series	1930	£5.50	£137.50
25	Cinema Studies	1929	£1.20	£30.00
F54	Life At Whipsnade Zoo	1934	£0.50	£27.00
50	Links With The Past	1925	£0.25	£12.50
25	(Australia)	1926	£1.00	–
25	(New Zealand)...	1926	£0.80	£20.00
L50	Links With The Past	1925	£0.25	£12.50
L25	(Australia)	1926	£1.00	–
L25	(New Zealand)...	1926	£0.60	£15.00
L25	(Presentation Issue)	1926	£2.00	–
25	Museum Series..	1927	£0.30	£7.50
25	(New Zealand)...	1927	£0.70	£17.50
L25	Museum Series..	1927	£0.30	£7.50
L25	(Australia)	1927	£1.00	–

NICOLAS SARONY & CO. – cont.

Qty		Date	Odds	Sets
L25	(New Zealand)	1927	£1.00	–
L25	(Presentation Issue)	1927	£1.00	£25.00
F36	National Types Of Beauty	1928	£0.30	£11.00
MF36	National Types Of Beauty	1928	£0.35	£12.50
15	Origin Of Games	1923	£5.00	£85.00
L15	Origin Of Games	1923	£6.00	£100.00
50	Saronicks	1929	£0.50	£25.00
M50	Saronicks	1929	£0.60	£30.00
50	Ships Of All Ages	1929	£1.20	£60.00
M50	Ships Of All Ages	1929	£1.20	£60.00
25	Tennis Strokes	1923	£3.60	£90.00

T.S. SAUNT

Qty		Date	Odds	Sets
30	Army Pictures, Cartoons, etc.	1916	£140.00	–

SCOTTISH C.W.S.LTD

Qty		Date	Odds	Sets
25	Burns (Large Numeral)	1924	£1.60	£40.00
25	Small Numeral)	1924	£2.80	£70.00
25	(Plain Back)	1924	£7.50	–
20	Dogs	1925	£12.00	–
25	Dwellings Of All Nations (Large No.)	1924	£2.00	£50.00
25	(Small No.)	1924	£3.60	£87.50
25	(Plain Back)	1924	£7.50	–
L25	Famous Pictures	1924	£8.00	–
L25	Famous Pictures-Glasgow Gallery			
L25	(Adhesive)	1927	£1.40	£35.00
L25	(Non-Adhesive)	1927	£2.40	£60.00
L25	Famous Pictures-London Galleries			
L25	(Adhesive)	1927	£1.40	£35.00
L25	(Non-Adhesive)	1927	£2.40	£60.00
50	Feathered Favourites (Adhesive)	1926	£1.80	£90.00
50	(Non-Adhesive, Grey Border)	1926	£2.50	£125.00
50	(Non-Adhesive, White Border)	1926	£2.30	£115.00
25	Racial Types	1925	£8.00	£200.00
50	Triumphs Of Engineering (Brown Border)	1926	£2.40	£120.00
50	(White Border)	1926	£2.50	–
50	Wireless	1924	£4.50	£225.00

SELBY'S TOBACCO STORES

Qty		Date	Odds	Sets
M12	Manikin Cards	1915	£130.00	–

SHARPE & SNOWDEN

Qty		Date	Odds	Sets
?1	Views Of England	1905	£750.00	–
?23	Views Of London	1905	£350.00	–

W.J. SHEPHERD

Qty		Date	Odds	Sets
25	Beauties "FECKSA"	1901	£110.00	–

SHORT'S

Qty		Date	Odds	Sets
L?13	House Views (Numbered)	1924	£65.00	–
L10	House Views (Unnumbered)	1924	£40.00	–

SIMONETS LTD. (Channel Isles)

Qty		Date	Odds	Sets
MF36	Beautiful Women	1928	£6.00	£215.00
F24	Cinema Scene Series	1926	£7.50	£180.00
F27	Famous Actors And Actresses	1929	£6.50	£175.00
50	Local Footballers	1925	£6.00	£300.00
25	Picture Series	1925	£5.00	£125.00
F27	Sporting Celebrities	1929	£10.00	—
LF50	Views Of Jersey (Plain Back)	1926	£2.50	—

JOHN SINCLAIR LTD.

Qty		Date	Odds	Sets
M?92	Actresses	1902	£85.00	—
F48	Birds (Numbered)	1924	£3.20	£155.00
F?50	("Specimen Cigarette Card")	1924	£8.50	—
LF50	Birds	1924	£6.50	£325.00
50	British Sea Dogs	1928	£6.00	£300.00
F54	Champion Dogs, A Series	1938	£1.25	£67.50
LF52	Champion Dogs, A Series	1938	£1.25	£65.00
F54	Champion Dogs, 2nd Series	1939	£3.50	£190.00
LF52	Champion Dogs, 2nd Series	1939	£3.75	£195.00
F50	English & Scottish Football Stars	1935	£1.70	£85.00
F54	Film Stars ("Series Of 54 Real Photos")	1934	£2.25	£121.50
F54	Film Stars ("Series Of Real Photos")	1937	£1.80	£97.50
F54	Film Stars (55-108)	1937	£1.60	£85.00
M12	Flags (Numbered, Silk, 25-36)	1914	£14.00	—
M24	Flags (Unnumbered, Silk) (Blue Caption)	1914	£8.50	—
M24	(Bright Green)	1914	£8.00	—
M24	Flags (Unnumbered, Silk) (Olive Green)	1914	£7.50	—
M24	(Red Caption)	1914	£8.50	—
M25	Flags (Unnumbered, Silk) (Grey Caption)	1914	£12.50	—
M50	Flags, Fourth Series (Silk)	1914	£6.25	—
M50	Flags, Fifth Series (Silk)	1914	£6.25	—
D50	Flags, Sixth Series (Silk)	1914	£7.50	—
G10	Flags, Seventh Series (Silk)	1914	£65.00	—
F96	Flowers & Plants (Numbered)	1924	£2.40	£235.00
F?100	("Specimen Cigarette Card")	1924	£7.50	—
51	Football Favourites (51-101)	1908	£175.00	—
4	North Country Celebrities	1904	£75.00	£300.00
F55	Northern Gems	1902	£70.00	—
50	Picture Puzzles & Riddles Series	1916	£27.50	—
F54	Radio Favourites	1935	£1.60	£85.00
L50	Regimental Badges (Silk)	1915	£6.25	—
D24	Regimental Colours (Silk) (38-61)	1914	£14.00	—
K53	Rubicon Cards (Miniature P/C)	1933	£5.00	—
K53	(Red Overprint)	1933	£7.50	—
P1	The Allies Flags (No.37, Silk)	1915	—	£35.00
50	Trick Series	1916	£30.00	—
50	Well Known Footballers-N.E.Counties	1938	£1.50	£75.00
50	Well Known Footballers-Scottish	1938	£1.40	£70.00
50	Worlds Coinage	1914	£20.00	£1,000.00

ROBERT SINCLAIR TOBACCO CO. LTD.

Qty		Date	Odds	Sets
X4	Battleships & Crests (Silk)	1915	£60.00	—
10	Billiards, First Set	1928	£9.00	£90.00
15	Billiards, Second Set	1928	£11.00	—
3	Billiards, Third Set	1928	£16.50	—

ROBERT SINCLAIR TOBACCO CO. LTD. – cont.

Qty		Date	Odds	Sets
28	Dominoes	1902	£65.00	—
M10	Flags (Silk)	1915	£25.00	—
?9	Footballers (Black & White On Card)	1898	£1,000.00	—
?3	Footballers (Mauve On Paper)	1898	£1,500.00	—
P6	Great War Area (Silk)	1915	£50.00	—
M10	Great War Heroes (Silk)	1915	£37.50	—
12	Policemen Of The World	1899	£225.00	—
X1	Red Cross Nurse (Silk)	1915	—	£50.00
M5	Regimental Badges (Silk)	1915	£32.50	—
12	The Smiler Series	1924	£7.50	—
L12	The Smiler Series	1924	£12.50	—

J. SINFIELD

Qty		Date	Odds	Sets
24	Beauties "HUMPS"	1899	£1,500.00	—

SINGLETON & COLE LTD.

Qty		Date	Odds	Sets
50	Atlantic Liners	1910	£24.00	£1,200.00
25	Bonzo Series	1928	£8.00	£200.00
50	Celebrities-Boer War Period	1901	£22.00	£1,100.00
110	Crests & Badges Of The British Army (Silk)	1915	£4.25	—
35	Famous Boxers (Numbered)	1930	£16.50	—
35	(Unnumbered)	1930	£45.00	—
25	Famous Film Stars	1930	£11.00	£275.00
35	Famous Officers	1915	£15.00	£700.00
35	(Subtitled Hero Series)	1915	£400.00	—
50	Footballers	1905	£150.00	—
40	Kings & Queens	1902	£24.00	£960.00
M12	Manikin Cards	1915	£130.00	—
25	Maxims Of Success (Orange Border)	1906	£27.00	£675.00
25	(Yellow Border)	1906	£250.00	—
10	Orient Line (Anonymous, 5 Ports On Back)	1904	£42.50	£425.00
10	(Anonymous, 11 Ports On Back)	1904	£50.00	—
8	Orient Pacific Line (Anonymous)	1904	£65.00	—
8	Orient Royal Mail Line (Firm's Name)	1904	£45.00	£340.00
25	The Wallace-Jones Keep Fit System	1910	£27.00	£675.00

F. & J. SMITH

Qty		Date	Odds	Sets
24	Advertisement Cards	1897	£240.00	—
50	A Tour Round The World (Postcard Back)	1904	£40.00	£2,000.00
50	(Script Back)	1904	£20.00	£1,000.00
50	A Tour Round The World (Descriptive, Multi-Backed)	1906	£11.00	£550.00
50	Battlefields Of Great Britain (15 Backs)	1913	£16.00	£800.00
25	Boer War Series (Black & White)	1901	£75.00	—
50	Boer War Series (Coloured)	1901	£30.00	£1,500.00
50	Champions Of Sport (Blue Back)	1902	£90.00	—
50	Champions Of Sport (Red Multi-Backed)	1902	£85.00	—
25	Cinema Stars (8 Brands)	1920	£12.00	£300.00
50	Cricketers (1-50)	1912	£16.00	£800.00
20	Cricketers, 2nd Series (51-70)	1912	£27.50	£550.00
50	Derby Winners	1913	£15.00	£750.00
50	Famous Explorers	1911	£16.00	£800.00
50	Football Club Records	1917	£17.50	£875.00
50	Football Club Records (Different)	1922	£19.00	£950.00
120	Footballers (Brown Back)	1906	£45.00	—

F. & J. SMITH – cont.

Qty		Date	Odds	Sets
100	Footballers (Blue Back, No Series Title)	1909	£14.00	£1,400.00
150	Footballers (Titled, Dark Blue Backs)	1912	£14.00	£2,100.00
150	(Titled, Light Blue Backs)	1912	£14.00	–
50	Fowls, Pigeons & Dogs	1908	£10.00	£500.00
25	Holiday Resorts	1925	£7.50	£187.50
50	Medals (Numbered, Smith Multi-Backed)	1902	£11.00	£550.00
50	(Numbered, Imperial Tobacco Co.,Multi-Backed)	1903	£35.00	–
50	(Numbered, Imperial Tobacco Company, Multi-Backed)	1906	£11.00	£550.00
20	(Unnumbered)	1905	£15.00	£300.00
G1	Medal Album (Printed)	1902	–	£200.00
50	Nations Of The World	1923	£7.00	£350.00
50	Naval Dress & Badges			
50	(Descriptive, Multi-Backed)	1911	£11.00	£550.00
50	(Non-Descriptive, Multi-Backed)	1914	£10.00	£500.00
50	Phil May Sketches (Brown, 4 Brands)	1924	£7.00	£350.00
50	(Grey Multi-Backed)	1908	£9.00	£450.00
25	Prominent Rugby Players	1924	£12.50	£312.50
40	Races Of Mankind (No Title, Multibacked)	1900	£65.00	–
40	(Titled, Multi-Backed)	1900	£47.50	–
25	Shadowgraphs (7 Brands)	1915	£8.00	£200.00
25	War Incidents A Series	1914	£8.00	£200.00
25	War Incidents 2nd Series	1915	£8.00	£200.00

F.L. SMITH LTD. (Albany Cigarettes)

L?20	Advertising Inserts	1957	£6.50	–

SNELL & CO.

25	Boer War Celebrities "STEW"	1901	£250.00	–

SOROKO

6	Jubilee Series	1935	£200.00	–
L6	Jubilee Series	1935	£200.00	–

S.E. SOUTHGATE & SON

25	Types Of British & Colonial Troops	1900	£135.00	–

SOUTH WALES TOB.MFG.CO.LTD.

30	Army Pictures, Cartoons, etc."	1915	£135.00	–
?92	Game Of Numbers	1912	£80.00	–
25	Views Of London	1912	£26.00	£650.00

T. SPALTON

30	Army Pictures, Cartoons, etc.	1916	£130.00	–

SPIRO VALLERI & CO.

?10	Noted Footballers	1908	£2,000.00	–

G. STANDLEY

M12	Manikin Cards	1915	£130.00	–

A & A E STAPLETON

M12	Manikin Cards	1915	£130.00	–

There are many instances in the enlarged catalogue when a set by one issuer is noted as occurring in more than one back. For example, each card in Wills Seaside Resorts can be found with six different brands advertised, while in the case of Smith Battlefields of Great Britain each number can have no less than 15 different advertisements!

In addition to these varieties there are also many series, particular among the earlier issues, where there are different backs, but not every front may be found with every back. These are known as multi-backs. A good example of this is the Wills set Sports of All Nations, which like Seaside Resorts also has six advertisements; however in this case each number only occurs with two different brands, and these run in distinct groups of numbers. The issues of Smith are also an excellent source of multi-

including Champions of Sport, Medals and Phil May Sketches featuring prominently. Indeed the Smith issues are so complicated that it has been necessary to publish a separate Reference Book detailing all the varieties known.

In the catalogue we now show when a series is multi-backed, but without indicating all the options available: this would have been too complicated, especially for a series such as Adkin Pretty Girl Series RASH, with its 50 different backs! Most type collectors would probably wish to obtain one of each of these multi-backs, and full information is normally to be found in the Cartophilic Society's Reference Books.

One additional term worth remembering is "vari-backed". This is used when there are different advertisements on the back, but where each front can be found with one back

DISSIMILAR SERIES

When a firm decides to issue a new set of cards it may have undertaken some market research, but it will never be certain how successful it may become. If the response is positive it may then produce an extra set, which would normally be distinguished as 2nd or continuation series. In the case of Lea's Pottery or Ogden Boy Scouts this extended to five series. Sometimes when a subject appeared popular, different aspects would be covered by sets with different titles, as in the case of Player with their aircraft sets and Ogden with its racing series.

Sometimes a popular series was extended by producing it in different sizes. Apart from the better known multi sized sets such as those of International T.C. and Jackson, there are examples where the small and large cards depict different subjects. These include Wills English Period Costumes, Baker Actresses and Carreras Old Staffordshire Figures.

Another quite complicated situation can occur when a Company decides to issue a completely new series under the same title as an earlier set. Wills were very fond of this, with two or more series titled Wild Flowers, Association Footballers, Garden Flowers and Speed.

Ogden too issued a later set of Boy Scouts some years after its first five, but its newer series of Bird's Eggs and British Birds were easily distinguishable by being cut-outs!

Finally, there is a group of series which are not quite the same. There are series where the pictures have been re-drawn, and show minor differences. These include two sets by Gallaher – Boy Scouts and the first series of Champions; also half the set of Carreras Famous Footballers and Huntley & Palmers Sports.

WHITSTABLE WHELKER

STAR OF THE WORLD

Qty		Date	Odds	Sets
20	Boer War Cartoons	1901	£160.00	—
?32	Boer War Celebrities "JASAS"................................	1901	£225.00	—
30	Colonial Troops...	1901	£100.00	—

H. STEVENS & CO.

20	Dogs	1923	£11.00	£220.00
25	Zoo Series..	1926	£6.50	—

A. STEVENSON

50	War Portraits...	1916	£130.00	—

ALBERT STOCKWELL

30	Army Pictures, Cartoons, etc.................................	1916	£135.00	—

STRATHMORE TOBACCO CO.LTD

M25	British Aircraft	1938	£3.20	£80.00

SWEET ALVA CIGARETTES

?32	Boer War Celebrities "JASAS"..............................	1901	£175.00	—

T.S.S.

24	Nautical Expressions	1900	£125.00	—

TADDY & CO.

72	Actresses, Collotype..	1897	£120.00	—
25	Actresses With Flowers	1899	£85.00	£2,125.00
37	Admirals & Generals-The War (2 Backs)...............	1914	£17.50	£900.00
25	Admirals & Generals-The War (South Africa)........	1914	£35.00	£875.00
25	Autographs	1912	£22.00	£550.00
20	Boer Leaders	1901	£27.50	£550.00
50	British Medals & Decorations, Series 2 (Steel Blue Back)....	1912	£13.00	£650.00
50	(Black Back)	1912	£35.00	—
50	British Medals & Ribbons	1912	£13.00	£650.00
20	Clowns & Circus Artistes ....Unissued		£900.00	—
30	Coronation Series	1902	£25.00	£750.00
238	County Cricketers...	1907	£40.00	—
50	Dogs	1900	£32.00	£1,600.00
5	English Royalty	1897	£800.00	—
25	Famous Actors/Famous Actresses........................	1903	£24.00	£600.00
50	Famous Horses And Cattle	1912	£115.00	—
25	Famous Jockeys (No Frame)	1910	£35.00	£875.00
25	(With Frame)	1910	£32.00	£800.00
50	Footballers (New Zealand)	1906	£100.00	—
25	Heraldry Series	1913	£22.00	£550.00
25	Honours & Ribbons...	1915	£26.00	£650.00
10	Klondyke Series	1900	£67.50	£675.00
60	Leading M.L.A.'S (South Africa)............................	1900	£850.00	—
25	Natives Of The World..	1899	£70.00	£1,750.00
25	Orders Of Chivalry	1911	£22.00	£550.00
25	Orders Of Chivalry, Second Series........................	1912	£26.00	£650.00
595	Prominent Footballers (No Footnote).....................	1907	£25.00	—
?403	Prominent Footballers (With Footnote).................	1908	£25.00	—
?410	Prominent Footballers (London Mixture)	1914	£42.50	—

TADDY & CO. – cont.

Qty		Date	Odds	Sets
20	Royalty, Actresses & Soldiers	1898	£225.00	–
25	Royalty Series	1903	£20.00	£500.00
25	Russo Japanese War (1-25)	1904	£22.00	£550.00
25	Russo Japanese War (26-50)	1904	£26.00	£650.00
15	South African Cricket Team, 1907	1907	£60.00	£900.00
26	South African Football Team, 1906-7	1906	£27.50	£715.00
25	Sports & Pastimes	1912	£23.00	£600.00
25	Territorial Regiments	1908	£25.00	£625.00
25	Thames Series	1903	£35.00	£875.00
20	Victoria Cross Heroes (1-20)	1901	£75.00	£1,500.00
20	Victoria Cross Heroes (21-40)	1901	£65.00	£1,300.00
20	V.C. Heroes-Boer War (41-60)	1902	£23.00	£460.00
20	V.C. Heroes-Boer War (61-80)	1902	£23.00	£460.00
20	V.C. Heroes-Boer War (81-100)	1902	£24.00	£500.00
25	Victoria Cross Heroes (101-125)	1904	£62.50	–
2	Wrestlers	1910	£275.00	£550.00

TADDY & CO.(RE-REGISTERED)
(No Connection with Original Company)

Qty		Date	Odds	Sets
D8	Advertisement Cards	1980	£0.50	£4.00
26	Motor Cars (Clown Cigarettes)	1980	–	£8.00
26	(Myrtle Grove Cigarettes)	1980	–	£12.00
26	Railway Locomotives (Clown Cigarettes)	1980	–	£12.50
26	(Myrtle Grove Cigarettes)	1980	–	£8.00

W. & M. TAYLOR

Qty		Date	Odds	Sets
8	The European War Series (Bendigo Cigs)	1915	£42.50	–
8	(Tipperary)	1915	£40.00	–
25	War Series (Bendigo Cigarettes)	1915	£22.00	£550.00
25	(Tipperary Cigarettes)	1915	£20.00	£500.00

TAYLOR WOOD

Qty		Date	Odds	Sets
18	Motor Cycle Series	1914	£115.00	–

TEOFANI & CO. LTD.

Qty		Date	Odds	Sets
25	Aquarium Studies From The London Zoo	1925	£12.00	–
50	Cinema Celebrities (Broadway Novelties)	1926	£4.00	–
50	(Anonymous)	1926	£3.60	–
25	Cinema Stars (Blue Band Cigarettes)	1924	£7.50	–
25	("Favourites" Printed)	1924	£7.50	–
25	("Favourites" Stamped)	1924	£7.50	–
25	(Three Star Cigarettes)	1924	£7.50	–
25	(Three Star Magnums, 2 Printings)	1924	£7.00	£175.00
X25	Cinema Stars	1924	£7.50	–
25	Famous Boxers	1925	£12.00	£300.00
F32	Famous British Ships And Officers	1934	£3.75	£120.00
L50	Famous Racecourses (Favourite Cigs)	1926	£20.00	–
50	Famous Racehorses	1923	£11.00	–
12	Film Actors & Actresses (Plain Back)	1936	£0.75	£9.00
20	Great Inventors	1924	£5.00	£100.00
20	Head-dress Of All Nations (Plain Back)	1926	£16.50	£330.00
LF50	Icelandic Girls	1929	£6.50	–
LF50	Icelandic Stage Scenes & Artistes	1929	£25.00	–
12	London Views (Plain Back)	1936	£0.50	£6.00

TEOFANI & CO. LTD. – cont.

Qty		Date	Odds	Sets
12	London Views (8 Different Printed Backs)	1936	£4.00	£50.00
48	Modern Movie Stars & Cinema Celebrities	1934	£1.40	£70.00
50	Natives In Costume (Plain Back)	1926	£17.50	—
24	Past & Present "A"-The Army (No Frame)	1938	£2.00	£48.00
24	(With Frame Line On Back)	1938	£2.25	£54.00
24	Past & Present "B"-Weapons Of War	1938	£1.25	£30.00
4	Past & Present "C"-Transport	1939	£5.50	£22.00
50	Public Schools & Colleges	1923	£3.40	£170.00
50	Ships And Their Flags	1925	£4.00	£200.00
25	Sports & Pastimes (Plain Back)	1924	£5.50	£150.00
25	(Printed Back)	1924	£13.00	—
22	Teofani Gems	1925	£2.25	£50.00
28	Teofani Gems	1925	£1.25	—
36	Teofani Gems	1925	£2.25	£81.00
48	Transport Then & Now	1939	£0.65	£32.50
50	Views Of London	1925	£3.50	—
F36	Views Of The British Empire	1927	£1.25	£45.00
24	Well-known Racehorsxes	1923	£10.00	—
50	World's Smokers (Plain Back)	1926	£17.00	£850.00
50	Zoological Studies	1924	£4.00	—
L50	Zoological Studies	1924	£7.00	—

TETLEY & SONS

Qty		Date	Odds	Sets
1	The Allies	1915	£1,250.00	—
50	War Portraits	1916	£110.00	—
25	Worlds Coinage	1914	£70.00	—

THEMANS & CO.

Qty		Date	Odds	Sets
?2	Anecdotes & Riddles	1913	£1,000.00	—
55	Dominoes	1913	£80.00	—
18	Motor Cycle Series	1914	£85.00	—
50	War Portraits	1915	£65.00	—
14	War Posters	1916	£400.00	—

SILK ISSUES (MAINLY ANONYMOUS)

Qty		Date	Odds	Sets
M12	Crests Of Warships (Series B4)	1914	£7.50	—
L4	Crests Of Warships (Series C4)	1914	£10.00	—
M48	Film Stars (Series B6)	1914	£7.50	—
P14	Film Stars (Series D6)	1914	£7.50	—
M12	Flags (Series B1)	1914	£7.00	—
M12	Flags (Series B2)	1914	£7.00	—
L12	Flags (Series C1)	1914	£12.00	—
L4	Flags (Series C2)	1914	£12.00	—
P2	Flags (Series D1)	1914	£15.00	—
P1	Flags (Series D2)	1914	£15.00	—
M12	Regimental Badges (Series B3)	1914	£7.50	—
L4	Regimental Badges (Series C3)	1914	£10.00	—
P1	Regimental Badges (Series D3)	1914	£16.00	—
M12	Views Of Blackpool (Series B5)	1914	£20.00	—
P7	Views Of Blackpool (Series D5)	1914	£20.00	—

THOMSON & PORTEOUS

Qty		Date	Odds	Sets
50	Arms Of British Towns	1905	£17.00	£850.00
25	Boer War Celebrities "STEW"	1901	£62.50	—
25	Shadowgraphs	1902	£45.00	—

THOMSON & PORTEOUS – cont.

Qty		Date	Odds	Sets
20	The European War Series	1915	£15.00	£300.00
41	V.C. Heroes (Firm's Name At Bottom)	1916	£14.00	£625.00
41	(Firm's Name At Top)	1916	£50.00	—

TOM NODDY

P12	Children Of The Year Series	1904	£90.00	—

TOPSY CIGARETTES

F?13	Actresses	1896	£750.00	—

TURKISH MONOPOLY CIGARETTE CO. LTD.

X?16	Boer War Scenes	1901	£600.00	—

UNITED KINGDOM TOBACCO CO. LTD.

50	Aircraft	1938	£1.70	£85.00
P48	Beautiful Britain, A Series (2 Printings)	1929	£1.75	£85.00
P48	Beautiful Britain, Second Series"	1929	£1.60	£80.00
25	British Orders Of Chivalry & Valour (2 Printings)	1936	£1.80	£45.00
24	Chinese Scenes	1933	£0.75	£18.00
32	Cinema Stars	1933	£1.80	£58.00
50	Cinema Stars (With Firm's Name)	1934	£1.80	£90.00
50	(Anonymous)	1934	£2.60	—
36	Officers Full Dress	1936	£2.25	£81.00
52	Soldiers (Metal)	1935	£13.50	—
36	Soldiers Of The King	1937	£2.25	£80.00

UNITED SERVICES MFG. CO. LTD.

50	Ancient Warriors	1938	£2.40	£120.00
25	Ancient Warriors	1957	£4.00	£100.00
50	Bathing Belles	1939	£0.90	£45.00
100	Interesting Personalities	1935	£3.25	£325.00
50	Popular Footballers	1936	£6.00	£300.00
50	Popular Screen Stars	1937	£3.75	£187.50

UNITED TOBACCONISTS ASSOCIATION LTD.

10	Actresses "MUTA"	1901	£250.00	—
12	Pretty Girl Series "RASH"	1900	£500.00	—

WALKERS TOBACCO CO. LTD. (W.T.C.)

60	British Beauty Spots	1924	£20.00	—
28	Dominoes (Old Monk)	1908	£65.00	—
28	Dominoes (W.T.C.)	1924	£6.00	—
F30/32	Film Stars (Tatleys)	1936	£2.00	£60.00
F48	Film Stars (Walkers)	1935	£4.75	—
K?5	Footballers	1924	£75.00	—

WALTERS TOBACCO CO. LTD.

L6	Angling Information	1939	£1.50	£9.00

E.T. WATERMAN

30	Army Pictures, Cartoons, etc.	1916	£135.00	—

WEBB & RASSELL

Qty		Date	Odds	Sets
50	War Portraits	1916	£120.00	—

HENRY WELFARE & CO.

| 22 | Prominent Politicians | 1912 | £75.00 | — |

WESTMINSTER TOBACCO CO. LTD.

F36	Australia, First Series	1932	£0.30	£10.00
F36	Australia, 2nd Series (Plain Back)	1933	£0.25	£9.00
F48	British Royal And Ancient Buildings			
	(Unnumbered)	1925	£0.75	£36.00
	(Numbered)	1925	£1.00	£48.00
F48	British Royal And Ancient Buildings			
	Second Series	1926	£0.30	£15.00
F36	Canada, First Series	1926	£0.50	£18.00
F36	Canada, Second Series	1928	£0.50	£18.00
F48	Indian Empire, First Series	1925	£0.25	£12.00
F48	Indian Empire, Second Series	1926	£0.25	£12.00
F36	New Zealand, First Series	1928	£0.25	£9.00
F36	New Zealand, Second Series	1929	£0.25	£9.00
F36	South Africa, First Series	1928	£0.60	£20.00
F36	South Africa, Second Series	1928	£0.60	£20.00

OVERSEAS ISSUES

L?200	Adamson's Oplevelser	1926	£20.00	—
MF50	Beauties	1924	£3.25	—
MF?97	Beautiful Women	1915	£3.00	—
M50	Birds, Beasts & Fishes	1923	£2.80	£140.00
102	British Beauties (Hand Coloured)	1915	£3.50	—
?57	(Uncoloured)	1915	£4.00	—
F48	British Royal And Ancient Buildings	1925	£1.00	£48.00
50	Butterflies & Moths	1920	£3.00	—
F36	Canada, First Series	1926	£1.00	£36.00
F36	Canada, Second Series	1928	£1.00	£36.00
30	Celebrated Actresses	1921	£5.50	£165.00
X25	Champion Dogs	1934	£4.60	£115.00
100	Cinema Artistes (Green Back)	1928	£3.25	—
50	Cinema Artistes (Grey Back)	1931	£3.25	—
48	Cinema Celebrities (C)	1935	£3.25	—
F50	Cinema Stars	1927	£3.00	—
MF50	Cinema Stars (Coloured)	1926	£3.50	—
MF50	(Uncoloured)	1930	£3.25	—
M27	Dancing Girls	1917	£6.00	£160.00
50	Do You Know? (3 Printings)	1922	£2.00	—
24	Fairy Tales (Booklets)	1926	£7.00	—
M100	Famous Beauties (Blue Caption)	1916	£2.75	—
M100	Famous Beauties (Brown Caption)	1916	£2.25	£225.00
P35	Famous Fighting Ships Of Various Nations	1910	£50.00	—
MF52	Film Favourites (Coloured)	1928	£4.00	—
MF52	(Uncoloured)	1928	£4.00	—
M50	Film Personalities	1931	£4.50	—
M50	Garden Flowers Of The World	1917	£3.00	£150.00
L50	Garden Flowers Of The World (Silk, 2 Printings)	1913	£6.00	£300.00
M?16	Icelandic History	1925	£40.00	—
F48	Indian Empire, First Series	1925	£1.00	£48.00
F48	Indian Empire, Second Series	1926	£1.00	—

WESTMINSTER TOBACCO CO. LTD. – cont.

Qty		Date	Odds	Sets
MF50	Islenzkar Eimskipamyndir (Trawlers)	1931	£3.00	£150.00
MF50	Islenzkar Landslagsmyndir (Views)	1928	£2.30	£115.00
MF50	Islenzkar Landslagsmyndir Nr2 (Views)	1929	£2.30	£115.00
40	Merrie England Studies	1914	£7.50	–
X24	Miniature Rugs	1924	£17.50	–
36	Modern Beauties	1938	£3.25	–
M?3	Monsterbeskyttet	1926	£40.00	–
MF52	Movie Stars	1925	£3.75	–
F36	New Zealand, First Series	1928	£1.25	–
F36	New Zealand, Second Series	1929	£1.25	–
53	Playing Cards (P.O.Box 78)	1934	£2.00	–
53	(Special Blend)	1934	£2.25	–
M55	Playing Cards (Blue Back)	1934	£2.00	–
M55	(Red Back)	1934	£2.00	–
F50	Popular Film Stars	1926	£3.50	–
50	Safety First	1936	£1.50	£75.00
L?200	Skjeggen's Oplevelser	1926	£20.00	–
F36	South Africa, First Series	1928	£1.00	–
F36	South Africa, Second Series	1928	£1.00	–
M49	South African Succulents	1937	£0.25	£12.50
M100	Stage & Cinema Stars (Black Caption)	1921	£3.00	–
M100	Stage & Cinema Stars (Grey Caption)	1921	£2.25	£225.00
MF50	Stars Of Filmland (Firm In Brown)	1927	£3.50	–
MF50	(Firm In White)	1927	£3.75	–
50	Steamships Of The World	1920	£10.00	–
40	The Great War Celebrities	1914	£8.50	£340.00
50	The World Of Tomorrow	1938	£1.50	£75.00
M50	Uniforms Of All Ages	1917	£12.00	£600.00
F50	Views Of Malaya	1930	£7.00	£350.00
25	Wireless(Several Printings)	1923	£5.00	£125.00
M50	Women Of Nations	1922	£4.50	£225.00

WHALE & COMPANY

?13	Conundrums	1900	£425.00	–

M.WHITE & CO.

20	Actresses "BLARM"	1900	£225.00	

WHITFIELD'S

30	Army Pictures, Cartoons, etc."	1916	£135.00	–

WHITFORD & SONS

20	Inventors	1924	£45.00	

WHOLESALE TOBACCO CO.

25	Armies Of The World	1903	£67.50	–
40	Army Pictures (Home & Colonial Regiments)	1902	£100.00	–

P. WHYTE

30	Army Pictures, Cartoons, etc.	1916	£140.00	–

W. WILLIAMS & CO.

30	Aristocrats Of The Turf, A Series	1924	£8.00	–
36	Aristocrats Of The Turf, Second Series	1924	£14.00	–
25	Boer War Celebrities "STEW"	1901	£75.00	–

W. WILLIAMS & CO. – cont.

Qty		Date	Odds	Sets
25	Boxing	1923	£10.00	–
50	Interesting Buildings	1912	£14.00	–
12	Views Of Chester	1912	£35.00	£420.00
12	Views Of Chester (As It Was), 2nd Series	1913	£35.00	£420.00

W.D. & H.O. WILLS LTD.

Qty		Date	Odds	Sets
?20	Actresses (Typeset Back)	1895	£1,000.00	–
52	Actresses (Brown Back, P/C Inset)	1898	£18.00	£935.00
52	Actresses (Grey Back, P/C Inset)	1897	£18.00	£935.00
52	(Grey Back, No Inset)	1897	£18.00	£935.00
25	Actresses, Collotype (Wills', Brands Back)	1894	£85.00	–
25	(Wills', No Brands)	1894	£85.00	–
?46	Actresses & Celebrities, Collotype			
	(Wills's, Four Brands on Back)	1894	£90.00	–
	(Wills's, Export Manufacturers Back)	1894	£100.00	–
1	Advertisement Card (Serving Maid)	1890	–	£800.00
4	Advertisement Cards (Cigarette Packets)	1891	£2,000.00	–
11	Advertisement Cards (Tobacco Packings)	1891	£1,000.00	–
3	Advertisement Cards (Showcards, 7 Brands)	1893	£325.00	–
6	Advertisement Cards (Showcards)	1893	£325.00	–
1	Advertisement Card-Three Castles	1965	–	£1.40
L1	Advertisement Card-Wants List	1935	–	£0.60
P4	Advertisement Postcards	1902	£140.00	–
50	Air Raid Precautions	1938	£1.00	£50.00
40	(Eire)	1938	£1.40	£56.00
50	Allied Army Leaders (2 Printings)	1917	£1.70	£85.00
50	Alpine Flowers	1913	£0.80	£40.00
49	And When Did You Last See Your Father (Sect.)	1932	£1.00	£49.00
50	Animals & Birds (Descriptive)	1900	£19.00	£950.00
50	Animals & Birds In Fancy Costume	1896	£40.00	£2,000.00
48	Animalloys (Sect.)	1934	£0.25	£12.00
L25	Animals And Their Furs	1929	£2.00	£50.00
50	Arms Of Companies	1913	£0.75	£37.50
50	Arms Of Foreign Cities (2 Printings)	1912	£65.00	£32.50
L42	Arms Of Oxford & Cambridge Colleges	1922	£1.35	£57.50
L25	Arms Of Public Schools, 1st Series	1933	£2.20	£55.00
L25	Arms Of Public Schools, 2nd Series	1934	£2.00	£50.00
50	Arms Of The Bishopric	1907	£0.90	£45.00
50	Arms Of The British Empire	1910	£0.65	£32.50
L25	Arms Of The British Empire, 1st Series	1933	£1.80	£45.00
L25	Arms Of The British Empire, 2nd Series	1933	£1.80	£45.00
L25	Arms Of Universities	1923	£1.50	£37.50
50	Association Footballers (Frame On Back)	1935	£1.40	£70.00
50	Association Footballers (No Frame On Back)	1939	£1.30	£65.00
50	(No Frame, Eire)	1939	£2.50	£125.00
L25	Auction Bridge	1926	£2.40	£60.00
50	Aviation	1910	£2.60	£130.00
?20	Beauties, Collotype (Firefly)	1894	£175.00	–
?20	(Wills Cigarettes)	1894	£175.00	–
?155	Beauties Actresses & Children	1894	£100.00	–
K52	Beauties, Playing Card Inset (2 Printings)	1896	£26.00	–
52	Beauties, Playing Card Inset	1897	£22.00	£1,140.00
10	Alternative Subjects	1897	£70.00	–
?53	Beauties (No Inset, Scroll Back)	1897	£175.00	–
?29	(No Inset, Type Set Back)	1897	£250.00	–

Qty		Date	Odds	Sets
?9	Beauties, Girl Studies	1895	£1,250.00	–
L25	Beautiful Homes	1930	£2.60	£65.00
48	Between Two Fires (Sect.)	1930	£0.25	£12.00
50	Billiards	1909	£2.20	£110.00
K9	Boer War Medallions (6 Brands)	1900	£85.00	–
50	Borough Arms (Scroll Back, Numbered)	1903	£10.00	£500.00
50	Borough Arms (Scroll Back, Unnumbered)	1903	£1.00	£50.00
50	(1-50 Descriptive)	1904	£1.00	£50.00
50	Second Edition (1-50)	1906	£0.90	£45.00
50	Borough Arms, Second Series (51-100)	1904	£0.60	£30.00
50	Second Edition (51-100)	1906	£0.60	£30.00
50	Borough Arms, 3rd Series (101-150 Red)	1905	£0.70	£35.00
50	(101-150 Grey)	1905	£0.80	£40.00
50	Second Edition (101-150)	1906	£0.60	£30.00
50	Borough Arms, Fourth Series (151-200)	1905	£0.60	£30.00
24	Britain's Part In The War	1917	£0.80	£20.00
50	British Birds	1915	£1.40	£70.00
50	British Butterflies	1927	£1.00	£50.00
L25	British Castles	1925	£2.80	£70.00
1	British Commanders In The Transvaal War (booklet)	1900	–	£90.00
L25	British School Of Painting	1927	£1.20	£30.00
M48	British Sporting Personalities	1937	£1.00	£48.00
50	Builders Of The Empire	1898	£8.00	£400.00
L40	Butterflies & Moths	1938	£0.90	£36.00
1	Calendar For 1911	1910	–	£11.00
1	Calendar 1912	1911	–	£6.00
L25	Cathedrals	1933	£4.80	£120.00
L25	Celebrated Pictures (2 Printings)	1916	£1.80	£45.00
L25	Celebrated Pictures 2nd Series	1916	£2.00	£50.00
50	Celebrated Ships	1911	£1.20	£60.00
25	Cinema Stars, 1st Series	1928	£1.60	£40.00
25	Cinema Stars, 2nd Series	1928	£1.50	£37.50
50	Cinema Stars, 3rd Series	1931	£2.00	£120.00
P12	Cities Of Britain	1929	£9.00	£108.00
25	Conundrums (No Album Clause)	1898	£10.00	£250.00
25	(With Album Clause)	1898	£10.00	£250.00
60	Coronation Series (Narrow Arrows)	1902	£6.50	£390.00
60	(Wide Arrows)	1902	£5.50	£330.00
50	Cricketers	1896	£85.00	£4,250.00
25	Cricketer Series 1901 (Plain Background)	1901	£26.00	£650.00
50	(With Vignettes)	1901	£22.00	£1,100.00
25	Cricketers ("WILLS'S")	1908	£9.00	£225.00
50	("WILLS's")	1908	£7.50	£375.00
50	Cricketers, 1928	1928	£1.80	£90.00
50	Cricketers 2nd Series	1929	£1.80	£90.00
50	Dogs	1937	£0.70	£35.00
50	(Eire)	1937	£1.30	£65.00
L25	Dogs, A Series	1914	£3.80	£95.00
L25	Dogs, 2nd Series"	1915	£3.60	£90.00
50	Double Meaning	1898	£9.00	£450.00
52	(P/C Inset)	1898	£10.00	£520.00
50	Do You Know, A Series	1922	£0.45	£22.50
50	Do You Know, 2nd Series	1924	£0.40	£20.00
50	Do You Know, 3rd Series	1926	£0.40	£20.00
50	Do You Know, 4th Series	1933	£0.50	£25.00

W.D. & H.O. WILLS LTD. – cont.

Qty		Date	Odds	Sets
50	Engineering Wonders	1927	£1.00	£50.00
50	English Period Costumes	1929	£0.90	£45.00
L25	English Period Costumes	1927	£2.60	£65.00
L40	Famous British Authors	1937	£1.75	£70.00
L30	Famous British Liners, A Series	1934	£5.50	£165.00
L30	Famous British Liners, 2nd Series	1935	£4.00	£120.00
L25	Famous Golfers	1930	£16.00	£450.00
50	Famous Inventions	1915	£1.00	£50.00
50	First Aid (No Album Clause)	1913	£1.80	£90.00
50	(With Album Clause)	1913	£1.50	£75.00
50	Fish & Bait	1910	£3.00	£150.00
25	Flags Of The Empire, A Series	1926	£1.20	£30.00
25	Flags Of The Empire, 2nd Series	1929	£1.00	£25.00
50	Flower Culture In Pots	1925	£0.40	£20.00
L30	Flowering Shrubs	1934	£1.00	£30.00
50	Flowering Trees & Shrubs	1924	£0.50	£25.00
66	Football Series	1902	£10.00	£660.00
50	Garden Flowers	1933	£0.70	£35.00
50	Garden Flowers By Sudell	1939	£0.25	£12.50
50	Eire)	1939	£0.50	£25.00
L40	Garden Flowers-New Varieties, A Series	1938	£0.70	£28.00
L40	Garden Flowers-New Varieties, 2nd Series	1939	£0.60	£24.00
50	Garden Hints	1938	£0.30	£15.00
50	(Eire)	1938	£0.45	£22.50
50	Gardening Hints	1923	£0.30	£15.00
50	Garden Life	1914	£0.50	£25.00
50	Gems Of Belgian Architecture	1915	£0.65	£32.50
50	Gems Of French Architecture	1916	£1.25	£62.50
50	Gems Of Italian Architecture (Coloured)	Unissued	£200.00	–
F50	Reproductions)	Unissued	–	£35.00
50	Gems Of Russian Architecture	1917	£0.65	£32.50
L25	Golfing	1924	£9.00	£225.00
X32	Happy Families	1939	£5.00	£160.00
L25	Heraldic Signs & Their Origin	1925	£1.80	£45.00
50	Historic Events	1912	£1.20	£60.00
F54	Homeland Events	1932	£0.40	£35.00
50	Household Hints (Title In White)	1927	£0.50	£25.00
50	Household Hints, 2nd Series	1930	£0.60	£30.00
50	Household Hints (Different)	1936	£0.30	£15.00
50	(Eire)	1936	£0.50	£25.00
50	Hurlers (Eire)	1927	£2.00	£100.00
2	Indian Series	1900	£275.00	£550.00
P12	Industries Of Britain	1930	£10.00	£120.00
25	Irish Beauty-Spots	1924	£4.60	£115.00
25	Irish Holiday Resorts	1924	£4.60	£115.00
50	Irish Industries ("Ask Your Retailer..")	1937	£1.00	£50.00
50	("This Surface...")	1937	£3.50	–
25	Irish Rugby Internationals	1926	£12.00	–
50	Irish Sportsmen	1936	£4.50	£225.00
50	Japanese Series	1900	£36.00	£1,800.00
50	Kings & Queens (Short Card, Brown Back)	1898	£10.00	£500.00
50	(Short Card, Grey Back)	1898	£6.50	£325.00
50/51	(Long, "Wills" At Base)	1902	£6.50	£325.00
51	(Complete Set)	1902	–	£375.00
50	(Long, "Wills" At Top)	1902	£12.50	–

97

Qty		Date	Odds	Sets
L25	Lawn Tennis, 1931	1931	£10.00	£250.00
50	Life In The Hedgerow (Unissued)	Unissued	£0.50	£25.00
50	Life In The Royal Navy	1939	£0.40	£20.00
50	Life In The Tree Tops	1925	£0.40	£20.00
50	Locomotives & Rolling Stock (No Clause)	1901	£8.00	£400.00
7	Additional Subjects	1902	£30.00	£210.00
50	(With ITC Clause)	1902	£8.50	£425.00
50	Lucky Charms	1923	£0.60	£30.00
100	Maori Series (White Borders)	1900	£85.00	—
?44	(Green Borders)	1900	£90.00	—
3	(Green Borders, Numbered Top Left)	1900	£200.00	—
4	(Green Borders, Unnumbered)	1900	£200.00	—
50	Medals	1906	£2.60	£130.00
50	Merchant Ships Of The World	1924	£1.40	£70.00
50	Military Motors (Not Passed By Censor)	1916	£1.70	£85.00
50	(Passed By Censor)	1916	£1.70	£85.00
53	Miniature Playing Cards			
	(Blue Back, Numbered, 5 Printings)	1931	£0.40	£20.00
	(Blue Back, Unnumbered)	1931	£0.40	£20.00
	(Blue Back, Red Overprint)	1931	£0.40	£20.00
	(3 Pink Backs)	1931	£0.50	£26.00
	(Eire, 9 Backs)	1931	£1.00	—
50	Mining	1916	£1.50	£75.00
L25	Modern Architecture	1931	£1.60	£40.00
L30	Modern British Sculpture	1928	£1.20	£36.00
48	Mother And Son (Sect.)	1931	£0.25	£12.00
50	Musical Celebrities	1912	£2.40	£120.00
50	Musical Celebrities Second Series	1914	£3.50	£175.00
8	(Original Subjects)	1914	£275.00	—
25	National Costumes	1895	£200.00	—
?	National Types	1893	£1,250.00	—
50	Naval Dress & Badges	1909	£3.50	£175.00
50	Nelson Series	1905	£5.50	£275.00
50	Old English Garden Flowers	1910	£1.30	£65.00
50	Old English Garden Flowers, Second Series	1913	£0.85	£42.50
L25	Old Furniture, 1st Series	1923	£2.80	£70.00
L25	Old Furniture, 2nd Series	1924	£2.80	£70.00
L40	Old Inns, A Series	1936	£2.75	£110.00
L40	Old Inns, Second Series	1939	£1.65	£66.00
L25	Old London	1929	£3.60	£90.00
L30	Old Pottery & Porcelain	1934	£1.20	£36.00
L25	Old Silver	1924	£2.50	£62.50
L25	Old Sundials	1928	£2.80	£70.00
20	Our Gallant Grenadiers	1902	£32.50	£650.00
50	Our King & Queen	1937	£0.20	£10.00
50	Overseas Dominions (Australia)	1915	£0.80	£40.00
50	Overseas Dominions (Canada)	1914	£0.60	£30.00
50	Physical Culture	1914	£1.00	£50.00
25	Pond & Aquarium, 1st Series	Unissued	—	£6.00
25	Pond & Aquarium, 2nd Series	Unissued	—	£10.00
50	Portraits Of European Royalty (1-50)	1908	£1.25	£62.50
50	Portraits Of European Royalty (51-100)	1908	£1.50	£75.00
L25	Public Schools	1927	£2.50	£62.50
L25	Punch Cartoons, First Series	1916	£3.40	£85.00
L25	Punch Cartoons, Second Series	1917	£18.00	£450.00

W.D. & H.O. WILLS LTD. – cont.

Qty		Date	Odds	Sets
L40	Racehorses & Jockeys,1938	1939	£2.40	£95.00
50	Radio Celebrities, A Series	1934	£0.70	£35.00
50	(Eire)	1934	£1.50	–
50	Radio Celebrities, Second Series	1934	£0.50	£25.00
50	(Eire)	1934	£1.25	–
50	Railway Engines	1924	£1.25	£62.50
50	Railway Engines (Adhesive)	1936	£1.00	£50.00
50	(Eire)	1936	£1.60	–
50	Railway Equipment	1938	£0.40	£20.00
50	Railway Locomotives	1930	£1.80	£90.00
12	Recruiting Posters	1915	£7.50	£90.00
L25	Rigs Of Ships	1929	£4.00	£100.00
50	Romance Of The Heavens	1928	£1.10	£55.00
50	Roses A Series (1-50)	1912	£1.60	£80.00
50	Roses Second Series (51-100)	1914	£1.50	£75.00
50	Roses (Different)	1926	£1.00	£50.00
L40	Roses (Different)	1936	£1.65	£66.00
M48	Round Europe	1936	£0.20	£10.00
50	Rugby Internationals	1929	£2.20	£110.00
50	Safety First	1934	£1.00	£50.00
50	(Eire)	1934	£2.00	–
50	School Arms	1906	£0.65	£32.50
50	(With "Series Of 50")	1906	£65.00	–
50	Seaside Resorts (Mixed Backs)	1899	–	£600.00
	(Best Bird's Eye)	1899	£12.00	–
	(Capstan)	1899	£12.00	–
	(Gold Flake)	1899	£12.00	–
	(Three Castles)	1899	£12.00	–
	(Traveller)	1899	£12.00	–
	(Westward Ho)	1899	£12.00	–
40	Shannon Electric Power Scheme (Eire)	1931	£1.65	£66.00
25	Ships (Three Castles Back)	1895	£30.00	£750.00
25	(No "WILLS" On Front)	1895	£28.00	£700.00
50	(With "WILLS" On Front)	1896	£20.00	£1,000.00
100	(Brownish Card)	1897	£20.00	£2,000.00
50	Ships' Badges	1925	£0.80	£40.00
50	Signalling Series	1911	£1.90	£95.00
50	Soldiers & Sailors (Blue Back)	1894	£40.00	£2,000.00
50	(Grey Back)	1894	£40.00	£2,000.00
100	Soldiers Of The World ("Ld." Back)	1895	£8.50	£850.00
100/101	(No Ld. On Back)	1895	£8.50	£850.00
52	(P/C Inset)	1896	£23.00	£1,200.00
100	South African Personalities, Collotype			
	(5 Different Printings)	1901	£130.00	–
50	Speed (Title In White)	1930	£1.60	£80.00
50	Speed (Different)	1938	£0.40	£20.00
50	(Eire)	1938	£0.80	£40.00
50	Sports Of All Nations (Multi-Backed)	1901	£10.00	£560.00
50	Strange Craft	1931	£1.00	£50.00
48	The Boyhood Of Raleigh (Sect.)	1931	£0.25	£12.00
P12	The British Empire	1929	£8.50	£100.00
50	The Coronation Series	1911	£1.00	£50.00
L40	The King's Art Treasures	1938	£0.30	£12.00
48	The Laughing Cavalier (Sect., 2 Backs)	1931	£0.25	£12.00
48	(Sect., Eire)	1931	£1.75	£84.00

W.D. & H.O. WILLS LTD. – cont.

Qty		Date	Odds	Sets
50	The Life Of H.M.King Edward VIII	Unissued	£20.00	–
50	The Reign Of H.M. King George V	1935	£0.70	£35.00
50	The Sea-Shore	1938	£0.25	£12.50
50	(Eire)	1938	£0.50	£25.00
48	The Toast (Sect.)	1931	£0.50	£24.00
48	(Sect., Eire)	1931	£1.75	£84.00
25	The World's Dreadnoughts	1910	£3.00	£75.00
50	Time & Money In Different Countries (2 Printings)	1908	£1.70	£85.00
50	Transvaal Series (Black Border)	1901	£8.50	–
66	(White Border)	1901	£1.65	£110.00
66	(Non Descriptive)	1902	£5.75	£380.00
L40	Trees	1937	£1.60	£64.00
L25	University Hoods & Gowns	1926	£3.20	£80.00
50	Vanity Fair Series (Unnumbered)	1902	£7.00	£350.00
50	Vanity Fair, 1st Series	1902	£7.00	£350.00
50	Vanity Fair, 2nd Series	1902	£7.00	£350.00
50	Waterloo (Unissued)	1915	£125.00	–
50	Wild Animals Of The World (Green Scroll Back)	1900	£6.50	£325.00
?16	(Grey Descriptive Back)	1902	£30.00	£480.00
52	(P/C Inset)	1900	£12.00	£625.00
50	Wild Flowers(2 Printings)	1923	£0.70	£35.00
50	Wild Flowers, A Series (Adhesive)	1936	£0.40	£20.00
50	(Eire)	1936	£0.75	£37.50
50	Wild Flowers, 2nd Series	1937	£0.20	£9.00
50	(Eire)	1937	£0.73	£37.50
50	Wonders Of The Past	1926	£0.70	£35.00
50	Wonders Of The Sea	1928	£0.40	£20.00
	MODERN ISSUES (CASTELLA)			
L30	Britain's Motoring History	1991	£1.25	£37.50
P6	Britain's Motoring History	1993	–	£4.50
L30	Britain's Steam Railways	1998	£1.20	£36.00
X30	British Aviation	1994	£1.20	£36.00
P6	British Aviation	1994	£0.50	£3.00
L30	Classic Sports Cars	1996	£1.20	£36.00
X30	Donington Collection	1993	£1.25	£37.50
P6	Donington Collection	1993	–	£6.00
X10	Golden Era	1999	–	£12.00
X30	In Search Of Steam	1992	£1.20	£36.00
X30	Soldiers Of Waterloo	1995	£1.25	£37.50
L30	The Tank Story	1997	£1.25	£37.50
	MODERN ISSUES (EMBASSY)			
56	Caribbean Treasure Cruise	1985	£1.25	–
M56	Caribbean Treasure Cruise	1985	£0.65	–
T48	Familiar Phrases	1986	£1.00	£48.00
L30	History Of Britain's Railways	1987	£1.25	£37.50
L30	History Of Motor Racing	1987	£1.60	–
T5	Pica Punchline	1984	£1.00	£5.00
L144	Punch Lines	1983	£0.75	–
T288	Punch Lines	1983	£0.75	–
T48	Ring The Changes (Anonymous)	1985	£1.25	–
T48	(Wills Name)	1985	£1.00	£48.00
56	Showhouse (33 X 60mm)	1988	£1.25	–
56	(35 X 80mm)	1988	£0.50	–
M56	Showhouse (47 X 68mm)	1988	£1.25	–
M56	(47 X 80mm)	1988	£0.50	£28.00

W.D. & H.O. WILLS LTD. – cont.

Qty		Date	Odds	Sets
T56	Showhouse (47 X 90mm)	1988	£0.50	–
T10	Spot The Shot	1986	£2.50	£25.00
?	Wheel Of Fortune	1985	£1.25	–
M?	Wheel Of Fortune	1985	£0.50	–
56	Wonders Of The World	1986	£0.90	–
M56	Wonders Of The World	1986	£0.65	£36.50
T56	Wonders Of The World	1986	£0.55	£30.00
M36	World Of Firearms	1982	£0.30	£10.00
M36	World Of Speed	1981	£0.30	£10.00
	AUSTRALIAN ISSUES			
100	Actresses (Capstan)	1903	£3.25	£325.00
100	(Vice Regal)	1903	£3.25	–
1	Advertisement Card (Capstan)	1902	–	£250.00
60	Animals (Cut-Outs, Specialities)	1913	£0.85	£51.00
60	(Cut-Outs, Havelock)	1913	£2.00	–
50	Arms & Armour (Capstan, "ALSO OBTAINABLE")	1910	£2.25	–
50	(Capstan, No Extra Words)	1910	£1.75	£87.50
50	(Vice Regal)	1910	£1.75	£87.50
50	(Havelock)	1910	£3.25	–
50	Arms Of The British Empire (Specialities)	1910	£0.85	£42.50
50	(Havelock)	1910	£1.75	–
M50	Arms Of The British Empire (Silk)	1910	£3.00	£150.00
50	A Tour Round The World (Blue Caption)	1907	£2.70	£135.00
50	(Mauve Caption)	1907	£2.80	–
25	Australian & English Cricketers (Numbered)	1903	£17.00	£425.00
25	Australian & English Cricketers			
25	(Blue Border, Capstan)	1909	£16.00	£400.00
25	(Blue Border, Vice Regal)	1909	£16.00	£400.00
25	(Red Border, Capstan)	1909	£16.00	£400.00
25	(Red Border, Vice Regal)	1909	£16.00	£400.00
59	Australian & English Cricketers, Titled	1911	–	£800.00
50	Capstan, "SERIES OF 50"	1911	£13.50	–
50	Capstan, "SERIES OF "	1911	£13.50	–
9	51-59, Capstan, "SERIES OF 59"	1911	£16.50	–
50	Vice Regal, "SERIES OF 50"	1911	£13.50	–
50	Vice Regal, "SERIES OF "	1911	£13.50	–
9	51-59, Vice Regal, "SERIES OF 59"	1911	£16.50	–
50	Havelock	1911	£37.50	–
60	Australian & South African Cricketers	1910	–	£900.00
60	Light Background,Blue Border	1910	£16.00	–
60	Light Background,Red Border	1910	£16.00	–
24	Dark Backgound, mixed printing	1910	–	£400.00
24	Dark Backgound,Blue Border, Capstan	1910	£16.50	–
24	Dark Backgound,Blue Border, Vice Regal	1910	£16.50	–
24	Dark Backgound,Red Border, Capstan	1910	£16.50	–
24	Dark Backgound,Red Border, Vice Regal	1910	£16.50	–
60	Light Background, Havelock	1910	£37.50	–
M50	Australian Butterflies (Silk)	1914	£2.80	£140.00
40/46	Australian Club Cricketers	1905	–	£700.00
40	Blue Back, With State	1905	£17.50	–
40	Blue Back, No State"	1905	£17.50	–
40	Green Back	1905	£18.50	–
39/46	Blue Back, Brown Frame Line	1905	£25.00	–
MF100	Australian Scenic Series	1925	£0.80	£80.00
50	Australian Wild Flowers (Specialities)	1913	£0.80	£40.00

Qty		Date	Odds	Sets
50	Australian Wild Flowers (Havelock)	1913	£1.75	—
1	Australia Day	1915	—	£15.00
75	Aviation (Black Back, Capstan)	1910	£2.20	£165.00
75	(Black Back, Vice Regal)	1910	£2.20	£165.00
75	(Black Back, Havelock)	1910	£3.00	—
75	(Green Back, Capstan)	1910	£2.40	—
75	Aviation (Green Back, Vice Regal)	1910	£2.40	—
75	(Green Back, Havelock)	1910	£3.50	—
85	(Capstan)	1910	£2.75	—
85	(Vice Regal)	1910	£2.75	—
50	Best Dogs Of Their Breed (Specialities)	1914	£5.00	£250.00
50	(Havelock)	1914	£7.50	—
M50	Birds And Animals Of Australia (Silk)	1915	£3.20	£160.00
100	Birds Of Australasia (Green, Capstan)	1912	£1.50	£150.00
100	(Green, Vice Regal)	1912	£1.50	£150.00
100	(Green, Havelock)	1912	£2.50	—
100	(Yellow Back)	1912	£1.50	£150.00
100	(Yellow, Havelock)	1912	£2.25	—
50	Britain's Defenders (1-50)	1915	£1.30	£60.00
50	(Havelock)	1915	£2.80	£140.00
7	Britain's Defenders (51-57)	1915	£10.00	—
50	British Empire Series (Capstan)	1912	£0.85	£42.50
50	(Vice Regal)	1912	£0.85	£42.50
50	(Havelock)	1912	£1.80	£90.00
M68	Crests And Colours Of Australian Universities Colleges And Schools	1929	£0.75	£51.00
M50	Crests & Colours Of Australian Universities Colleges & Schools (Silk)	1916	£2.80	£140.00
M1	Crests And Colours Of Australian Schools (Silk, Unnumbered)	1929	—	£25.00
50	Cricketer Series (Grey Scroll Back, No Frame)	1901	£125.00	—
25	Cricketer Series (Grey Scroll Back, Fancy Frame)	1902	£120.00	—
F63	Cricketers (Plain Back)	1924	£8.00	£500.00
F40/48	Cricket Season, 1928-29	1929	£3.50	£140.00
L20	Dogs, A Series (Three Castles & Vice Regal)	1927	£3.25	£65.00
L20	(World Renowned, Album Clause)	1927	£3.50	£70.00
L20	(World Renowned, No Album Clause)	1927	£3.50	—
L20	Dogs, 2nd Series"	1928	£3.50	£70.00
L25	English Period Costumes	1929	£1.80	£45.00
100	Famous Film Stars	1934	£1.50	£150.00
M100	Famous Film Stars	1933	£2.30	£230.00
MF100	Famous Film Stars	1933	£3.25	£325.00
M20	Fiestas (Cartons)	1968	£0.75	—
50	Fish Of Australasia (Capstan)	1912	£1.20	£60.00
50	(Vice Regal)	1912	£1.20	£60.00
50	(Havelock)	1912	£2.25	—
50	Flag Girls Of All Nations, mixed editions	1908	—	£80.00
50	Capstan, Small Captions	1908	£2.00	—
24	Capstan, Large Captions	1908	£3.00	—
50	Vice Regal, Small Captions	1908	£1.80	£90.00
24	Vice Regal, Large Captions	1908	£3.00	—
8	Flags (Shaped, Metal, 6 Printings)	1915	£9.00	—
M13	Flags (Lace)	1916	£5.00	£65.00
28	Flags Of The Allies (Silk, Capitals)	1915	£2.25	£63.00
23	(Silk, Small Letters)	1915	£2.25	£52.00

Qty		Date	Odds	Sets
25	Flags Of The Empire	1926	£7.00	–
28	Football Club Colours & Flags (Capstan)	1913	£5.50	£154.00
28	(Havelock)	1913	£7.00	–
200	Footballers 1933	1933	£1.60	£320.00
M200	Footballers 1933	1933	£3.50	–
?5	Footballers (Shaped)	1910	£130.00	–
?27	Football Pennants (Shaped, Capstan)	1905	£60.00	–
?27	(Shaped, Havelock)	1905	£65.00	–
50	Girls Of All Nations (Capstan)	1908	£2.75	£137.50
50	(Vice Regal)	1908	£2.75	£137.50
X?2	Havelock Comics	1904	£200.00	–
50	Historic Events (Specialities)	1913	£1.20	£60.00
50	(Havelock)	1913	£2.00	£100.00
L25	History Of Naval Dress	1929	£35.00	–
50	Horses Of Today (Capstan)	1906	£3.20	£160.00
50	(Vice Regal)	1906	£3.20	£160.00
50	(Havelock)	1906	£5.00	–
50	Interesting Buildings	1905	£2.40	£120.00
5	Islands Of The Pacific	1917	£200.00	–
38	Kings & Queens Of England (Silk)	1910	£5.00	£190.00
45	Melbourne Cup Winners	1906	£8.50	–
40	Merrie England Studies	1916	£7.00	£280.00
50	Modern War Weapons (Specialities)	1915	£1.70	£85.00
50	(Havelock)	1915	£2.75	
50	Past & Present Champions (Cigarettes)	1908	£12.00	–
50	(Tobacco)	1908	£12.00	–
M50	Popular Flowers (Silk, Large Packets)	1913	£4.50	–
M50	(Silk, 1/- Packets)	1913	£4.00	£200.00
L70	Practical Wireless	1923	£7.25	
50	Prominent Australian And English Cricketers (1-50)	1907	£13.50	£775.00
23	Prominent Australian And English Cricketers (51-73, Grey Captions)	1907	£17.00	£390.00
8	Prominent Australian And English Cricketers (66-73, Red Captions)	1907	£17.00	£136.00
10	Recruiting Posters (Anon Back)	1915	£7.00	£70.00
50	Riders Of The World	1913	£1.70	£85.00
50	(Havelock)	1913	£3.50	–
50	Royal Mail (Capstan)	1913	£3.80	£190.00
50	(Vice Regal)	1913	£3.80	£190.00
50	(Anonymous Printed Back)	1913	£6.50	–
50	(Anonymous Plain Back)	1913	£6.50	–
50	(Havelock, 2 Printings)	1913	£5.00	–
50	Signalling Series (Capstan)	1912	£1.30	£65.00
50	(Vice Regal)	1912	£1.30	£65.00
50	(Havelock)	1912	£2.40	–
39/40	Sketches In Black & White	1905	£2.30	£90.00
?39/40	(White On Black)	1905	£125.00	–
50	Soldiers Of The World	1902	£9.00	£450.00
25	Sporting Terms (Capstan)	1905	£14.00	£350.00
25	(Vice Regal)	1905	£14.00	£350.00
50	Sports Of The World	1917	£5.00	£250.00
50	Stage & Music Hall Celebrities (Capstan)	1904	£3.50	£175.00
50	(Vice Regal)	1904	£3.50	–
50	(Havelock)	1904	£4.50	–
50	Stage & Music Hall Celebrities (Square Frame)	1904	£3.50	£175.00

Qty		Date	Odds	Sets
L25	The Nation's Shrines....................................	1928	£1.40	£35.00
25	The World's Dreadnoughts (Capstan)	1910	£2.50	£62.50
25	(Vice Regal)...............	1910	£2.50	£62.50
50	Time & Money In Different Countries..................			
	(Capstan)...	1907	£1.50	–
	(Vice Regal, Album Clause)...............	1907	£1.40	£70.00
	(Vice Regal, No Album Clause)	1907	£1.40	£70.00
	(Havelock)	1907	£2.70	£135.00
50	Types Of The British Army..........................			
	(Capstan, 2 Printings)	1912	£2.20	£110.00
	(Vice-Regal, 2 Printings).............	1912	£2.20	£110.00
50	Types Of The Commonwealth Forces			
	(Capstan, 2 Printings)	1910	£2.40	£120.00
	(Vice Regal, 2 Printings)	1910	£2.40	£120.00
	(Havelock)	1910	£4.50	–
P1	Union Jack (Silk)	1915	–	£30.00
25	United States Warships (Capstan)................	1911	£3.00	£75.00
25	(Vice Regal)	1911	£3.00	£75.00
25	(Havelock)	1911	£5.00	–
25	Victoria Cross Heroes (Specialities)...............	1915	£2.50	£62.50
25	(Havelock)	1915	£4.00	£100.00
29	Victorian Football Pennants............................			
	(Capstan, Multi-Backed)	1910	£4.50	–
	Vice-Regal, Multi-Backed)	1910	£4.50	–
	Havelock, Multi-Backed)................	1910	£6.50	–
FS165	Views Of The World (Capstan).......................	1908	£0.85	–
FS165	(Vice Regal)	1908	£0.85	–
50	War Incidents, A Series (Specialities)	1915	£2.40	£120.00
50	(Havelock)...............	1915	£3.50	–
50	War Incidents, 2nd Series (Specialities)...........	1915	£3.20	£160.00
50	(Havelock)	1915	£4.00	–
L67	War Medals (Silk)	1916	£3.50	£230.00
50	War Pictures (Specialities)............................	1915	£1.25	£62.50
50	War Pictures (Havelock)...............................	1915	£2.40	£120.00
?1	Warships..	1905	£300.00	–
50	Wild Animals' Heads....................................	1934	£0.65	£32.50
M25	Wild Animals (Heads)..................................	1934	£1.20	£30.00
50	Wild Animals Of The World............................	1906	£6.00	£300.00
LF50	Zoological Series	1922	£1.80	£90.00
	BRAND ISSUES			
	(A) AUTOCAR CIGARETTES			
40	Chinese Trades...	1905	£7.00	–
	(B) FLAG CIGARETTES			
67	International Footballers,1909-1910.....................	1911	£11.00	–
50	Jiu-Jitsu	1911	£6.00	£300.00
50	Types Of The British Army............................	1912	£5.50	–
	(C) FOUR ACES CIGARETTES			
52	Birds Of Brilliant Plumage (P/C Inset).............	1924	£3.25	£169.00
75	Film Favourites	1928	£1.80	£135.00
25	Modes Of Conveyance.................................	1928	£2.00	£50.00
50	Stage & Film Stars (Numbered)	1926	£1.70	£85.00
50	(Unnumbered).................	1926	£2.00	£100.00
F52	Stars Of The Cinema	1926	£6.00	–
	(D) PIRATE CIGARETTES			
G?	Advertisement Cards	1910	£80.00	–

W.D. & H.O. WILLS LTD. – cont.

Qty		Date	Odds	Sets
?95	Baseball Series	1912	£500.00	–
52	Birds Of Brilliant Plumage			
	(P/C Inset, Frame Line)	1916	£3.75	£195.00
	(P/C Inset, No Frame)	1916	£3.25	£169.00
100	China's Ancient Warriors (Multibacked)	1911	£3.00	£300.00
28	Chinese Actors & Actresses	1907	£3.00	£84.00
50	Chinese Beauties (Multi-Backed)	1909	£1.80	£90.00
50	Chinese Costumes	1928	£5.00	–
P25	Chinese Pagodas	1911	£50.00	
50	Chinese Proverbs (Brown, 2 Backs)	1928	£1.50	£75.00
50	(Coloured, 4 Backs)	1915	£1.50	£75.00
33	Houses Of Parliament	1914	£1.30	£44.00
50	Products Of The World	1913	£1.20	£60.00
	(E) PURPLE MOUNTAIN CIGARETTES			
20	Chrysanthemums (Numbered)	1914	£12.00	–
100	Chrysanthemums (Unnumbered)	1915	£10.00	–
25	Roses (Wills On Front)	1912	£6.50	–
25	(Without Wills On Front)	1912	£6.00	£150.00
	(F) RUBY QUEEN CIGARETTES			
30	Birds & Animals(2 Backs)	1911	£3.00	–
50	Birds Of The East (Multi-Backs/Fronts)	1912	£1.50	£75.00
30	Chinese Children's Games (2 Backs)	1911	£2.50	–
50	Chinese Proverbs	1927	£5.00	–
41	Chinese Transport (3 Backs)	1914	£3.50	–
	(G) SCISSORS CIGARETTES			
50	Actresses (Black & White)	1904	£9.00	–
50	Actresses (Four Colour Surround)	1904	£6.50	–
30	Actresses (Green Surround)	1905	£3.25	£97.50
30	Actresses (Mauve Surround)	1916	£1.60	£48.00
30	(Orange Surround)	1916	£2.25	£67.50
30	Actresses (Purple Brown, Brown Back)	1908	£2.50	£75.00
30	(Purple Brown, Red Back)	1908	£1.80	£54.00
30	Actresses (Purple Brown, Long Card)	1909	£2.00	£60.00
25	Army Life	1914	£2.40	£60.00
30	Beauties (Green Surround)	1921	£5.00	£150.00
52	Beauties (P/C Inset-Lattice Back)	1911	£3.25	£169.00
52	(P/C Inset-No Lattice Back)	1911	£6.50	–
52	(P/C Inset-No Packets)	1911	£40.00	–
32	Beauties (Picture Hats)	1914	£3.75	£120.00
40	Beauties (Brown Tint)	1913	£1.60	£64.00
30	Beauties & Children	1910	£2.50	£90.00
36	Boxers	1911	£9.00	£324.00
50	Britain's Defenders (Green Back)	1915	£1.80	£90.00
50	(Red Back & Front)	1915	£1.70	£85.00
50	Britain's Defenders (Blue Front)	1915	£1.60	£80.00
43	British Army Boxers Series	1913	£5.50	£235.00
25	Cinema Stars	1916	£2.50	£62.50
F50	Cinema Stars	1926	£5.00	–
27	Dancing Girls (27 Subjects)	1915	£2.60	£70.00
27/28	(28 Subjects)	1915	£2.70	£75.00
25	Derby Day Series	1914	£8.00	£200.00
25	Series A (No Series Title)	1914	£10.00	–
32	Drum Horses (Horizontal Back)	1909	£6.75	£216.00
32	(Vertical Back)	1909	£8.50	£265.00
50	Famous Footballers	1914	£10.00	£500.00

Qty		Date	Odds	Sets
25	Flag Girls Of All Nations (Numbered)	1908	£9.00	£225.00
25	(Unnumbered)	1908	£11.00	–
50	Football Club Colours	1907	£9.00	£450.00
25	Governors-General Of India	1912	£7.00	£175.00
30	Heroic Deeds	1913	£4.50	£135.00
50	Indian Regiments Series	1912	£8.50	£425.00
67	International Footballers,1909-1910	1910	£10.00	–
50	Jiu-Jitsu	1910	£6.50	£325.00
53	Jockeys & Owners Colours (P/C Inset)	1914	£8.00	£424.00
25	Military Portraits	1917	£4.00	£100.00
50	Music Hall Celebrities	1911	£6.50	£325.00
K52	Playing Cards	1906	£10.00	–
25	Puzzle Series (Green, United Service Backs)	1910	£7.00	£175.00
25	(Yellow, United Service Backs)	1910	£7.50	–
50	Regimental Colours & Cap Badges	1907	£1.60	£80.00
33	Regimental Pets	1911	£6.00	£200.00
30	Sporting Girls	1913	£8.50	£255.00
50	Types Of The British Army	1908	£5.50	£275.00
25	Victoria Cross Heroes	1915	£3.20	£80.00
50	War Incidents	1915	£2.60	£130.00
30	What It Means	1916	£1.25	£37.50
F50	"Zoo"	1927	£4.00	–

(H) UNITED SERVICE CIGARETTES

Qty		Date	Odds	Sets
50	Arms & Armour	1910	£3.20	£160.00
32	Drum Horses	1909	£6.00	£192.00
25	Flag Girls Of All Nations	1908	£2.80	£70.00
67	International Footballers, 1909-1910"	1910	£10.00	–
	Puzzle Series - See Scissors Cigarettes			
50	Regimental Colours & Cap Badges (Blue Back)	1907	£1.40	£70.00
50	(Red Back)	1907	£1.50	£75.00

(I) WILD WOODBINE CIGARETTES

Qty		Date	Odds	Sets
50	British Army Uniforms	1909	£6.00	£300.00

CHANNEL ISLANDS ISSUES

Qty		Date	Odds	Sets
50	Air Raid Precautions	1938	£1.25	£62.50
50	Association Footballers	1935	£2.50	£125.00
50	Dogs	1937	£1.20	£60.00
50	Garden Flowers By Sudell	1939	£0.40	£20.00
50	Garden Hints	1938	£0.40	£20.00
50	Household Hints	1936	£0.40	£20.00
50	Life In The Royal Navy	1939	£0.45	£22.50
50	Our King & Queen	1937	£0.40	£20.00
50	Railway Equipment	1938	£0.70	£35.00
50	Speed	1938	£0.60	£30.00
50	The Sea-Shore	1938	£0.40	£20.00
50	Wild Flowers, A Series	1936	£0.60	£30.00
50	Wild Flowers, 2nd Series	1937	£0.50	£25.00

NEW ZEALAND ISSUES

Qty		Date	Odds	Sets
F50	A Sporting Holiday In New Zealand	1928	£0.80	£40.00
LF50	A Sporting Holiday In New Zealand (Different)	1928	£1.00	£50.00
F50	Beautiful New Zealand	1928	£0.25	£12.50
50	Birds, Beasts And Fishes	1924	£0.50	£25.00
F48	British Royal And Ancient Buildings	1925	£0.35	£17.50
45	British Rugby Players	1930	£2.60	£117.00
50	Children Of All Nations	1925	£0.60	£30.00
50	Coaches And Coaching Days	1925	£2.20	£110.00

Qty		Date	Odds	Sets
50	Dogs	1926	£1.00	£50.00
P10	English Views And Buildings	1925	£13.00	–
F25	English Cricketers	1926	£3.20	£80.00
26	Etchings (Dogs)	1925	£2.60	£68.00
L26	Etchings (Dogs)	1925	£5.00	£130.00
P10	Famous Castles	1926	£11.00	£110.00
50	Famous Inventions	1926	£0.90	£45.00
L25	Heraldic Signs & Their Origin	1925	£1.60	£40.00
F50	Homeland Events	1927	£0.60	£40.00
50	Household Hints (Wills At Top Back)	1927	£0.30	£15.00
50	(Scroll At Top Back)	1927	£1.50	–
50	Lighthouses	1926	£2.40	£120.00
50	Merchant Ships Of The World	1925	£1.20	£60.00
48	Motor Cars	1923	£2.30	£110.00
F50	Motor Cars	1926	£1.60	£80.00
50	Motor Cycles	1926	£3.20	£160.00
50	New Zealand Birds	1925	£1.00	£50.00
F50	New Zealand-Early Scenes & Maori Life	1926	£0.25	£12.50
F50	New Zealand Footballers	1927	£1.60	£80.00
50	New Zealand Race Horses	1928	£0.90	£45.00
50	N.Z. Butterflies, Moths & Beetles	1925	£0.90	£45.00
25	Past & Present	1929	£1.20	£30.00
25	Picturesque People Of The Empire	1928	£1.20	£30.00
25	Pirates & Highwaymen	1925	£1.50	£37.50
50	Products Of The World	1929	£0.30	£15.00
50	Railway Engines	1925	£1.25	£62.50
50	Railway Working	1927	£2.25	–
50	Regimental Standards And Cap Badges	1928	£0.65	£32.50
50	Riders Of The World	1926	£1.00	£50.00
50	Romance Of The Heavens	1928	£1.50	£75.00
50	Safety First	1935	£0.80	£40.00
F50	Ships And Shipping	1928	£0.85	£42.50
50	Ships' Badges	1925	£0.80	£40.00
P10	Splendours Of New Zealand	1927	£10.00	£100.00
F50	The Royal Family At Home And Abroad	1927	£1.60	–
F50	The Royal Navy	1929	£1.70	£85.00
F50	Units Of The British Army And R.A.F.	1928	£0.60	£30.00
50	U.S.S. Co's. Steamers	1930	£2.60	£130.00
50	V.C's	1926	£2.00	£100.00
25	Village Models Series	1925	£1.20	£30.00
L25	Village Models Series	1925	£6.00	–
50	Warships	1926	£1.80	£90.00
25	Wonders Of The World	1926	£0.70	£17.50
F50	"Zoo"	1926	£0.25	£12.50
	OTHER OVERSEAS ISSUES			
50	Actors & Actresses "WALP" (Black)	1905	£3.25	–
50	(Flesh Tint)	1905	£2.75	£137.50
250	Actresses "ALWICS" (Black & Red Front)	1905	£1.80	£450.00
50	(All Red Front)	1905	£3.00	–
?3	(All Black Front)	1905	£20.00	–
?88	(No Address On Back)	1905	£3.75	–
25	Actresses, Tabs Type (101-125)	1902	£20.00	£500.00
50	Actresses, Four Colour Surround (Matt)	1904	£3.00	£150.00
50	(Varnished)	1904	£3.00	£150.00
50	Aeroplanes	1926	£3.50	£175.00

W.D. & H.O. WILLS LTD. – cont.

Qty		Date	Odds	Sets
50	Animals And Birds (With Series Title)	1912	£5.00	£250.00
50	(No Series Title)	1909	£5.00	£250.00
50	Arms Of The British Empire	1911	£0.80	£40.00
50	Art Photogravures-Set 1	1912	£0.50	£25.00
M50	Art Photogravures-Set 1 (2 Printings)	1912	£0.60	£30.00
50	Art Photogravures-Set 2	1913	£0.50	£25.00
50	Aviation Series (Wills On Back)	1911	£3.50	—
50	(Anon Back, Album Clause)	1911	£3.50	—
50	(Anon Back, No Clause)	1911	£3.40	£170.00
50	Beauties "LAWHA" (Red Tinted)	1905	£2.50	£125.00
40	Beauties (Brown Tint)	1913	£3.00	£120.00
52	Beauties (P/C Inset)	1911	£5.00	—
32	Beauties (Picture Hats)	1914	£5.50	£176.00
M72	Beauties	1923	£12.00	—
MF50	Beauties (Hand Coloured)	1925	£3.75	—
F25	Beauties	1925	£3.20	—
F50	Beauties, 2nd Series"	1925	£3.20	—
52	Birds Of Brilliant Plumage (P/C Inset)	1914	£4.25	£221.00
36	Boxers	1911	£9.00	£324.00
50	Britain's Defenders	1915	£2.00	£100.00
101	British Beauties	1915	£2.25	£225.00
50	British Costumes From 100 BC To 1904 (Unissued)	1905	£65.00	—
50	Chateaux	1925	£5.50	£275.00
50	Conundrums	1903	£13.00	£650.00
25	Derby Day Series A	1914	£9.00	—
32	Drum Horses	1909	£7.00	£224.00
26	Etchings (Gold Flake Cigarettes)	1925	£7.00	—
26	(Dutch Text, Frame On Back)	1925	£8.00	—
26	(Dutch Text, No Frame Line)	1925	£8.00	—
50	Famous Footballers	1914	£9.00	£450.00
25	Flag Girls Of All Nations	1908	£2.80	£70.00
126	Flags & Ensigns	1904	£1.60	£200.00
6	Flags Of The Allies (Shaped)	1915	£12.50	£75.00
50	Girls Of All Nations	1908	£2.60	—
32	Houses Of Parliament	1912	£2.20	£70.00
50	Indian Regiments Series	1912	£9.00	—
24	Merveilles Du Monde	1927	£6.50	—
M25	Miniatures (Metal)	1914	£55.00	£1,375.00
F48	Movie Stars	1927	£3.25	—
50	National Flags And Arms	1936	£1.40	—
FS50	Nature Studies	1928	£1.50	£75.00
25	Police Of The World	1910	£10.00	£250.00
25	Products Of The World	1913	£1.60	£40.00
50	Races Of Mankind	1911	£12.50	£625.00
100	Royalty, Notabilities & Events, 1900-2	1902	£2.75	£275.00
27	Rulers Of The World	1912	£7.50	£200.00
100	Russo Japanese Series (Black Front, 2 Printings)	1905	£2.00	£200.00
50	(Red Front)	1905	£8.00	—
LF48	Scenes From The Empire	1939	£2.00	£96.00
30	Semaphore Signalling	1910	£3.50	£105.00
36	Ships & Their Pennants	1913	£5.50	£200.00
75	Soldiers Of The World	1903	£10.00	—
F52	Stars Of The Cinema	1926	£5.00	—
25	The Evolution Of The British Navy	1915	£3.00	£75.00
25	The World's Dreadnoughts	1910	£2.60	£65.00
50	Wild Animals Of The World (Star, Circle & Leaves)	1906	£8.50	—

WILSON & CO.

Qty		Date	Odds	Sets
50	War Portraits	1916	£130.00	—

W. WILSON

30	Army Pictures, Cartoons, etc.	1916	£135.00	—

HENRI WINTERMANS (UK) LTD

T30	Disappearing Rain Forest	1991	£0.35	£10.00
T30	Wonders Of Nature	1993	£0.35	£10.00

A. & M. WIX

D250	Cinema Cavalcade	1940	£1.30	£325.00
D250	Cinema Cavalcade, Volume II	1940	£1.50	£375.00
100	Film Favourites	1937	£2.75	—
100	Film Favourites, 2nd Series	1938	£2.75	—
100	Film Favourites, 3rd Series	1939	£1.60	£160.00
L?23	Maxims Of Max (Package Issue, Various Formats)	1952	£25.00	—
X100	Men Of Destiny	1934	£2.25	£225.00
D250	Speed-Through The Ages (English Text)	1938	£0.40	—
D250	(2 Languages)	1938	£0.30	£75.00
D250	This Age Of Power & Wonder	1935	£0.30	£75.00

J. WIX & SONS LTD.

F?	Animals	1928	£60.00	—
P80	Bridge Favours & Place Cards	1930	£17.50	—
P50	Bridge Hands	1930	£30.00	—
L48	British Empire Flags (Silk)	1934	£1.00	£48.00
L48	("Printed In USA")	1934	£0.85	£40.00
50	Builders Of Empire	1937	£0.65	£32.50
42	Card Tricks	1938	£5.50	—
M42	Card Tricks	1938	£6.00	—
50	Coronation (Kensitas)	1937	£0.30	£15.00
50	(Wix)	1937	£0.25	£12.50
L50	Henry	1935	£0.80	£40.00
P25	Henry	1935	£3.20	£80.00
L50	Henry, 2nd Series (No Album Price)	1936	£3.50	—
L50	(With Album Price)	1936	£1.20	£60.00
P25	Henry, 2nd Series (Last Line Of Text "throat")	1936	£3.20	£80.00
P25	(Last Line Of Text "your throat.")	1936	£6.50	—
L50	Henry, 3rd Series"	1936	£0.80	£40.00
L50	Henry, 4th Series"	1936	£0.70	£35.00
L50	Henry, 5th Series"	1937	£0.70	£35.00
L102	Jenkynisms, 1st Series (Yellow)	1932	£1.00	—
L50	Jenkynisms, 2nd Series (Yellow)	1932	£1.00	—
L25/30	Jenkynisms, 3rd Series (Yellow)	1932	£1.00	—
L1	Jenkynisms, 4th Series (Yellow)	1932	—	£2.50
?21	Jenkynisms (Red Borders, Unnumbered)	1931	£4.25	—
?44	Jenkynisms (Red Borders, Numbered)	1931	£4.00	—
?30	Jenkynisms (Red Borders, Series B)	1931	£4.25	—
?19	Jenkynisms (Red Borders, Series C)	1931	£4.00	—
?34	Jenkynisms (Red Borders, Series D)	1931	£4.00	—
6	Jenkynisms (Red Borders, Vertical)	1931	£5.00	—
M?21	Jenkynisms (Red Borders, Unnumbered)	1931	£4.50	—
M?44	Jenkynisms (Red Borders, Numbered)	1931	£4.00	—
?M30	Jenkynisms (Red Borders, Series B)	1931	£4.25	—

J. WIX & SONS LTD. – cont.

Qty		Date	Odds	Sets
?M19	Jenkynisms (Red Borders, Series C)	1931	£4.00	—
?M34	Jenkynisms (Red Borders, Series D)	1931	£4.25	—
M6	Jenkynisms (Red Borders, Vertical)	1931	£6.00	—
P96	Ken-Cards	1969	£0.25	£24.00
60	Kensitas Flowers (Silk, Plain Back)	1934	£3.00	£180.00
60	(Silk, 3 Printed Backs)	1934	£3.00	£180.00
L60	Kensitas Flowers (Silk, Plain Back)	1934	£4.50	£270.00
L60	(Silk, 3 Printed Backs)	1934	£4.50	£270.00
P30	Kensitas Flowers (Silk, Plain Backs)	1934	£40.00	£1,200.00
P30	(Silk, 3 Printed Backs)	1934	£40.00	£1,200.00
40	Kensitas Flowers Second Series (Silk)	1935	£5.00	£350.00
L40	Kensitas Flowers Second Series (Silk)	1935	£5.75	£450.00
25	Love Scenes From Famous Films, 1st Series	1932	£3.00	£75.00
L25	Love Scenes From Famous Films, 1st Series	1932	£3.00	£75.00
P25	Love Scenes From Famous Films, 1st Series	1932	£6.50	—
19/25	Love Scenes From Famous Films, 2nd Series	1932	£2.60	£50.00
L19/25	Love Scenes From Famous Films, 2nd Series	1932	£3.25	£60.00
P19/25	Love Scenes From Famous Films, 2nd Series	1932	£8.00	—
K53	Miniature Playing Cards (Blue Scroll)	1938	£0.20	£10.00
K53	(Red Scroll)	1938	£0.20	£10.00
K53	(Revenge)	1938	£0.25	£13.00
K53	(Victory)	1938	£0.25	£13.00
L60	National Flags (Silk)	1934	£1.00	£70.00
F24	Royal Tour In New Zealand	1928	£12.50	—
25	Scenes From Famous Films, Third Series	1932	£3.00	£75.00
P25	Scenes From Famous Films, Third Series	1932	£7.50	—

T. WOOD & SON

30	Army Pictures, Cartoons, etc.	1916	£135.00	—

WOOD BROS.

28	Dominoes	1910	£70.00	—

JOHN J. WOODS

?23	Views Of London	1905	£275.00	—

W.H. & J. WOODS LTD.

25	Aesop's Fables	1932	£1.80	£45.00
F50	Modern Motor Cars	1936	£6.00	£300.00
25	Romance Of The Royal Mail	1931	£1.60	£40.00
25	Types Of Volunteer & Yeomanry	1902	£35.00	£875.00

J. & E. WOOLF

?5	Beauties "KEWA"	1898	£1,250.00	—

M.H. WOOLLER

25	Beauties "BOCCA"	1899	£1,500.00	—

T.E. YEOMANS & SONS LTD.

M72	Beauties	1900	£250.00	—
50	War Portraits	1916	£130.00	—

JOHN YOUNG & SONS LTD.

Qty		Date	Odds	Sets
12	Naval Skits	1904	£150.00	—
12	Russo Japanese Series	1904	£90.00	—

A. ZICALIOTTI

Qty		Date	Odds	Sets
1	Milly-Totty Advertisement Card	1900	—	£2,000.00

Part 2

OVERSEAS TOBACCO MANUFACTURERS

AFRICAN TOBACCO MANUFACTURERS (S.A.)

Qty		Date	Odds	Sets
L29	All Blacks South African Tour,1928	1928	£20.00	—
60	Animals (2 Types)	1922	£3.50	£210.00
MF48	British Aircraft	1926	£5.00	£240.00
M100	Caravanning In South Africa	1939	£40.00	—
50	Chinese Transport	1923	£4.50	—
MF48	Cinema Artistes	1926	£4.00	£190.00
50	Cinema Stars "OMBI"	1923	£2.00	£100.00
50	Cinema Stars "OMBI" Second Series	1923	£2.20	£110.00
M50	Famous & Beautiful Women	1938	£2.50	—
L50	Famous & Beautiful Women	1938	£3.00	—
33	Houses Of Parliament	1923	£6.00	—
?58	Miniatures	1924	£6.25	—
MF48	National Costumes	1926	£3.50	£168.00
53	Playing Cards (MP)	1929	£3.00	—
53	(Scots)	1929	£1.75	—
MF48	Popular Dogs	1926	£5.00	£240.00
M100	Postage Stamps-Rarest Varieties	1930	£1.50	£150.00
M80	Prominent N.Z.& Australian Rugby Players & Springbok 1937 Touring Team (2 Types)	1937	£5.00	—
L80	Prominent N.Z.& Australian Rugby Players & Springbok 1937 Touring Team (2 Types)	1937	£3.50	—
29	S.A. Rugby Football Team, 1912-1913	1912	£35.00	—
L30	Some Beautiful Roses (Silk)	1928	£9.00	£270.00
M?125	S.A. Members Of Legislative Assembly	1919	£40.00	—
25	The Arcadia Fair	1923	£10.00	—
25	The Race Course	1923	£10.00	—
M100	The World Of Sport	1939	£4.25	—
L100	The World Of Sport	1939	£3.25	£450.00
L25	Types Of British Birds (Silk)	1928	£9.00	£225.00
L20	Types Of British Butterflies (Silk)	1928	£10.00	—
L25	Types Of Railway Engines (Silk)	1928	£25.00	—
L25	Types Of Sea Shells (Silk)	1928	£13.50	—

AGUERE (Belgium) (Imitation Cigar Bands)

24	Military Head-Dress	1975	-	£6.00

M. V. ALBERT (France)

12	Film Actors & Actresses	1936	£2.50	—

ALLEN TOBACCO CO. (U.S.A.)

X250	Views & Art Studies (55 x 90mm)	1912	£4.50	—
X?117	Views & Art Studies (80 x 72mm)	1912	£4.50	—

ALLEN & GINTER (U.S.A.)

50	American Editors	1887	£34.00	£1,700.00
X50	American Editors	1887	£42.00	—
50	Arms Of All Nations	1887	£26.00	£1,300.00
50	Birds Of America	1888	£15.00	£750.00
X50	Birds Of America	1890	£30.00	£1,500.00
50	Birds Of The Tropics	1889	£17.00	£850.00
X50	Birds Of The Tropics	1889	£30.00	—
50	Celebrated American Indian Chiefs	1888	£40.00	£2,000.00
50	City Flags	1888	£15.00	£750.00
50	Fans Of The Period	1889	£27.00	£1,350.00

Qty		Date	Odds	Sets
50	Fish From American Waters	1889	£16.00	£800.00
X50	Fish From American Waters	1889	£32.00	£1,600.00
48	Flags Of All Nations (7 Types)	1887	£10.00	£480.00
50	Flags Of All Nations, Second Series	1890	£13.00	£650.00
47	Flags Of The States And Territories (2 Printings)	1888	£13.00	£610.00
50	Fruits	1891	£25.00	£1,250.00
50	Game Birds	1889	£15.00	£750.00
X50	Game Birds	1889	£30.00	—
50	General Government & State Capitol Buildings Of The United States	1889	£15.00	£750.00
50	Great Generals	1886	£42.00	—
50	Natives In Costume	1886	£36.00	£1,800.00
50	Naval Flags	1887	£16.00	£800.00
50	Parasol Drill	1888	£25.00	£1,250.00
F?	Photographic Cards (Many Types)	1885	£6.50	—
F66	Photographic Cards (Girl Cyclists)	1885	£42.50	—
50	Pirates Of The Spanish Main	1888	£40.00	£2,000.00
50	Prize & Game Chickens	1892	£26.00	£1,300.00
50	Quadrupeds	1890	£17.00	£850.00
X50	Quadrupeds	1890	£32.00	—
50	Racing Colors Of The World (No Border)	1888	£27.00	£1,350.00
50	(White Border)	1888	£25.00	£1,250.00
50	Song Birds Of The World	1890	£15.00	£750.00
X50	Song Birds Of The World	1890	£32.00	
X50	The American Indian	1888	£55.00	—
50	The World's Beauties	1888	£24.00	£1,200.00
50	The World's Beauties, Second Series	1888	£24.00	£1,200.00
50	The World's Champions	1888	£50.00	—
50	The World's Champions, Second Series	1889	£60.00	—
X50	The World's Champions, Second Series	1889	£110.00	—
50	The World's Decorations	1890	£16.00	£800.00
X50	The World's Decorations	1890	£28.00	£1,400.00
50	The World's Racers	1888	£28.00	£1,400.00
50	Types Of All Nations	1889	£26.00	£1,300.00
50	Wild Animals Of The World	1888	£18.00	£900.00
50	World's Dudes	1889	£25.00	£1,250.00
50	World's Smokers	1888	£22.00	£1,100.00
50	World's Sovereigns	1889	£32.00	£1,600.00
	"SPECIAL ISSUES" (U.S.A. & BRITAIN)			
F?137	Actresses, Celebrities & Children, Gold Border	1887	£55.00	—
25	Actresses, Collotype	1887	£85.00	—
25	Actresses (Group 3, Coloured)	1891	£10.00	—
20	Children, Gold Background, Set 1 (U.S.A.)	1887	£80.00	—
20	(Holborn Viaduct Address)	1887	£140.00	—
?49	Children, Gold Background, Set 2, Plain Back	1887	£90.00	—
30	Children, Gold Background, Set 3	1887	£80.00	—
?67	Sepia-Litho Series	1887	£60.00	—
10	Dickens Characters Burlesqued	1887	£225.00	—
9	Women Baseball Players (2 Types)	1887	£80.00	—
?93	Woodburytype Series	1887	£75.00	—
	PRINTED ALBUMS (EXCHANGED FOR COUPONS)			
	American Editors	1887	—	£350.00
	Birds Of America	1888	—	£160.00
	Birds Of The Tropics	1889	—	£160.00
	Celebrated American Indian Chiefs	1888	—	£600.00

ALLEN & GINTER(U.S.A.) – cont.

Qty		Date	Odds	Sets
	City Flags	1888	–	£160.00
	Decorations Of The Principal Orders	1890	–	£170.00
	Fish From American Waters	1889	–	£160.00
	Flags Of All Nations	1890	–	£160.00
	Game Birds	1889	–	£150.00
	General Government & State Capitol Buildings			
	Of The United States	1889	–	£150.00
	George Washington	1889	–	£200.00
	Napoleon	1889	–	£185.00
	Our Navy	1889	–	£185.00
	Paris Exhibition 1889	1889	–	£160.00
	Quadrupeds	1890	–	£185.00
	Racing Colors Of The World	1888	–	£300.00
	Song Birds Of The World	1890	–	£175.00
	With The Poets In Smokeland	1890	–	£160.00
	World's Beauties, 1st Series	1888	–	£275.00
	World's Beauties, 2nd Series	1888	–	£275.00
	World's Champions, 1st Series	1888	–	£3,000.00
	World's Champions, 2nd Series	1889	–	£3,000.00
	World's Inventors	1888	–	£175.00
	World's Racers	1888	–	£325.00

AMERICAN CIGARETTE CO. (China)

Qty		Date	Odds	Sets
10	Admirals & Generals	1900	£60.00	–
25	Beauties (Black Back)	1902	£18.50	–
?15	Beauties (Green Back)	1901	£32.00	–
53	Beauties, Playing Card Inset	1901	£53.00	–
?5	Chinese Girls	1900	£90.00	–
50	Flowers	1902	£15.00	£750.00

AMERICAN EAGLE TOBACCO CO. (U.S.A.)

Qty		Date	Odds	Sets
20	Actresses, Blue Border (Double 5)	1886	£65.00	–
15	Actresses, Brown Front	1886	£75.00	–
36	Flags Of All Nations	1890	£35.00	–
36	Flags Of States	1890	£35.00	–
50	Occupations For Women	1892	£65.00	–
F?	Photographic Cards	1886	£20.00	–
LF?	Photographic Cards	1886	£26.00	–
23	Presidents Of The U.S.	1890	£52.00	–

AMERICAN TOBACCO CO. (U.S.A.)
EARLY ISSUES

Qty		Date	Odds	Sets
25	Actresses (Plain Back)	1902	£12.50	–
F?126	Actresses (Black Back)	1901	£4.00	–
F300	Actresses (Blue Back, 2 Types)	1901	£3.00	–
F?42	Actresses (Richmond Straight Cut)	1902	£40.00	–
MF?48	Actresses (Richmond Straight Cut)	1902	£35.00	–
44	Australian Parliament	1901	£5.50	£240.00
25	Battle Scenes	1901	£13.00	£325.00
150	Beauties (Typeset Back)	1901	£2.75	–
?364	Beauties (Old Gold Back)	1901	£2.50	–
?112	Beauties (Label Back)(2 Types)	1901	£4.00	–
?564	Beauties (Green Net Back)	1901	£2.50	–
75	Beauties (Blue Net Back)	1901	£13.00	–

AMERICAN TOBACCO CO. (U.S.A.) – cont.

Qty		Date	Odds	Sets
24	Beauties (Plain Back, Carton)	1901	£5.00	–
25	Beauties, Black Background	1900	£13.00	£325.00
25	Beauties, Blue Frame Line	1900	£22.50	–
25	Beauties, Curtain Background	1900	£13.00	£325.00
28	Beauties, Domino Girls (Blue Net Back)	1895	£20.00	£560.00
28	(Type Set Back)	1895	£20.00	£560.00
25	Beauties, Flower Girls	1900	£10.00	£250.00
25	Beauties, Flowers Inset (Green Back)	1900	£12.00	£300.00
25	(Yellow Back)	1900	£10.00	£250.00
25	Beauties, Fruit Girls	1903	£35.00	–
25	Beauties, International Code Of Signals			
	1st Series, Green Back	1900	£12.50	–
	1st Series, Yellow Back	1900	£10.00	£250.00
25	Beauties, International Code Of Signals			
	2nd Series, Green Back	1900	£11.00	£275.00
	2nd Series, Yellow Back	1900	£11.00	£275.00
50	Beauties, Marine & Universe Girls	1900	£30.00	–
25	Beauties, Numbered (Black Front)	1900	£17.50	–
25	(Mauve Front)	1900	£16.00	£400.00
25	Beauties, Orange Framelines	1900	£30.00	–
25	Beauties, Palette Girls (Plain Border)	1900	£12.00	£300.00
25	(Red Border)	1900	£30.00	–
F?40	Beauties, Photographic	1894	£15.00	–
52	Beauties, Playing Card Inset, Set 1	1900	£12.00	–
52	Beauties, Playing Card Inset, Set 2 (Green Net Back)	1900	£11.00	£570.00
52	(Type Set Back)	1900	£10.00	£520.00
	Beauties, Playing Card Superimposed			
52	("52 Subjects")	1900	£11.00	£570.00
53	("53 Subjects")	1900	£10.00	£530.00
25	Beauties, Star Girls (Green Net Back)	1900	£17.50	–
25	(Type Set Back)	1900	£16.00	–
25	Beauties, Star Series	1900	£16.50	–
25	Beauties, Stippled Background	1900	£12.00	£300.00
100	Beauties, Thick Border	1895	£30.00	–
25	Boer War, Series A (Numbered)	1901	£6.00	£150.00
25	(Unnumbered)	1901	£7.00	£175.00
25	(No Series Letter)	1901	£8.00	–
22	Boer War, Series B	1901	£8.50	£187.00
L47	Boer War Celebrities (Kimball)	1901	£37.50	–
L10	Boer War Celebrities "RUTAN"	1901	£40.00	£400.00
50	Butterflies	1895	£27.50	–
32	Celebrities	1900	£7.00	£225.00
25	Chinese Girls	1900	£12.50	–
1	Columbian & Other Postage Stamps	1895	–	£12.50
25	Comic Scenes	1901	£9.00	£225.00
50	Congress Of Beauties, World's Fair (Backlisted)	1893	£22.50	–
50	(Type Set Back)	1893	£50.00	–
25	Constellation Girls	1894	£25.00	–
25	Dancers	1895	£13.00	–
50	Dancing Women	1895	£22.50	–
50	Fancy Bathers	1895	£22.50	–
25	Fish From American Waters (Green Net)	1900	£10.00	£250.00
50	(Back listed)	1895	£12.50	–
28	Flags, Dominoes Superimposed (Carton)	1900	£6.50	£180.00
50	Flags Of All Nations	1895	£9.00	–

Qty		Date	Odds	Sets
X25	French Novelties	1891	£75.00	–
50	Heroes Of The Spanish American War(Carton)	1900	£7.00	–
?47	Japanese Girls	1900	£65.00	–
50	Jokes	1906	£17.50	–
25	Military Uniforms, A	1894	£16.00	–
25	Military Uniforms, B	1896	£13.00	£325.00
25	Military Uniforms, C (Green Net Back)	1900	£9.00	£245.00
27	(Typeset Back)	1900	£10.00	£270.00
27		1900		
25	Military Uniforms, D	1900	£14.00	£350.00
50	Musical Instruments	1895	£16.00	–
50	National Flags & Arms (Green Net Back)	1895	£10.00	–
50	(Type Set Back)	1895	£11.00	–
25	National Flags & Flower-Girls	1900	£22.00	–
25	Old Ships, 1st Series	1900	£6.00	£150.00
25	Old Ships, 2nd Series	1900	£10.00	£250.00
50	Savage & Semi Barbarous Chiefs & Rulers	1895	£24.00	–
25	Songs A (2 Types)	1900	£15.00	£375.00
25	Songs B	1900	£15.00	£375.00
25	Songs C, 1st Group	1900	£10.00	£250.00
25	Songs C, 2nd Group	1900	£12.50	–
25	Songs D	1900	£9.00	£225.00
27	Songs E	1900	£13.00	£350.00
25	Songs F (2 Types)	1900	£12.00	£300.00
25	Songs G	1900	£11.00	£275.00
25	Songs H	1900	£18.00	£450.00
25	Songs I	1900	£23.00	–
X25	Stars Of The Stage	1891	£75.00	–
F150	Views	1901	£2.50	–

LATER ISSUES

Qty		Date	Odds	Sets
L50	Actors	1911	£6.50	£325.00
L50	Actresses "Between The Acts"	1902	£10.00	–
G25	Actresses "Turkish Trophies"(Premiums)	1902	£22.00	£550.00
M85	Actress Series	1909	£7.00	–
L80	Animals	1909	£2.40	£190.00
L25	Arctic Scenes	1910	£6.00	£150.00
?55	Art Reproductions	1910	£5.00	–
21	Art Series (Grand Duke)	1902	£16.50	–
P10	Artistic Pictures	1910	£11.00	–
18	Ask Dad	1916	£13.00	–
L50	Assorted Standard Bearers Of Different Countries	1914	£6.00	–
M25	Auto-Drivers	1910	£15.00	£375.00
M50	Automobile Series	1910	£14.00	£700.00
L50	Baseball Folders	1907	£32.00	–
M121	Baseball Series (T204)	1907	£50.00	–
208	Baseball Series (T205, Gold Border)	1907	£24.00	–
522	Baseball Series (T206, White Border)	1907	£24.00	–
200	Baseball Series (T207, Brown Background)	1911	£30.00	–
?642	Baseball Series (T210, Red Borders)	1907	£35.00	–
75	Baseball Series (T211, Southern Assoc.)	1907	£35.00	–
?406	Baseball Series (T212, "Obak")	1907	£35.00	–
?184	Baseball Series (T213, "Coupon")	1907	£35.00	–
?51	Baseball Series (T214, Victory Tobacco)	1907	£110.00	–
?172	Baseball Series (T215, Red Cross)	1907	£35.00	–
L76	Baseball Triple Folders	1907	£45.00	–
50	Bird Series (Gold Border)	1910	£2.50	£125.00

AMERICAN TOBACCO CO. (U.S.A.) – cont.

Qty		Date	Odds	Sets
50	Bird Series (White Border)	1910	£2.50	£125.00
30	Bird Series (Fancy Gold Frame)	1911	£3.00	£90.00
M360	Birthday Horoscopes	1911	£2.00	—
P80	Bridge Favors & Place Cards	1930	£7.00	—
P50	Bridge Game Hands	1930	£12.50	—
M24	British Buildings	1939	£3.00	£72.00
M42	British Sovereigns	1939	£3.00	£125.00
M50	Butterfly Series	1910	£4.50	£225.00
L153	Champion Athlete & Prizefighter Series	1910	£7.50	—
X50	Champion Athlete & Prizefighter Series (Prizefighters only)	1910	£13.50	—
L50	Champion Pugilists	1910	£22.50	—
X100	Champion Women Swimmers	1906	£9.00	—
M150	College Series	1909	£2.70	£400.00
G25	College Series (Premiums)	1910	£40.00	—
M50	Costumes And Scenery For All Countries Of The World	1911	£3.50	£175.00
X49	Cowboy Series	1911	£7.50	£370.00
M?41	Cross Stitch	1906	£9.00	—
L?17	Embarrassing/Emotional Moments	1906	£35.00	—
M50	Emblem Series	1911	£3.50	£175.00
L100	Fable Series	1910	£3.00	£300.00
PF?60	Famous Baseball Players, American Athletic Champions & Photoplay Stars	1910	£55.00	—
100	Fish Series	1910	£2.50	£250.00
200	Flags Of All Nations Series	1909	£1.75	£350.00
L100	Flags Of All Nations Series (Red Cross)	1909	£16.00	—
50	Foreign Stamp Series A	1911	£6.50	—
L505	Fortune Series	1910	£2.20	—
G12	Hamilton King Girls (1-12, Sketches)	1902	£27.50	—
G12	Hamilton King Girls (13-24, Girls)	1902	£18.00	£220.00
G12	Hamilton King Girls (25-36, Bathing Girls)	1902	£18.00	£220.00
G25	Hamilton King Girls (37-61, Period Gowns)	1902	£17.00	£425.00
G25	Hamilton King Girls (62-86, Flag Girls)	1902	£16.50	£412.50
G25	Hamilton King Girls (1-25)	1912	£20.00	—
L?76	Helmar Girls	1902	£50.00	—
M79	Henry	1937	£2.40	£200.00
X50	Heroes Of History	1912	£8.50	£425.00
M50	Historic Homes	1910	£5.00	£250.00
X24/25	Historical Events Series	1911	£8.00	—
M15	Home Art Gallery Pictures	1915	£5.00	£75.00
M25	Hudson-Fulton Series	1909	£7.00	£175.00
45	Imitation Cigar Bands	1909	£2.50	—
L50	Indian Life In The "60's"	1910	£8.50	£425.00
L?268	Jig Saw Puzzle Pictures	1910	£7.50	—
L50	Light House Series	1910	£7.50	£375.00
X50	Men Of History 2nd Series	1912	£8.50	£425.00
M100	Military Series (White Border)	1910	£5.00	£500.00
50	Military Series (Gold Border)	1911	£6.00	£300.00
50	Military Series (Recruit)	1908	£6.00	—
50	Movie Stars	1915	£5.00	—
L100	Movie Stars	1915	£5.00	—
M25	Moving Pictures (Flip Books)	1910	£30.00	—
M?84	Moving Picture Stars Series	1915	£22.50	—
X50	Murad Post Card Series	1905	£9.00	—
?100	Mutt & Jeff Series (Black & White)	1908	£5.00	—
?183	Mutt & Jeff Series (Coloured)	1908	£5.00	—

AMERICAN TOBACCO CO. (U.S.A.) – cont.

Qty		Date	Odds	Sets
F16	Nat. League & American League Teams	1910	£55.00	—
X50	Postcard Series	1910	£13.50	—
G126	Prominent Baseball Players & Athletes (Premium)	1911	£85.00	—
50	Pugilistic Subjects	1908	£30.00	—
X18	Puzzle Picture Series	1904	£16.50	—
L200	Riddle Series	1910	£2.50	—
X?60	Royal Bengal Souvenir Cards	1906	£9.00	—
M150	Seals Of The United States & Coats Of Arms Of All Countries Of The World	1909	£1.75	£260.00
L?24	Series Of Champions	1912	£30.00	—
X50	Sights & Scenes Of The World	1912	£4.00	£200.00
X50	Silhouettes	1908	£8.50	—
L25	Song Bird Series	1905	£40.00	—
50	Sports Champions	1910	£35.00	—
45	Stage Stars (Transfers)	1910	£8.00	—
M25	State Girl Series	1910	£8.00	£200.00
L50	Theatres Old And New Series	1912	£8.00	—
L?100	The World's Best Short Stories	1910	£15.00	—
L25	The World's Greatest Explorers	1914	£6.00	£150.00
L50	Toast Series (Sultan)	1910	£9.00	—
M550	Toast Series (Mogul)	1909	£2.00	—
L25	Toasts	1910	£15.00	—
50	Types Of Nations Series	1912	£2.75	£137.50
M25	Up To Date Baseball Comics	1908	£30.00	—
L26	Up To Date Comics	1908	£9.00	—
250	Up To The Minute War Pictures	1916	£2.00	—
F?481	World Scenes & Portraits	1914	£2.50	—
X50	World's Champion Athletes	1909	£12.00	—
	SILK ISSUES			
M?113	Actresses	1910	£4.50	—
X?10	Actresses	1910	£60.00	—
L15	Animals	1910	£6.50	—
P250	Athlete And College Seal	1910	£17.50	—
G250	Athlete And College Seal	1910	£20.00	—
M25	Automobile Pennants	1910	£55.00	—
M?117	Baseball-Actress Series	1910	£6.50	—
M?122	Baseball Players	1910	£22.00	—
G25	Baseball Players	1910	£65.00	—
M25	Bathing Beach Girls	1910	£11.00	£275.00
G6	Bathing Girls	1910	£16.50	£100.00
T50	Birds, Set 1	1910	£5.00	—
M26	Birds, Set 2	1910	£5.00	—
L26	Birds, Set 2	1910	£5.00	—
M30	Birds, Set 3	1910	£5.00	—
L20	Birds In Flight	1910	£6.00	£120.00
L25	Breeds Of Dogs	1910	£16.00	£400.00
L10	Breeds Of Fowls	1910	£16.50	£165.00
P6	Butterflies	1910	£14.00	£84.00
L25	Butterflies & Moths, Set 1	1910	£6.00	—
L50	Butterflies & Moths, Set 2	1910	£5.00	£225.00
L25	Butterflies & Moths, Set 3	1910	£5.00	—
M77	City Seals	1910	£3.75	—
G50	College Flag, Seal, Song, Yell	1910	£12.50	—
T44	College Pennants	1910	£7.00	—
M144	College Seals	1910	£2.75	—

Qty		Date	Odds	Sets
G?14	College Yells	1910	£20.00	–
L10	Comics	1910	£10.00	–
M25	Domestic Animals' Heads	1910	£8.00	£200.00
G6	Domestic Animals' Heads	1910	£16.50	£100.00
M50	Emblem Series	1910	£5.00	–
L15	Famous Queens	1910	£10.00	£150.00
L11	Feminine Types	1910	£10.00	£110.00
D322	Flags & Arms (Woven)	1910	£2.00	–
P24	Flag Girls Of All Nations	1910	£10.00	£240.00
G24	Flag Girls Of All Nations	1910	£12.00	–
X50	Flowers, Set 1	1910	£6.00	–
M25	Flowers, Set 2	1910	£5.00	–
L50	Flowers, Set 2	1910	£6.00	–
L54	Flowers, Set 3	1910	£5.50	–
M?28	Foreign Postage Stamps	1910	£25.00	–
L10	Fruits	1910	£7.50	£75.00
G5	Generals	1910	£100.00	–
M10	Girls (Portrait In Circle)	1910	£30.00	–
L10	Girls (Portrait In Circle)	1910	£50.00	–
G10	Girls (Portrait In Circle)	1910	£75.00	–
G15	Great War Leaders	1915	£75.00	–
G?38	Hatbands	1910	£12.00	–
M50	Indian Portraits	1910	£10.00	£500.00
G6	Indian Portraits	1910	£25.00	–
L25	Indian Portraits & Scenes	1910	£12.00	–
P10	Indian Portraits & Scenes	1910	£17.50	–
G12	King Girls	1910	£15.00	£180.00
G20	Kink Series	1910	£65.00	–
M51	Military & Lodge Medals	1910	£4.00	£200.00
L?77	Miniature National Flags	1910	£20.00	–
L10	Mottoes & Quotations	1910	£8.50	£85.00
L25	National Arms (Silko)	1910	£4.00	£100.00
M42	National Arms (Woven)	1910	£3.50	£150.00
L154	National Flags	1910	£1.75	–
T?22	National Flags (Egyptian Banner Cigarettes)	1910	£25.00	–
G?157	National Flags (Many Styles)	1910	£3.00	–
L25	National Flags & Arms	1910	£2.50	–
X40	National Flags & Arms	1910	£2.50	–
P53	National Flags & Arms (Many Styles)	1910	£2.50	–
X27	National Flag, Song & Flower	1910	£5.00	–
P20	National Flag, Song & Flower	1910	£6.00	–
G17	National Flag, Song & Flower	1910	£7.00	–
E5	National Flag, Song & Flower	1910	£8.00	–
M?37	Orders & Military Medals	1910	£6.00	–
M24	Presidents Of U.S.	1910	£10.00	–
P24	Ruler With National Arms	1910	£15.00	–
P10	Rulers Of The Balkans & Italy	1910	£16.00	£160.00
L120	Silk National Flags (Paper Backs)	1910	£3.00	–
M36	State Flags	1910	£4.50	–
M?11	State Flowers (80 X 45Mm)	1910	£12.50	–
M25	State Flowers (Different, 80 X 47Mm)	1910	£7.50	–
L25	State Girl & Flower	1910	£8.50	–
M50	State Maps & Maps Of Territories	1910	£7.50	–
M48	State Seals	1910	£4.50	–
X?81	Twelfth Night Miscellany	1910	£9.00	–

OXO RECIPE NO 20
JELLIED MEAT LOAF

The Liebig Extract of Meat Co. Ltd. was formed in 1856 and was acquired by Brooke Bond in 1971. In Britain their product was renamed Oxo, which it is known as today. In a period of 100 years from 1872 the Company issued a large number of sets of cards, including postcards, menus, calendars, place cards and other novelty issues. The first series were issued in France, but eventually cards could be obtained all over Europe, in languages such as Danish, Czech, Spanish, and even Russian. Many series were printed in English, including the Oxo insert series, and issued in Britain and the U.S.A.

In all the company issued 2,000 different sets of cards. These covered an enormous variety of subjects, including the Trans-Siberian Railway, Shadowgraphs, Gulliver, Fans, Education in Ancient Greece, and the Left Bank of the River Po. There is even a set showing the life of Justus von Liebig, founder of the firm, and another showing how the cards themselves are prepared and printed.

Because of the size of the subject a separate catalogue is available (price £4.95) listing all the issues, and a small selection of series is listed on pages 257 and 258.

IL GIOCO DEGLI SCACCHI
2 - La Regina
Gelatina rapida Liebig:
Pronta in 2 minuti!

Flintlock Duelling Pistol

The last few years have seen but a trickle of cigarette cards, albeit in cigar packets such as Doncella and Tom Thumb. For the most part however collectors have had to be satisfied with trade cards for their new acquisitions.

The most significant of these has been Brooke Bond, which has been issuing cards continuously since 1954 (British Birds) and has now issued over 40 different sets, usually with special albums, in Britain, North America, and Africa. One would like to think that the success of the Company, which incidentally also owns Liebig, owes as much to the quality and appeal of the cards as to the tea itself. Its rivals failed to sustain any competition in card issues, although many, such as Lyons, Horniman and Lipton, made some attempts.

Confectionery is another prolific area for card collectors, chiefly with sweet cigarettes (now discreetly called "Candy Sticks") and bubble gum. Barratt/Bassett is the premier issuer of the former, and A. & B. C./Topps of the latter, although the competition in these items is intense. Many other firms appear in these pages such as Dandy, Monty, Primrose & Somportex, and often collectors try to obtain the box or wrapper in addition to the set of cards.

Cereal products are also a fruitful source for the cartophilist. Kello Nabisco and Welgar regularly inclu among their free incentive inse collectable series of cards, often novel form such as transfers or cut-ou

The last rewarding area for cards that of periodicals. A new feature these has been the appearance Panini, with free inserts in magazi and newspapers, followed by t opportunity to complete the very l sets by purchasing packets of car Often these sets are of footballers, Panini invests some of its profits (w further advertising) in sponsoring fan enclosures at soccer grounds.

FREE POP TOKEN

AMERICAN TOBACCO CO. (U.S.A.) – cont.

Qty		Date	Odds	Sets
M25	Women Of Ancient Egypt	1910	£12.00	£300.00
L10	Zira Girls	1910	£10.00	£100.00
	BLANKET ISSUES			
P?	Animal Pelts	1908	£8.50	–
G90	Baseball Players	1908	£45.00	–
P?50	Butterflies	1908	£6.00	–
G?50	Butterflies	1908	£6.00	–
P250	College Athlete, Pennant, Seals	1908	£12.00	–
G?11	College Pennants	1908	£7.50	–
G?41	College Seals	1908	£4.00	–
X?	Conventional Rug Designs	1908	£3.50	–
P?	Conventional Rug Designs	1908	£4.00	–
G?	Conventional Rug Designs	1908	£5.00	–
X?5	Domestic Pets	1908	£8.00	–
P?	Miniature Indian Blankets	1908	£9.00	–
G?	Miniature Indian Blankets	1908	£9.00	–
E6	National Arms	1908	£5.00	–
P45	National Flags	1908	£3.00	–
G71	National Flags	1908	£3.00	–
E31	National Flags	1908	£3.50	–
G?20	National Flags, Arms And Medals	1908	£4.00	–
X?10	Nursery Rhymes	1908	£11.00	–
X12	Soldiers	1908	£14.00	£168.00
	LEATHER ISSUES			
M15	Breeds Of Dogs	1908	£11.00	–
X?100	College Building, Shield, Etc.	1908	£6.50	–
P19	College Buildings	1908	£6.50	–
M?15	College Fraternity Seals	1908	£8.00	–
M166	College Pennants	1908	£2.00	–
M?30	(Shaped)	1908	£2.50	–
X23	College Pennant, Yell, Emblem	1908	£6.50	–
M148	College Seals	1908	£2.00	–
M?122	(Shaped)	1908	£2.50	–
M53	(Card Suit Shaped)	1908	£3.50	–
M20	Comic Designs	1908	£4.50	–
M25	Flowers	1908	£4.50	–
M?11	Girls	1908	£8.00	–
M26	Girls (Alphabet Background)	1908	£9.00	–
M?96	Mottoes & Quotations	1908	£3.00	–
M97	Movie Film Personalities	1908	£8.50	–
M?23	National Flags	1908	£3.50	–
M?51	Nursery Rhymes Illustrated	1908	£5.00	–
M56	State Seals	1908	£1.50	–
M18	(Pennant Shaped)	1908	£2.00	–
	CELLULOID BUTTONS & PINS			
K?251	Actresses	1901	£3.25	–
K152	Baseball Players	1901	£20.00	–
K9	Boer War Leaders	1901	£85.00	–
K?370	Comic Pictures	1901	£3.25	–
K?449	Comic Sayings	1901	£3.00	–
K14	Cricketers	1901	£160.00	–
K?129	Flags	1901	£2.40	–
K?49	Girls' Heads	1901	£7.00	–
K?29	Jockeys	1901	£35.00	–

AMERICAN TOBACCO CO. (U.S.A.) – cont.

Qty		Date	Odds	Sets
K48	State Arms	1901	£3.00	£144.00
K187	Yellow Kid Designs	1901	£8.50	—

A.T.C. OF NEW SOUTH WALES (Australia)

25	Beauties, Group 1	1902	£13.00	£325.00
25	Beauties, Group 2	1902	£13.00	£325.00

A.T.C. OF VICTORIA LTD. (Australia)

100	Beauties	1902	£13.00	—

ANONYMOUS ISSUES

48	Famous Buildings And Monuments (Cigar Bands)	1976	—	£10.00
X100	Famous Men (Belgian)	1938	—	£30.00
48	Great Inventions (Cigar Bands)	1975	—	£7.50

THE ASHEVILLE TOBACCO WORKS CO. U. S. A

?39	Actresses "ASVERI"	1890	£65.00	—

ATLAM CIGARETTE FACTORY (Malta)

150	Beauties	1924	£6.00	—
M65	Beauties	1924	£2.75	—
M519	Celebrities	1924	£1.20	£625.00
L50	Views Of Malta	1924	£6.00	—
M128	Views Of The World	1924	£5.00	—

BANNER TOBACCO CO. (U.S.A.)

X?41	Actors & Actresses	1890	£75.00	—
X25	Beauties	1890	£37.00	—

AUG. BECK & CO. (U.S.A.)

?52	Beauties-Burdick 488	1888	£65.00	—
25	National Dances	1889	£60.00	—
F?	Photographic Cards	1886	£16.00	—
?44	Picture Cards	1893	£65.00	—
23	Presidents Of The U.S.A. (Coloured)	1890	£60.00	—
23	Presidents Of The U.S.A. (Sepia, Different)	1890	£60.00	—
?14	State Seals	1887	£70.00	—

DE BEER & CO. (Australia)

20	Admirals & Warships Of The U.S.A.	1908	£55.00	—
?16	Caricatures Of Cyclists	1908	£75.00	—

A. BENITEZ (Canary Islands)

50	Swiss Views	1912	£5.00	—

BOOKER TOBACCO CO. (U.S.A.)

35	Indian Series (2 Printings)	1906	£36.00	£1,260.00
?17	U.S. Battleships	1906	£36.00	—

NICOLA BOSIOS (Malta)

?86	Opera Personalities	1910	£37.50	—
K?23	Opera Singers	1910	£40.00	—

BRITISH AMERICAN TOBACCO CO. LTD. (BAT)

Qty		Date	Odds	Sets
	(1) SERIES WITH FIRM'S NAME			
30	Actrices	1905	£6.50	—
48	A Famous Picture Ser., The Toast (Sect)	1931	£3.00	—
MF50	Beauties	1925	£2.40	£120.00
MF40	Beauties	1925	£2.50	£100.00
25	Beauties, Art Series	1903	£12.50	—
25	Beauties, Black Background	1903	£11.50	—
25	Beauties, Blossom Girls	1903	£40.00	—
25	Beauties, Flower Girls	1903	£11.00	£275.00
25	Beauties, Fruit Girls	1903	£14.00	£350.00
25	Beauties, Girls In Costumes	1903	£14.00	£350.00
20	Beauties, Group 1	1903	£11.00	£220.00
25	Beauties, Lantern Girls	1903	£11.00	£275.00
50	Beauties, Marine & Universe Girls	1903	£12.00	£600.00
25	Beauties, Numbered	1903	£18.00	—
25	Beauties, Palette Girls (Plain Border)	1903	£11.00	£275.00
25	(Red Border)	1903	£14.00	—
53	Beauties, Playing Card Superimposed	1903	£11.00	£585.00
24	Beauties, Smoke Girls	1903	£16.00	£384.00
25	Beauties, Star Girls	1903	£16.50	—
25	Beauties, Stippled Background	1903	£11.00	£275.00
25	Beauties, Water Girls	1903	£11.00	£275.00
32	Beauties Of Old China	1933	£5.00	—
M50	Birds, Beasts & Fishes	1934	£1.80	£90.00
50	Buildings	1905	£10.00	—
25	Chinese Girls "A"	1904	£11.00	—
25	Chinese Girls "B" (Silver Borders)	1904	£11.00	—
25	Chinese Girls "C" (Sky Background)	1904	£11.00	£275.00
25	Chinese Girls "D" (2 Printings)	1904	£11.00	—
25	Chinese Girls "E"	1904	£11.00	—
25	Chinese Girls "F1" (2 Printings)	1904	£11.00	£275.00
25	Chinese Girls "F2" (2 Printings)	1904	£11.00	£275.00
50	Chinese Girls "F3" (2 Printings)	1904	£11.00	—
40	Chinese Trades	1904	£7.50	—
50	Danish Athletes	1905	£12.50	£625.00
28	Dominoes	1905	£6.50	—
48	Fairy Tales	1928	£4.00	—
25	New York Views	1908	£12.00	—
53	Playing Cards	1908	£12.00	—
M50	Wild Animals	1930	£2.40	£120.00
	(2) SERIES WITH BRAND NAMES			
	(A) ALBERT CIGARETTES (BELGIUM ETC.)			
L50	Aeroplanes (Civils)	1935	£10.00	—
50	Artistes De Cinema (1-50)	1932	£3.00	—
50	Artistes De Cinema (51-100)	1933	£3.00	—
50	Artistes De Cinema (101-150)	1934	£3.00	—
MF72	Beauties	1928	£4.50	—
M75	Belles Vues De Belgique	1928	£2.80	£210.00
M50	Birds, Beasts & Fishes	1934	£3.50	—
M50	Butterflies (Girls)	1926	£6.00	—
M50	Cinema Stars, Set 1 (Brown, 2 Printings)	1927	£3.00	—
M100	Cinema Stars, Set 2	1928	£3.00	—
M208	Cinema Stars, Set 3 (Unnumbered)	1928	£3.00	—
M100	Circus Scenes	1930	£3.00	—
M100	Famous Beauties	1916	£3.00	—

BRITISH AMERICAN TOBACCO CO.LTD. (BAT) – cont.

Qty		Date	Odds	Sets
M100	La Faune Congolaise	1934	£1.25	—
M50	L'Afrique Equatoriale de L'est a L'Ouest	1932	£3.00	—
M50	Les Grands Paquebots Du Monde	1924	£7.00	—
M50	Merveilles Du Monde	1927	£3.50	—
M50	Women Of Nations	1922	£4.00	—
	(B) ATLAS CIGARETTES (CHINA)			
50	Buildings	1907	£6.00	—
25	Chinese Beauties	1912	£4.00	—
?8	Chinese Trades Set 3	1912	£5.00	—
50	Chinese Trades, Set 4	1912	£3.00	—
85	Chinese Trades, Set 6	1912	£3.00	—
	(C) BATTLE AX CIGARETTES			
M100	Famous Beauties	1916	£5.00	£500.00
M50	Women Of Nations	1922	£6.00	£300.00
	(D) CAMEO CIGARETTES(AUSTRALIA)			
50	Horses Of To Day	1906	£10.00	—
	(E) COPAIN CIGARETTES (BELGIUM)			
52	Birds Of Brilliant Plumage (P/C Inset)	1927	£5.50	—
	(F) DOMINO CIGARETTES (MAURITIUS)			
25	Animaux Et Reptiles	1961	—	£2.75
25	Coursaires Et Boucaniers	1961	—	£3.00
25	Figures Historiques,Une Serie	1961	—	£6.00
25	Figures Historiques,Seconde Serie	1961	—	£13.50
25	Fleurs De Culture	1961	—	£2.75
25	Les Oiseaux Et L'Art Japonais	1961	—	£20.00
25	Les Produits Du Monde	1961	—	£2.75
50	Voitures Antiques	1961	—	£70.00
	(G) EAGLE BIRD CIGS. (CHINA & SIAM)			
50	Animals & Birds	1909	£2.00	—
50	Aviation Series	1912	£4.00	—
25	Birds Of The East	1912	£2.00	—
25	China's Famous Warriors	1911	£4.00	£100.00
25	Chinese Beauties, 1st Series (2 Types)	1908	£3.00	£75.00
25	Chinese Beauties, 2nd Series (2 Types)	1909	£2.80	£70.00
50	Chinese Trades	1908	£2.50	—
25	Cock Fighting	1911	£12.50	—
60	Flags & Pennons	1926	£1.25	£75.00
50	Romance Of The Heavens	1929	£2.50	£125.00
50	Siamese Alphabet (2 Types)	1922	£1.50	—
50	Siamese Dreams & Their Meaning	1923	£1.20	£60.00
50	Siamese Horoscopes	1916	£1.20	£60.00
50	Siamese Play-Inao	1916	£1.40	£70.00
50	Siamese Play-Khun Chang Khun Phaen 1	1917	£1.40	£70.00
50	Siamese Play-Khun Chang Khun Phaen 2	1917	£1.40	£70.00
36	Siamese Play-Phra Aphai, 1st	1918	£1.50	£54.00
36	Siamese Play-Phra Aphai, 2nd	1919	£1.35	£50.00
150	Siamese Play-Ramakien I	1913	£1.10	£165.00
50	Siamese Play-Ramakien II	1914	£1.30	£65.00
50	Siamese Uniforms	1915	£2.00	£100.00
50	Views Of Bangkok	1928	£4.00	—
50	Views Of Siam (2 Types)	1928	£3.00	£150.00
30	War Weapons	1914	£2.50	£75.00
	(H) GOLD DOLLAR CIGARETTES(GERMANY)			
M270	Auf Deutscher Scholle	1934	£1.50	—
M270	Der Weltkrieg (1914)	1933	£1.50	—

Qty		Date	Odds	Sets
M270	Deutsche Kolonien	1931	£1.50	–
M270	Die Deutsche Wehrmacht	1935	£1.50	–
?50	Do You Know?	1928	£5.00	–
M100	Filmbilder	1935	£1.35	£135.00
M100	In Prarie Und Urwald	1930	£1.25	£125.00
100	Wild-West	1932	£1.65	£165.00
	(I) KONG BENG CIGARETTES (CHINA)			
50	Animals	1912	£7.00	–
	(J) MASCOT CIGARETTES (GERMANY)			
100	Cinema Stars	1931	£3.00	–
M208	Cinema Stars	1924	£2.75	–
	(K) MOTOR CIGARETTES (DENMARK)			
50	Aviation Series(3 Printings)	1911	£8.00	–
50	Butterflies & Moths	1911	£4.50	–
50	Flag Girls Of All Nations	1908	£7.50	–
50	Girls Of All Nations	1908	£7.50	–
	(L) OLD JUDGE CIGARETTES(AUSTRALIA)			
50	Horses Of To Day	1906	£10.00	–
FS270	Views Of The World	1908	£7.00	–
	(M) PEDRO CIGARETTES (INDIA)			
50	Actors & Actresses	1906	£3.25	–
37	Nautch Girls (Red Border, 3 Types)	1905	£2.50	–
40	(Coloured)	1905	£2.50	–
52	(P/C Inset)	1905	£3.00	–
	(N) PINHEAD CIGARETTES (CHINA)			
50	Chinese Modern Beauties	1912	£3.50	–
33	Chinese Heroes, Set 1	1912	£3.50	–
50	Chinese Heroes, Set 2	1913	£3.50	–
50	Chinese Trades, Set III (2 Types)	1908	£3.50	–
50	Chinese Trades, Set IV	1909	£3.50	–
50	Chinese Trades, Set V	1910	£3.50	–
50	Types Of The British Army	1909	£4.50	–
	(O) RAILWAY CIGARETTES (INDIA)			
37	Nautch Girl Series (2 Types)	1907	£2.75	£100.00
	(P) SHANTUNG CIGARETTES (CHINA)			
50	Chinese Curios	1928	£8.00	–
	(Q) SUNFLOWER CIGARETTES (CHINA)			
50	Chinese Trades	1906	£7.00	–
	(R) TEAL CIGARETTES (SIAM)			
30	Chinese Beauties	1917	£5.00	–
50	Cinema Stars (Blue Back) (2 Printings)	1930	£2.20	£110.00
50	(Red Back) (2 Printings)	1930	£2.20	£110.00
50	Cinema Stars (51-100)	1931	£3.75	–
30	Fish Series	1916	£3.25	–
L30	Fish Series (Double Cards)	1916	£5.00	–
50	War Incidents	1916	£2.50	£125.00
	(S) TIGER CIGARETTES (INDIA)			
52	Nautch Girl Series (P/C Inset, 4 Types)	1911	£2.75	–
	(T) VANITY FAIR CIGARETTES(AUSTRALIA)			
50	Horses Of To Day	1906	£10.00	–
	(3) SERIES WITH PRINTED BACK, NO MAKER'S NAME OR BRAND			
	(See Also Imperial Tobacco Co. (Canada), United Tobacco Co)			
250	Actresses "ALWICS"(Design Back)	1906	£3.75	–
50	Aeroplanes (Gilt Border)	1926	£3.20	£160.00

BRITISH AMERICAN TOBACCO CO.LTD. (BAT) – cont.

Qty		Date	Odds	Sets
50	Aeroplanes Of Today	1936	£1.25	£62.50
25	Angling	1930	£5.00	£125.00
25	Animaux Prehistoriques	1925	£6.00	£150.00
L25	Arabic Proverbs (Silk)	1913	£13.50	—
50	Arms & Armour	1910	£6.00	—
L50	Arms Of The British Empire (Silk, Blue)	1911	£3.00	£150.00
L50	(Silk, Brown Back)	1911	£4.00	—
25	Army Life	1908	£6.50	—
50	Art Photogravures	1912	90p	—
L50	Australian Wild Flowers (Silk)	1913	£3.50	£175.00
22	Automobielen	1923	£8.00	—
22	Automobiles (as above)	1923	£8.00	—
75	Aviation	1910	£4.50	—
50	Aviation Series	1911	£4.00	—
50	Beauties, Red Tinted (Design Back)	1906	£3.20	—
52	Beauties, Tobacco Leaf Back (P/C Inset)	1908	£3.50	£180.00
52	(No Inset)	1908	£4.25	—
F50	Beauties	1925	£2.25	—
MF50	Beauties (Hand Coloured)	1925	£1.75	£87.50
F50	Beauties, 2nd Series	1926	£1.60	£80.00
F50	Beauties, 3rd Series	1926	£1.40	£70.00
F50	Beauties Of Great Britain	1930	60p	£30.00
F50	Beautiful England	1928	40p	£20.00
M?28	Belgian Footballers	1913	£9.00	—
M75	Belles Vues De Belgique	1928	£3.00	—
50	Best Dogs Of Their Breed	1913	£4.40	£220.00
L50	Best Dogs Of Their Breed (Silk)	1913	£5.60	£280.00
50	Billiards	1929	£2.20	£110.00
50	Birds, Beasts And Fishes (Cut-Outs)	1937	70p	£35.00
M50	Birds, Beasts & Fishes (Cut-Outs)	1937	£1.25	£62.50
24	Birds Of England	1924	£2.50	—
50	Boy Scouts	1930	£2.70	£135.00
50	Britain's Defenders (Blue Front)	1914	£2.00	—
50	Britain's Defenders (Mauve Front)	1914	£1.80	£90.00
50	British Butterflies	1930	£1.00	£50.00
50	British Empire Series	1913	£2.75	—
25	British Trees & Their Uses	1930	£2.00	£50.00
50	British Warships And Admirals	1915	£4.25	£212.50
50	Butterflies & Moths	1911	£2.00	£100.00
50	Butterflies (Girls)	1928	£5.00	£250.00
M50	Butterflies (Girls)	1928	£7.50	£375.00
M50	Celebrities Of Film And Stage (2 Types)	1930	£2.00	£100.00
LF48	Channel Islands, Past & Present (2 Types)	1939	40p	£20.00
40	Characters From The Works Of Dickens	1919	—	£50.00
38/40	Characters From The Works Of Dickens	1919	70p	£28.00
50	Cinema Artistes (Black & White 1-50)	1928	£1.70	£85.00
50	Cinema Artistes (Black &White 101-150)	1930	£1.70	£85.00
60	Cinema Artistes, Set 1 (Brown, 2 Types)	1929	£2.30	£138.00
50	Cinema Artistes, Set 2 (Brown, 2 Types)	1931	£1.80	£90.00
M48	Cinema Artistes, Set 3	1932	£2.00	—
48	Cinema Celebrities (C)	1935	£1.25	£60.00
L48	Cinema Celebrities (C)	1935	£1.50	£72.00
L56	Cinema Celebrities (D)	1937	£2.60	£145.00
50	Cinema Favourites	1929	£2.00	£100.00
50	Cinema Stars, Set 2 (1-50)	1928	£1.00	£50.00

BRITISH AMERICAN TOBACCO CO.LTD. (BAT) – cont.

Qty		Date	Odds	Sets
50	Cinema Stars, Set 3 (51-100)	1930	£3.00	—
50	Cinema Stars, Set 4 (101-150)	1932	£1.00	—
100	Cinema Stars (Coloured)	1931	£2.25	—
F50	Cinema Stars, Set 1	1924	£1.50	—
F50	Cinema Stars, Set 2	1924	£1.00	£50.00
F50	Cinema Stars, Set 3	1925	£1.50	£75.00
MF52	Cinema Stars, Set 4	1925	£1.75	£91.00
MF52	Cinema Stars, Set 5	1926	£1.60	—
MF52	Cinema Stars, Set 6	1927	£2.50	—
LF48	Cinema Stars, Set 7	1927	£3.00	—
F50	Cinema Stars, Set 8	1928	£1.20	£60.00
F50	Cinema Stars, Set 9 (51-100)	1929	£2.50	—
F50	Cinema Stars, Set 10 (101-150)	1930	£2.50	—
F50	Cinema Stars, Set 11 (151-200)	1931	£2.50	—
110	Crests & Badges Of British Army (Silk)	1915	£2.50	—
M108	Crests & Badges Of British Army (Silk)	1915	£2.25	—
M50	Crests And Colours Of Australian Universities, Colleges & Schools (Silk)	1916	£2.50	—
25	Derby Day Series A	1914	£9.00	—
50	Do You Know?	1930	35p	£17.50
50	Do You Know? 2nd Series	1931	35p	£17.50
25	Dracones Posthistorici	1931	£9.00	—
?10	Dutch Footballers	1913	£10.00	—
25	Dutch Scenes	1928	£3.00	£75.00
50	Engineering Wonders (2 Types)	1929	60p	£30.00
40	English Costumes Of Ten Centuries	1919	£1.50	£60.00
F25	English Cricketers	1926	£3.00	£75.00
26	Etchings (Of Dogs)	1926	£2.50	£65.00
F50	Famous Bridges	1935	£1.00	£50.00
50	Famous Footballers, Set 1	1923	£4.50	£225.00
50	Famous Footballers, Set 2	1924	£4.50	£225.00
50	Famous Footballers, Set 3	1925	£4.50	£225.00
25	Famous Racehorses	1926	£3.00	£75.00
25	Famous Railway Trains	1929	£2.20	£55.00
50	Favourite Flowers	1923	80p	£40.00
50	Film And Stage Favourites	1926	£1.80	£90.00
75	Film Favourites	1928	£1.50	£112.50
50	Flags Of The Empire	1928	70p	£35.00
50	Foreign Birds	1930	70p	£35.00
50	Game Birds And Wild Fowl	1929	£1.40	£70.00
LF45	Grace And Beauty (1-45)	1938	40p	£18.00
LF45	Grace And Beauty (46-90)	1939	30p	£13.50
LF48	Guernsey, Alderney & Sark	1937	40p	£19.00
LF48	Guernsey, Alderney & Sark (Second Series)	1938	30p	£15.00
L80	Guernsey Footballers, Priaulx League	1938	60p	£48.00
F52	Here There & Everywhere	1929	30p	£15.00
25	Hints & Tips For Motorists	1929	£2.50	£62.50
48	Hints On Association Football (Chinese)	1934	25p	£8.00
F50	Homeland Events	1928	60p	£40.00
50	Horses Of To Day	1906	£5.00	—
32	Houses Of Parliament (Red Back)	1912	£1.75	£56.00
32	Houses Of Parliament (Brown Back With Verse)	1912	£9.00	—
50	Indian Chiefs	1930	£9.00	£450.00
50	Indian Regiments Series	1912	£10.00	—
50	International Air Liners	1937	80p	£40.00

BRITISH AMERICAN TOBACCO CO.LTD. (BAT) – cont.

Qty		Date	Odds	Sets
25	Java Scenes	1929	£8.50	
LF48	Jersey Then & Now	1935	£1.00	£48.00
LF48	Jersey Then & Now, Second Series	1937	75p	£36.00
50	Jiu-Jitsu Series	1911	£3.50	£175.00
?82	Joueurs De Football Belges	1923	£9.00	—
50	Keep Fit	1939	80p	£40.00
M?166	La Belgique Monumentale & Pittoresque (4 Series)	1926	£3.25	—
50	Leaders Of Men	1929	£3.50	—
50	Life In The Tree Tops	1931	40p	£20.00
50	Lighthouses	1926	£2.00	£100.00
40	London Ceremonials	1929	£1.40	£56.00
F50	London Zoo	1927	60p	£30.00
50	Lucky Charms	1930	£1.50	£75.00
25	Marvels Of The Universe Series	1925	£2.50	£62.50
45	Melbourne Cup Winners	1906	£7.50	£337.50
50	Merchant Ships Of The World	1925	£4.50	—
25	Merchant Ships Of The World	1925	£3.50	—
25	Military Portraits	1917	£2.80	£70.00
LF36	Modern Beauties	1939	£1.25	£45.00
XF36	Modern Beauties	1936	£1.10	£40.00
36	Modern Beauties First Series	1938	£1.00	£36.00
MF54	Modern Beauties	1937	85p	£45.00
36	Modern Beauties Second Series	1938	50p	£18.00
MF54	Modern Beauties Second Series	1938	85p	£45.00
XF36	Modern Beauties Second Series	1936	70p	£25.00
MF36	Modern Beauties Third Series	1938	£1.50	£54.00
XF36	Modern Beauties Third Series	1937	75p	£27.00
MF36	Modern Beauties Fourth Series	1939	85p	£31.00
XF36	Modern Beauties Fourth Series	1937	£1.50	£54.00
XF36	Modern Beauties Fifth Series	1938	£1.00	£36.00
XF36	Modern Beauties Sixth Series	1938	75p	£27.00
XF36	Modern Beauties Seventh Series	1938	£1.25	£45.00
LF36	Modern Beauties Eighth Series	1939	£1.25	£45.00
LF36	Modern Beauties Ninth Series	1939	£1.50	£54.00
50	Modern Warfare	1936	£1.00	£50.00
M48	Modern Wonders	1938	£1.75	£84.00
25	Modes Of Conveyance	1928	£2.00	£50.00
48	Motor Cars (Coloured)	1926	£4.00	—
36	Motor Cars (Brown)	1929	£6.00	—
50	Motor Cycles	1927	£3.60	£180.00
FS50	Native Life In Many Lands (Stereo)	1932	£1.50	—
F50	Natural And Man Made Wonders Of World	1937	50p	£25.00
FS50	Nature Studies	1928	50p	£25.00
50	Naval Portraits	1917	£2.80	£140.00
32	Nederlandsche Leger (Dutch Army)	1923	£5.00	£160.00
25	Notabilities	1917	£2.50	£62.50
25	Past & Present	1929	£1.60	£40.00
FS48	Pictures Of The East	1930	£1.50	£72.00
M48	Picturesque China	1925	£1.60	£75.00
M53	Playing Cards	1940	20p	£9.00
36	Popular Stage, Cinema & Society Celebrities	1928	£3.50	—
25	Prehistoric Animals	1931	£3.20	£80.00
50	Prominent Australian And English Cricketers	1911	£40.00	—
25	Puzzle Series	1916	£6.00	£150.00
50	Railway Working	1927	£1.75	£87.50

Qty		Date	Odds	Sets
33	Regimental Pets..	1911	£6.75	—
50	Regimental Uniforms	1936	£1.60	£80.00
50	Romance Of The Heavens (2 Types)	1929	80p	£40.00
FS50	Round The World In Pictures...	1931	£1.20	—
50	Royal Mail	1912	£4.00	—
27	Rulers Of The World	1911	£8.00	—
40	Safety First..	1931	£2.00	—
25	Ships Flags & Cap Badges, A Series..................................	1930	£3.00	—
25	Ships Flags & Cap Badges, 2nd Series...............................	1930	£3.00	—
F50	Ships And Shipping	1928	80p	£40.00
50	Signalling Series	1913	£3.50	—
100	Soldiers Of The World (Tobacco Leaf Back)	1902	£12.00	£1,200.00
50	Speed	1938	65p	£32.50
25	Sports & Games In Many Lands...	1930	£5.00	£150.00
50	Stage & Film Stars	1926	£1.60	£80.00
M50	Stars Of Filmland	1927	£2.50	—
F50	The Royal Navy...	1930	£2.00	£100.00
F50	The World Of Sport...	1927	£2.00	—
100	Transfers, Set 1..	1930	£3.00	—
100	Transfers, Set 2..	1930	£3.00	—
32	Transport Of The World	1911	£8.00	—
20	Types Of North American Indians.......................................	1930	£14.00	£280.00
F50	Types Of The World	1936	75p	£37.50
F52	Ur Ollum Attum	1930	£4.00	—
FS270	Views Of The World	1908	£3.00	—
48	Volaille, Pigeons & Chiens	1915	£8.00	—
50	War Incidents (Blue Back)..	1915	£1.60	£80.00
50	War Incidents (Brown Back, Different)................................	1916	£1.75	£87.50
25	Warriors Of All Nations (Gold Panel)	1937	£1.60	£40.00
50	Warships...	1926	£5.00	—
25	Whaling	1930	£2.20	£55.00
F50	Who's Who In Sport (1926)..	1927	£1.60	£160.00
50	Wild Animals Of The World	1903	—	—
50	Wild Animals Of The World (Tobacco Leaf Back)..............	1903	£8.00	£400.00
25	Wireless	1923	£4.25	—
50	Wonders Of The Past..	1930	75p	£37.50
50	Wonders Of The Sea...	1929	60p	£30.00
25	Wonders Of The World	1928	60p	£15.00
40	World Famous Cinema Artistes	1933	£1.60	£64.00
L40	World Famous Cinema Artistes	1933	£1.40	£56.00
50	World's Products	1929	40p	£20.00
F50	Zoo..	1935	60p	£30.00
50	Zoological Studies	1928	50p	£25.00
M50	Zulu Chiefs (2 Types)	1932	£16.00	—
	(4) SERIES WITH PLAIN BACKS			
50	Actors & Actresses "WALP"	1906	£2.40	£120.00
50	Actresses "ALWICS"...	1907	£2.40	—
50	Actresses, Four Colours Surround	1905	£2.40	£120.00
30	Actresses, Unicoloured (Light Brown)	1910	80p	£24.00
30	(Purple Brown)	1910	£1.00	£30.00
50	Animals & Birds...	1912	£2.00	£100.00
60	Animals (Cut-Outs)..	1912	£1.00	£60.00
50	Art Photogravures	1912	£2.00	—
50	Aviation Series	1911	£4.00	£200.00
40	Beauties (Brown Tinted)..	1913	£2.25	—

BRITISH AMERICAN TOBACCO CO.LTD. (BAT) – cont.

Qty		Date	Odds	Sets
50	Beauties, Coloured Backgrounds	1911	£2.50	£125.00
50	Beauties, "LAWHA"	1906	£2.75	—
32	Beauties, Picture Hats I	1914	£3.00	£96.00
45	Beauties, Picture Hats II	1914	£3.00	£135.00
30	Beauties & Children	1912	£4.00	—
52	Birds Of Brilliant Plumage (P/C Inset)	1914	£2.75	£145.00
30	Boy Scouts Signalling (English Caption)	1922	£3.75	£112.50
30	(Siamese Caption)	1922	£3.75	—
50	Butterflies & Moths	1914	£1.60	£80.00
50	Cinema Artistes	1930	£2.50	—
50	Cinema Stars "BAMT" (1-50)	1927	£1.50	—
50	Cinema Stars (51-100)	1928	£1.50	—
50	Cinema Stars (101-150)	1930	£1.50	—
100	Cinema Stars (201-300)	1932	£1.00	£100.00
50	Cinema Stars Coloured	1928	£1.50	£75.00
50	Cinema Stars "FLAG"	1929	£1.50	—
27	Dancing Girls	1913	£1.50	£40.00
32	Drum Horses	1910	£4.75	£150.00
50	English Period Costumes	1929	80p	£40.00
50	Flag Girls Of All Nations	1908	£1.75	£87.50
165	Flags, Pennons & Signals	1907	£1.25	—
20	Flowers	1915	£1.25	£25.00
50	Girls Of All Nations	1908	£2.00	£100.00
30	Heroic Deeds	1913	£2.25	£67.50
25	Hindoo Gods	1909	£9.00	—
32	Houses Of Parliament	1914	£3.00	—
25	Indian Mogul Paintings	1909	£9.00	—
53	Jockeys & Owners Colours (P/C Inset)	1914	£3.00	£160.00
K36	Modern Beauties, 1st Series	1938	£2.75	£100.00
36	Modern Beauties, 2nd Series	1939	£2.75	—
F48	Movie Stars	1928	£1.50	£72.00
F50	New Zealand, Early Scenes & Maori Life	1929	£1.60	—
50	Poultry & Pigeons	1926	£6.50	—
25	Products Of The World	1914	85p	—
50	Royal Mail	1912	£5.00	—
36	Ships & Their Pennants	1913	£2.25	£81.00
75	Soldiers Of The World	1904	£8.00	—
30	Sporting Girls	1913	£5.50	—
50	Sports Of The World (Brown)	1917	£4.00	£200.00
50	(Coloured)	1917	£3.60	£180.00
M50	Stars Of Filmland	1927	£2.00	—
25	The Bonzo Series	1923	£3.60	£90.00
32	Transport Of The World	1917	£1.25	£40.00
50	Types Of The British Army (Numbered)	1908	£3.60	—
50	(Unnumbered)	1908	£3.20	£160.00
F50	Types Of The World	1936	£2.00	—
F50	Units Of The British Army & R. A. F.	1930	£2.00	—
FS50	Views Of The World	1908	£1.40	—
50	War Leaders And Scenes	1916	£5.00	—
M50	Women Of Nations (Flag Girls)	1922	£3.25	—
	(5) SIAMESE SERIES WITH BLUE FLAG BACKS			
50	Puzzle Sectional Series	1916	£1.80	£90.00
50	Siamese Dancers	1916	£1.30	£65.00
50	Siamese Life	1916	£1.30	£65.00

BRITISH AMERICAN TOBACCO CO.LTD. (BAT) – cont.

Qty		Date	Odds	Sets
50	Siamese Proverbs	1916	£1.50	£75.00
50	Types Of The British Army	1916	£2.40	£120.00

BRITISH-AUSTRALASIAN T. C. (Australia)

Qty		Date	Odds	Sets
?254	Flags Of All Nations (2 Types)	1910	£7.00	—

BRITISH CIGARETTE CO. (China)

Qty		Date	Odds	Sets
25	Actresses And Beauties "FECKSA"	1900	£75.00	—
25	South African War Scenes	1900	£32.00	£800.00

BRITISH LEAF TOBACCO CO. (India)

Qty		Date	Odds	Sets
?12	Actresses And Film Stars	1930	£10.00	—

BRITISH NEW GUINEA DEVELOPMENT CO.

Qty		Date	Odds	Sets
?41	Papuan Series 1	1910	£50.00	—

BROWN & WILLIAMSON TOBACCO CORP. (USA)

Qty		Date	Odds	Sets
M50	Modern American Airplanes Series A	1940	£3.70	£185.00
M50	(No Series Letter)	1940	£3.20	£160.00
M50	Modern Airplanes Series B	1941	£3.20	£160.00
M50	Modern Airplanes Series C	1942	£3.20	£160.00
50	Movie Stars	1940	£5.00	—

D. BUCHNER & CO. (U.S.A.)

Qty		Date	Odds	Sets
M48	Actors	1888	£32.00	—
X?97	Actresses	1888	£30.00	—
X60	American Scenes With A Policeman	1888	£65.00	—
M?143	Baseball Players	1888	£160.00	—
X?30	Butterflies & Bugs (2 Types)	1888	£70.00	—
P200	Defenders & Offenders	1888	£48.00	—
M31	Jockeys	1888	£48.00	—
X51	Morning Glory Maidens	1888	£55.00	—
X30	Morning Glory Maidens & American Flowers	1888	£85.00	—
X?23	Musical Instruments	1888	£60.00	—
X?20	New York City Scenes	1888	£65.00	—
M103	Police Inspectors	1888	£32.50	—
X?92	Police Inspectors & Captains	1888	£32.50	—
X12	Presidential Puzzle Cards	1888	£130.00	—
X?21	Yacht Club Colors	1888	£65.00	—

BUKHSH ELLAHIE & CO. (India)

Qty		Date	Odds	Sets
53	Indian Girl, Playing Card Inset (3 Series)	1902	£20.00	—

CALCUTTA CIGARETTE CO. (India)

Qty		Date	Odds	Sets
25	Actresses (Blue Front)	1906	£26.00	£650.00
25	(Brown Front)	1906	£30.00	—

A. G. CAMERON & CAMERON (U.S.A.)

Qty		Date	Odds	Sets
?12	Actresses (Burdick 488)..	1887	£80.00	–
24	Occupations For Women...	1893	£50.00	–
F?	Photographic Cards..	1893	£15.00	–
25	The New Discovery...	1892	£34.00	£850.00

V. CAMILLERI (MALTA)

MF104	Popes Of Rome	1922	£2.00	£200.00

CAMLER TOBACCO COY. (Malta)

F250	Footballers	1926	£9.00	
M96	Maltese Families Coats Of Arms	1925	£1.25	£120.00

M. C. CARATHANASSIS & CO.(Turkey)

48	The Post In Various Countries	1900	£35.00	–

CASTELANO BROS. LTD. (India)

52	Beauties, Playing Card Inset..................................	1899	£25.00	–
?3	Indian Series	1900	£65.00	–

HENRY CLAY & CO (Cuba)

M?1300	Album Universal..	1925	£1.00	–
M500	Alrededor Del Mundo...	1925	£1.00	–
M1670	Cuba En 1925	1925	£1.00	–
M1485	Espana y La America Latina	1926	£1.00	–
?	Photo Series (Postcard Back, Many Groups).......................	1920	£1.75	–
F?998	Views Of The World	1922	£1.50	–

J. CLIMENT & CO (Algeria)

F?	Photo Series (Many Groups)...................................	1910	£4.00	–

C. COLOMBOS (Malta)

F?206	Actresses	1902	£3.50	–
MF?60	Actresses	1902	£16.00	–
60	Actresses (Coloured)	1900	£15.00	–
MF?57	Celebrities	1900	£20.00	–
F136	Dante's Divine Comedy	1914	£2.50	£340.00
MF72	Famous Oil Paintings, Serie A	1910	90p	£65.00
MF108	Famous Oil Paintings, Serie B	1911	90p	£100.00
MF240	Famous Oil Paintings, Serie C	1912	90p	£215.00
MF100	Famous Oil Paintings, Serie D	1913	90p	£90.00
XF?91	Famous Oil Paintings..	1911	£7.00	–
MF100	Life Of Napoleon Bonaparte	1914	£2.60	£260.00
MF70	Life Of Nelson	1914	£3.20	£225.00
MF70	Life Of Wellington	1914	£2.60	£260.00
120	Masterpieces Of Contemporary Art........................	1913	85p	£100.00
MF100	National Types And Costumes	1908	£2.75	£275.00
F?30	Opera Singers...	1899	£32.50	–
M112	Royalty And Celebrities	1908	£3.25	–

COLONIAL TOBACCOS (PTY) LTD (S. Africa)

X150	World's Fairy Tales	1930	£3.75	–

CONDACHI BROTHERS & CO. (Malta)

Qty		Date	Odds	Sets
25	The Bride Retires	1905	£30.00	—

D. CONDACHI & SON (Malta)

?15	Artistes & Beauties	1910	£22.00	—

CONGRESS CUT PLUG (U.S.A.)

X12	Actresses	1890	£50.00	—

CONSOLIDATED CIGARETTE CO. (U.S.A.)

?24	Actresses (Consols)	1890	£65.00	—
25	Ladies Of The White House	1893	£32.00	£800.00
M14	Ladies Of The White House	1898	£40.00	£560.00
M25	Turn Cards (72 x 41mm)	1894	£50.00	—
M25	(78 x 51mm)	1894	£60.00	—

A. G. COUSIS & CO. (Malta)

254	Actors & Actresses	1924	£1.00	—
KF100	Actors & Actresses (Hand Coloured)	1906	£2.25	—
F100	Actors & Actresses (Hand Coloured)	1906	£2.25	—
F?3	Actresses (Cairo Address)	1907	£50.00	—
KF100	Actresses Serie I	1907	£1.75	—
KF80	Actresses Serie II	1907	£1.75	—
F1900	Actresses Serie I To Serie XIX	1907	£2.00	—
KF?2281	Actresses (Unnumbered)	1905	£1.25	—
F?1285	Actresses (Unnumbered)	1905	£1.25	—
MF?221	Actresses (White Border)	1902	£9.00	—
KF100	Actresses, Partners & National Costumes (Cousis')	1906	£2.25	—
KF200	Actresses, Partners & National Costumes (Cousis's)	1906	£2.50	—
F100	Actresses, Partners & National Costumes	1906	£2.75	—
50	Beauties, Couples & Children (Red Back)	1923	£2.25	—
MF50	Beauties, Couples & Children, Collection No.1	1908	£3.50	—
MF50	Beauties, Couples & Children, Collection No.2	1908	£3.50	—
MF50	Beauties, Couples & Children, Collection No.3	1908	£3.50	—
F100	Bullfighters	1901	£7.50	—
F402	Celebrities (Numbered)	1906	£1.75	—
KF?2162	Celebrities (Unnumbered)	1905	£1.25	—
F?2162	Celebrities (Unnumbered)	1905	£1.25	—
XF?104	Celebrities & Warships (White Border)	1902	£10.00	—
MF72	Grand Masters Of The Order Of St. John	1909	£3.50	—
F100	National Costumes	1908	£2.75	—
MF60	Paris Exhibition,1900	1900	£27.50	—
MF102	Paris Series	1902	£30.00	—
MF182	Popes Of Rome (To A.D.1241)	1904	£2.00	£365.00
MF81	Popes Of Rome (Dubec, After A.D.1241)	1904	£3.00	—
F100	Statues & Monuments (Numbered)	1905	£1.75	—
F100	(Unnumbered)	1905	£2.00	—
KF127	Views Of Malta	1903	£2.00	—
F?115	Views Of Malta (Numbered)	1903	£1.50	—
MF127	Views Of Malta (Numbered)	1903	£1.50	—
MF?59	(Unnumbered)	1903	£1.40	—
F?21	Views Of The Mediterranean	1903	£5.00	—
MF?123	Views Of The Mediterranean	1903	£4.00	—
F?559	Views Of The World	1903	£1.25	—
MF?559	Views Of The World	1903	£1.25	—

A. G. COUSIS & CO. (MALTA) – cont.

Qty		Date	Odds	Sets
F99	Warships (White Border)	1910	£3.50	—
KF850	Warships	1904	£1.90	—
MF850	Warships	1904	£2.00	—
MF?114	Warships & Liners (Dubec)	1904	£6.00	—
MF?22	Warships & Liners (Excelsior)	1904	£6.50	—
MF?40	Warships & Liners (Superior)	1904	£6.00	—

CRESCENT CIGAR FACTORY (U.S.A.)

Qty		Date	Odds	Sets
T?13	Actresses	1886	£70.00	—

CROWN TOBACCO CO. (India)

Qty		Date	Odds	Sets
X?26	Actresses	1900	£55.00	—
E?29	Celebrities	1900	£55.00	—
96	National Types, Costumes & Flags	1900	£40.00	—
T96	National Types, Costumes & Flags	1900	£45.00	—
MF?77	Photo Series	1900	£45.00	—

CHARLES C. DAVIS & CO. (U.S.A.)

Qty		Date	Odds	Sets
?15	Actresses	1890	£65.00	—

DIAMOND INDIAN CIGARETTES

Qty		Date	Odds	Sets
?20	Indian Beauties	1924	£12.50	—

M. W. DIFFLEY (U.S.A.)

Qty		Date	Odds	Sets
36	Flags Of All Nations	1890	£45.00	—

DIXSON (Australia)

Qty		Date	Odds	Sets
50	Australian M. P.s & Celebrities	1902	£20.00	—

DOMINION TOBACCO CO. (Canada)

Qty		Date	Odds	Sets
50	Photos (Actresses, "ALWICS")	1905	£30.00	—
100	Photos (Actresses, Plum Background)	1905	£30.00	—
50	The Smokers Of The World (2 Printings)	1904	£65.00	—

DOMINION TOBACCO CO. LTD (New Zealand)

Qty		Date	Odds	Sets
50	Coaches And Coaching Days	1927	£2.50	£125.00
50	People And Places Famous In New Zealand History	1933	£1.70	£85.00
50	Products Of The World	1929	80p	£40.00
50	U. S. S. Co's. Steamers	1928	£2.80	£140.00

DRUMMOND TOBACCO CO. (U.S.A.)

Qty		Date	Odds	Sets
?29	Actresses	1895	£65.00	—
?47	Bathing Girls	1895	£75.00	—
50	Beauties 'CHOAB'	1897	£80.00	—
X?10	Girls	1896	£65.00	—

DUDGEON & ARNELL (Australia)

Qty		Date	Odds	Sets
M16	1934 Australian Test Team	1934	£9.00	£144.00
M55	Famous Ships	1933	£3.75	—

W. DUKE & SONS LTD. (U.S.A)

Qty		Date	Odds	Sets
50	Actors And Actresses, Series 1 (2 Printings)	1889	£18.00	£900.00
M50	Actors And Actresses, Series 1	1889	£37.50	—
50	Actors And Actresses, Series 2 (2 Printings)	1889	£18.00	£900.00
M50	Actors And Actresses, Series 2	1889	£37.50	—
X30	Actors And Actresses (As Above)	1889	£34.00	—
25	Actresses (Tobacco War - Overseas)	1900	£9.00	—
X25	Albums Of American Stars	1886	£55.00	—
X25	Battle Scenes	1887	£42.00	—
X25	Beauties, Black Border	1886	£32.00	£800.00
P25	Beauties, Folders	1886	£55.00	£1,375.00
X25	Bicycle And Trick Riders	1891	£40.00	—
X25	Breeds Of Horses	1892	£37.00	£925.00
X25	Bridges	1890	£30.00	£750.00
X25	Burlesque Scenes	1889	£34.00	—
50	Coins Of All Nations (3 Printings)	1889	£18.00	£900.00
X25	Comic Characters	1887	£30.00	£750.00
X25	Cowboys Scenes	1888	£42.00	£1,050.00
X50	Fairest Flowers In The World	1887	£27.50	—
F45	Famous Ships	1884	£12.50	—
50	Fancy Dress Ball Costumes (2 Printings)	1887	£18.00	£900.00
M50	Fancy Dress Ball Costumes	1887	£37.50	—
X50	Fancy Dress Ball Costumes	1887	£29.00	—
50	Fishers And Fish	1888	£18.00	£900.00
X25	Fishes And Fishing	1888	£34.00	£850.00
X25	Flags And Costumes	1893	£34.00	£850.00
50	Floral Beauties & Language Of Flowers	1892	£16.00	£800.00
X25	French Novelties	1891	£32.00	—
X25	Gems Of Beauty (2 Types)	1884	£32.00	£800.00
50	Great Americans	1888	£26.00	£1,300.00
X16	Great Americans	1888	£42.00	—
25	Gymnastic Exercises (Duke In Blue)	1887	£32.00	—
25	(Duke In Brown)	1887	£28.00	£700.00
X25	Habitations Of Man	1890	£28.00	£700.00
50	Histories Of Generals (Booklets)	1889	£42.00	£2,100.00
X50	Histories Of Generals	1889	£42.00	—
50	Histories Of Poor Boys & Other Famous People (Booklets)	1889	£32.00	£1,700.00
50	Holidays	1890	£17.00	£850.00
X25	Honest Library (Booklets)	1896	£40.00	—
X25	Illustrated Songs	1893	£30.00	£750.00
X25	Industries Of The States	1889	£37.00	£925.00
50	Jokes (2 Types)	1890	£18.00	£900.00
X25	Jokes	1890	£32.00	£800.00
X25	Lighthouses (Die Cut)	1890	£30.00	£750.00
X25/26	Miniature Novelties	1891	£30.00	£750.00
50	Musical Instruments	1888	£24.00	£1,200.00
X25	Musical Instruments Of The World	1888	£34.00	—
36	Ocean And River Steamers	1887	£28.00	£1,000.00
F?	Photographic Cards	1885	£4.00	—
MF?	Photographic Cards	1885	£8.00	—
XF?	Photographic Cards	1885	£6.50	—
53	Playing Cards (2 Types)	1888	£12.00	£635.00
50	Popular Songs And Dancers	1894	£24.00	—
50	Postage Stamps (3 Types)	1889	£17.00	£850.00
X25	Presidential Possibilities	1888	£34.00	£850.00
X15	Puzzles	1887	£60.00	—

W. DUKE & SONS LTD. (U.S.A.) – cont.

Qty		Date	Odds	Sets
51	Ruler, Coat Of Arms, And Flag (Folders)	1888	£17.00	£850.00
X50	Rulers, Flags And Coats Of Arms	1889	£26.00	£1,300.00
50	Scenes Of Perilous Occupations	1888	£25.00	£1,250.00
X25	Sea Captains	1887	£36.00	£900.00
50	Shadows	1889	£18.00	£900.00
X25	Snapshots From 'Puck'	1889	£28.00	£700.00
X25	Stars Of The Stage (White Border)	1891	£32.00	£800.00
X25	Stars Of The Stage, Second Series	1891	£32.00	£800.00
X25	Stars Of The Stage, Third Series	1892	£32.00	£800.00
X25	Stars Of The Stage, 4th Series (Die Cut)	1893	£32.00	£800.00
48	State Governors, Arms & Maps (Folders)	1888	£17.00	£820.00
X48	State Governors, Arms & Maps	1888	£29.00	—
X25	Talk Of The Diamond	1893	£90.00	—
50	The Terrors Of America & Their Doings	1889	£18.00	£900.00
M50	The Terrors Of America & Their Doings	1889	£38.00	—
X50	The Terrors Of America & Their Doings	1889	£32.00	—
50	Tinted Photos	1887	£24.00	£1,200.00
50	Tinted Photos (Die-Cut)	1887	£16.00	—
X25	Transparencies	1888	£68.00	—
X24	Tricks With Cards	1887	£55.00	—
X25	Types Of Vessels (Die Cut)	1889	£30.00	£750.00
50	Vehicles Of The World	1888	£25.00	—
X50	Yacht Club Colors Of The World	1890	£34.00	—
50	Yacht Colors Of The World	1890	£18.00	£900.00
M50	Yacht Colors Of The World	1890	£37.50	—

PRINTED ALBUMS (EXCHANGED FOR COUPONS)

		Date	Odds	Sets
	Costumes Of All Nations (3 Series)	1890	—	£240.00
	Governors, Coats Of Arms & Maps	1889	—	£160.00
	Postage Stamp Album	1889	—	£185.00
	Shadows	1889	—	£185.00
	Sporting Girls	1888	—	£550.00
	The Heroes Of The Civil War	1889	—	£650.00
	The Rulers, Flags, Coats Of Arms	1889	—	£160.00
	The Terrors Of America	1889	—	£185.00
	Yacht Colors Of The World (3 Series)	1890	—	£235.00

DUNGEY, RALPH & CO. (Australia)

Qty		Date	Odds	Sets
50	Australian Footballers	1906	£80.00	—
?	Racehorses (Black Back)	1906	£60.00	—
?56	Racehorses And Incidents	1906	£40.00	—

EAGLE CIGARETTES (Australia)

Qty		Date	Odds	Sets
F50	Actresses & Sportsmen (Photographic)	1890	£85.00	—

EASTERN VIRGINIA CIGARETTE CO (Asia)

Qty		Date	Odds	Sets
60	Dutch East Indies Footballers	1926	£5.00	—

EGYPTIAN CIGARETTE COY. (Malta)

Qty		Date	Odds	Sets
F120	Actresses	1906	£8.50	—
XF30	Actresses	1906	£55.00	—
264	Decorations & Medals	1908	£12.50	—
F?95	Maltese Band Players	1910	£17.50	—

THEMATIC COLLECTING

Many people come into the hobby not because of an interest in cards themselves, but as an extension of an already existing interest. For there cannot be one subject that is not covered by at least one set of cards, in every case with an illustration and often with informative text.

One of the most popular themes to be collected is sport, and particularly cricket, golf and soccer. The value to the enthusiast can be shown by series such as Taddy County Cricketers and Prominent Footballers which depicted almost every first class player of the time, and the series of 2,462 different Footballers issued in the 1920's by Godfrey Phillips with their Pinnace Cigarettes. In the U.S.A. Baseball is the main cartophilic interest, while in Canada it is hockey. Other games sought by collectors are tennis, billiards, chess and archery.

Militaria, shipping and cinema are other themes that were issued in large numbers and have many devotees. Subjects such as aviation, opera, motoring, music hall and railways are also extensively covered, as are modern subjects such as space exploration and television. The significance of most of these is that they are contemporary records, and one can trace the development of the subject through a period of nearly a century.

E HENDREN

ARCHERY

WAR SERIES

GENERAL JOFFRE.
Commander-in-Chief French Army.

W. J. LYON.
ETON NORTH END

STANLEY HOLLOWAY

Tobacco Companies occasionally felt the need to reprint their own cards; the most notable example of this was Player after the Great War not having any new series prepared, and therefore re-issuing 'Cries of London 2nd Series, Miniatures, Players Past & Present and Characters from Dickens. However a new dimension was achieved by Brooke Bond, who have reprinted many of their earlier sets (with a different coloured back) SOLELY FOR SELLING TO COLLECTORS.

Several other commercial reprints appeared before Murray Cards (International) Ltd., began their "Nostalgia" reprints; these are carefully selected old series, which are very difficult to obtain in the original form, such as Wills 1896 Cricketers, Cope Golfers and Player Military Series. More recently Victoria Gallery and Imperial Publishing have printed under license from Imperial Tobacco Co. a number of their series, including two that were never actually issued! There have also been a number of reprints in North America, mainly of Baseball and Hockey cards, but also of the modern set, Mars Attacks. All these cards are clearly marked to show that they are reprints.

Early fears about the proliferation of reprints have proved to be unfounded. Their advantages are that on the one hand they have made available to a large number of collectors, cards that they would otherwise be unable to obtain or afford. In the other case they have fulfilled a demand for cards to be sold commercially in frames, and thereby relieved some of the pressure on supply of the originals, to the benefit of general collectors. In no case has the presence of reprints adversely affected the value of the originals.

One problem that has arisen, is the attempt by some dishonest people to remove all mention of the reprint and attempt to pass the cards off as originals. This has also happened in the case of Taddy Clowns and Wills Advertisement Cards, which have been cut from book illustrations and doctored. It therefore behoves the collector to be extremely careful when offered such

For your Cigarettes to be Handfilled,
with the Sand and Dust extracted, see
the name of
JONES BROS., Tottenham,
is on the Packet.

A NOSTALGIA REPRINT

18.   Dennis Eadie
in "Disraeli"

R. S. LUCAS
MIDDLESEX

BRUCE RIDPATH

COUNTY CRICKETERS

LORD HAWKE.
YORKSHIRE

EGYPTIAN CIGARETTES MFG. CO. (China)

Qty		Date	Odds	Sets
?79	Actresses("MUREG")	1900	£42.50	—
25	Armies Of The World	1900	£50.00	—
?3	Beauties In Late Qing Dynasty Dress	1900	£100.00	—
30	Beauties, Nymphs	1900	£55.00	—
35	Chinese & South African Series	1900	£60.00	—
25	National Flags & Flowers-Girls	1900	£50.00	—
30	Old Masters	1900	£45.00	—
?55	Russo-Japanese War Series	1904	£50.00	—
25	Types Of British & Colonial Troops	1900	£50.00	—
25	Warships	1900	£45.00	—

H. ELLIS & CO. (U.S.A.)

Qty		Date	Odds	Sets
25	Breeds Of Dogs (5 Types)	1890	£45.00	£1,125.00
25	Costumes Of Women	1890	£60.00	—
25	Generals Of The Late Civil War	1890	£85.00	—
F?	Photographic Cards	1887	£15.00	—

D. FANCIULLI & CO. (Malta)

Qty		Date	Odds	Sets
50	Il Paradiso Perduto	1906	£11.00	—

LA FAVORITA - E. FUENTES (Canary Islands)

Qty		Date	Odds	Sets
M30/58	Flags & Soldiers (Silk)	1915	80p	£24.00

JOHN FINZER & BROS. (U.S.A.)

Qty		Date	Odds	Sets
X10	Inventors & Inventions	1891	£50.00	£500.00

G. W. GAIL & AX (U.S.A.)

Qty		Date	Odds	Sets
X25	Battle Scenes	1891	£40.00	£1,000.00
X25	Bicycle And Trick Riders	1891	£42.50	—
X25	French Novelties	1891	£36.00	£900.00
X25	Industries Of The States	1891	£36.00	£900.00
X25	Lighthouses (Die Cut)	1891	£32.50	—
X25	Navy Library	1890	£45.00	—
X25	Novelties (Die Cut)	1890	£35.00	—
XF?	Photographic Cards	1885	£6.00	—
X25	Stars Of The Stage	1891	£32.50	—

GENERAL CIGAR CO. LTD. (Canada)

Qty		Date	Odds	Sets
X36	Northern Birds	1977	£1.25	£45.00

GENESEE TOBACCO WORKS (U.S.A.)

Qty		Date	Odds	Sets
?21	Actresses	1888	£65.00	—

ALEJANDRO GONZALEZ (Spain)

Qty		Date	Odds	Sets
X8	Typical Portuguese Costumes	1962	—	£5.00

G. G. GOODE LTD (Australia)

Qty		Date	Odds	Sets
17	Prominent Cricketer Series	1924	£90.00	—

GOODWIN & CO. (U.S.A.)

Qty		Date	Odds	Sets
50	Champions (2 Types)	1888	£55.00	—
50	Dogs Of The World (3 Types)	1890	£25.00	£1,250.00

GOODWIN & CO. (U.S.A.) – cont.

Qty		Date	Odds	Sets
50	Flowers	1890	£25.00	£1,250.00
50	Games And Sports Series	1889	£35.00	£1,950.00
50	Holidays	1889	£32.50	—
50	Occupations For Women	1887	£55.00	—
10	Old Judge Cards (Actresses)	1886	£80.00	—
F?	Photographic Cards	1886	£6.50	—
50	Vehicles Of The World	1888	£30.00	—
50	Wild Animals Of The World	1895	£22.50	—
	PRINTED ALBUMS (EXCHANGED FOR COUPONS)			
	Champions	1888	—	£3,000.00
	Floral Album	1890	—	£250.00
	Games & Sports	1889	—	£600.00
	Official League Ball	1888	—	£4,000.00

W. R. GRESH & SONS (U.S.A.)

Qty		Date	Odds	Sets
X25	Actresses (Coloured)	1890	£50.00	—
X?70	Actresses (Sepia)	1890	£45.00	—

L. O. GROTHE LTD. (Canada)

Qty		Date	Odds	Sets
52	Bridge Hands (3 Types)	1927	£5.50	—

THOS. H. HALL (U.S.A.)

Qty		Date	Odds	Sets
154	Actors & Actresses (Dull Background)	1881	£9.00	—
111	Actors & Actresses (Black Background)	1882	£11.00	—
?194	Actors & Actresses (Fancy Corners)	1884	£17.50	—
?159	Actors & Actresses (Sun's Rays)	1890	£17.50	—
?52	Actresses (Tiled Wall)	1888	£20.00	—
?12	Actresses (No Borders, Hall On Front)	1892	£37.50	—
25	Actresses (No Borders, No Hall On Front)	1892	£32.00	£800.00
T?11	Actresses ('Ours')	1885	£80.00	—
12	Athletes	1881	£70.00	—
8	Presidential Candidates & Actresses	1880	£75.00	—
22	Presidents Of The United States	1888	£37.50	£825.00
25	Theatrical Types	1890	£37.00	£925.00

HARTLEY'S TOBACCO CO. (S. Africa)

Qty		Date	Odds	Sets
53	Playing Cards (OK Cigarettes)	1929	£2.00	—
L19	S. African English Cricket Tour 1929	1929	£75.00	—

HERNANDEZ (Brazil)

Qty		Date	Odds	Sets
X24	Alphabet Cards	1960	—	£20.00

S. F. HESS & CO. (U.S.A.)

Qty		Date	Odds	Sets
F?	Photographic Cards	1885	£20.00	—
55	Poker Puzzle Cards (2 Types)	1890	£45.00	—
25	Terms Of Poker Illustrated	1890	£50.00	—

WM. G. HILLS (U.S.A.)

Qty		Date	Odds	Sets
X25	Actresses	1888	£65.00	—

HILSON CO. (U.S.A.)

Qty		Date	Odds	Sets
T25	Battleships & Signal Flags (2 Printings)	1898	£26.00	£650.00
T25	National Types	1900	£26.00	£650.00

HOUDE & GROTHE (Canada)

Qty		Date		
L24	Wildfowl (Package Issue)	1953		

T. S. H. HYPPO (BELGIUM) (Cigar Bands)

120	German Uniforms Of The 19th Century	1975		

IMPERIAL CIGARETTE & TOB. CO. (Canada)

?24	Actresses	1900		

IMPERIAL TOB. CO. OF CANADA LTD. (Canada)

Qty		Date		
50	Actresses, Framed Border (Plain Back)	1910	£2.60	£130.00
L55/66	Aircraft Spotter Series (Packets)	1941	£2.40	£132.00
60	Animals (Millbank, 4 Types)	1916	£1.25	£75.00
L55	Animal With Flag (Silk)	1915	£3.60	£200.00
50	Arms Of The British Empire	1911	£2.50	—
50	Around The World Series (Numbered)	1912	£3.50	—
50	(Unnumbered)	1912	£6.00	—
50	Aviation Series	1910	£4.50	—
90	Baseball Series	1912	£35.00	—
30	Beauties-Art Series (Plain Back)	1911	£12.50	—
30	(Bouquet Cigarettes)	1902	£55.00	—
50	Beauties (Coloured, Black Border)	1912	£2.50	£125.00
25	Beauties-Girls In Costume	1904	£55.00	—
24	Beauties-Smoke Girls	1904	£55.00	—
M50	Birds, Beasts & Fishes (2 Types) (Cut-Outs)	1923	£1.60	£80.00
30	Bird Series	1910	£2.50	£75.00
X100	Birds Of Canada	1924	£3.50	£350.00
X100	Birds Of Canada (Western Canada)	1925	£5.50	£550.00
50	Boy Scouts	1911	£5.50	£275.00
50	British Birds	1923	80p	£40.00
50	British Man Of War Series (Plain Back)	1910	£10.00	£500.00
50	Buildings (Plain Back)	1902	£8.50	£425.00
L55	Butterflies(Silk)	1912	£5.00	—
50	Butterflies & Moths	1911	£2.40	£120.00
T50	Canadian Cities (Silk)	1914	£8.00	—
50	Canadian Historical Portraits	1913	£3.00	—
48	Canadian History Series (I. T. C. Name)	1926	£1.75	£84.00
50	(Anon)	1926	£2.00	—
P50	Canadian History Series (Silk)	1914	£11.00	—
T121	Canadian Miscellany (Silk) ⨯ 10	1912	£4.00	—
50	Children Of All Nations	1924	75p	£37.50
23	Dogs Series	1924	£1.80	£40.00
50	Dogs, 2nd Series	1925	£1.50	£75.00
50	Famous English Actresses	1924	90p	£45.00
50	Film Favourites (4 Types)	1926	£3.00	£150.00
50	Fish & Bait	1924	£1.60	£80.00
50	Fishes Of The World	1924	£2.40	—
50	Fish Series	1912	£2.40	£120.00
L143	Flags (Silk)	1913	£2.00	—
50	Flower Culture In Pots	1925	65p	£32.50
50	Fowls, Pigeons & Dogs	1911	£3.25	—
30	Game Bird Series	1925	£2.00	£60.00
L55	Garden Flowers (Silk, Black Numerals)	1913	£2.50	£137.50
L50	(Silk, Red Numerals)	1913	£4.00	—
G5	Garden Flowers (Silk)	1913	£30.00	—

		Date	Odds	Sets
50	Gardening Hints	1923	50p	£25.00
L25	Heraldic Signs & Their Origin	1925	£1.30	£32.50
45	Hockey Players	1912	£25.00	—
36	Hockey Series (Coloured)	1911	£25.00	—
50	Hockey Series (Blue)	1910	£25.00	—
50	"How To Do It" Series	1911	£3.00	—
50	How To Play Golf	1925	£8.50	£425.00
50	Infantry Training (4 Types)	1915	£2.40	£120.00
100	Lacrosse Series, Set 1	1910	£7.50	—
98	Lacrosse Series, Set 2	1911	£7.50	—
50	Lacrosse Series, Set 3	1912	£7.50	—
50	L'Histoire Du Canada	1914	£1.20	£60.00
M48	Mail Carriers And Stamps	1903	£27.50	—
50	Merchant Ships Of The World	1924	£1.20	£60.00
25	Military Portraits (2 Types)	1917	£2.50	£62.50
50	Modern War Weapons	1915	£3.60	£180.00
56	Motor Cars	1925	£1.80	£100.00
50	Movie Stars	1925	£2.00	£100.00
50	Music Hall Artistes (Plain Back)	1911	£2.40	£120.00
50	Naval Portraits (2 Types)	1915	£2.20	£110.00
25	Notabilities (2 Types)	1917	£2.40	£60.00
L55	Orders & Military Medals (Silk)	1915	£3.00	£165.00
E6	Perils Of Early Golf	1926	£275.00	—
L50	Pictures Of Canadian Life (2 Types)	1912	£6.50	—
53	Poker Hands (Many Types)	1924	£1.30	£70.00
25	Poultry Alphabet	1924	£2.80	£70.00
G6	Premium Silk - Flag Girls	1913	£35.00	—
G1	Premium Silk - George V	1915	—	£40.00
G1	Premium Silk - Motor Boat	1915	—	£75.00
G1	Premium Silk - Royal Arms	1914	—	£30.00
G1	Premium Silk – "Staunch And True"	1914	—	£40.00
G1	Premium Silk - Union Jack	1913	—	£24.00
G2	Premium Silk - Yachts	1915	£65.00	—
P45	Prominent Canadian Hockey Players	1912	£200.00	—
50	Prominent Men Of Canada	1912	£3.75	—
50	Railway Engines (3 Types)	1924	£1.25	£62.50
L55	Regimental Uniforms Of Canada (Silk)	1914	£3.50	£200.00
P25/30	Rulers With Flags (Silk)	1910	£15.00	£375.00
127	Smokers Golf Cards (2 Types)	1926	£5.00	—
50	The Reason Why	1924	80p	£40.00
25	The World's Dreadnoughts	1910	£4.00	—
50	Tricks & Puzzles Series	1911	£5.50	—
50	Types Of Nations	1910	£2.75	—
25	Victoria Cross Heroes (Blue Back)	1915	£3.00	£75.00
L45	Views Of The World	1912	£6.00	£270.00
L25	Wild Animals Of Canada	1912	£10.00	—
M144	World War I Scenes & Portraits	1916	£2.25	£325.00
X49	Yacht Pennants & Views (Silk)	1915	£6.50	£325.00

IMPERIAL TOB. CO. OF INDIA LTD. (India)

Qty		Date	Odds	Sets
25	Indian Historical Views..	1910	£2.40	£60.00
K52	Miniature Playing Cards...	1933	£1.00	—
40	Nautch Girl Series (Pedro Cigarettes)....................	1908	£2.75	£110.00
40	(Railway Cigarettes)............................	1908	£2.75	£110.00
52	Nautch Girl Series (P/C Inset, Pedro)	1908	£2.75	£140.00
52	(P/C Inset, Railway)...............................	1908	£2.75	£140.00
53	Playing Cards (5 Types)...	1919	£1.50	—
1	Present Ticket...	1917	—	£3.50

IMPERIAL TOBACCO CO. (NFLD) LTD. (Canada)

M52	Playing Cards (2 Types)...	1930	£7.00	—

JACK & JILL CIGARS (U.S.A.)

T?49	Actresses "JAKE"	1890	£70.00	—

JAMAICA TOBACCO CO.

F?104	Miniature Post Card Series.......................................	1915	£7.50	—

BILL JONES (U.S.A.)

D?17	Girls (Various Sizes)	1885	£90.00	—

JUBILE (BELGIUM) (Cigar Bands)

24	Ancient Military Uniforms..	1975	—	£5.00
24	Inventions Of Leonardo Da Vinci	1975	—	£6.00
24	Paintings Of Manet...	1975	—	£5.00
24	Riders Of The World	1975	—	£7.50
24	Stained Glass Windows..	1975	—	£5.00
12	U.S. War Of Independence- Celebrities	1975	—	£4.50

DON JULIAN (SPAIN) (Cigar Bands)

X28	European Stamps - Series 7.....................................	1978	—	£25.00
X28	European Stamps - Series 8.....................................	1978	—	£20.00

KENTUCKY TOBACCOS (PTY) LTD. (S. Africa)

L120	The March Of Mankind..	1940	£2.25	—

KEY WEST FAVORS (U.S.A.)

T50	Actresses 'Jake'	1890	£70.00	—

KHEDIVIAL COMPANY (U.S.A.)

M10	Aeroplane Series No.103 (2 Types)	1912	£22.00	£220.00
M10	Prize Dog Series No.102 (2 Types)...........................	1911	£22.00	£220.00
M25	Prize Fight Series No.101 (2 Types).........................	1910	£26.00	—
M25	Prize Fight Series No.102	1911	£26.00	—

WM. S. KIMBALL & CO. (U.S.A.)

?42	Actresses, Collotype..	1887	£80.00	—
72	Ancient Coins (2 Types)..	1888	£32.00	—
48	Arms Of Dominions...	1888	£23.00	£1,100.00
50	Ballet Queens	1889	£25.00	£1,250.00
X20	Beautiful Bathers (2 Types)......................................	1889	£45.00	—
52	Beauties, Playing Card Inset....................................	1895	£25.00	—

WM. S. KIMBALL & CO. (U.S.A.) – cont.

Qty		Date	Odds	Sets
50	Butterflies..	1888	£25.00	£1,250.00
50	Champions Of Games And Sports (2 Types)......................	1888	£60.00	–
50	Dancing Girls Of The World	1889	£24.00	£1,200.00
50	Dancing Women	1889	£23.00	£1,150.00
50	Fancy Bathers...	1889	£24.00	£1,200.00
X25	French Novelties	1891	£42.50	–
X25	Gems Of Beauty	1891	£40.00	–
50	Goddesses Of The Greeks & Romans................................	1889	£30.00	£1,500.00
X25	Household Pets	1891	£37.00	£925.00
X15	National Flags	1887	£34.00	–
F?	Photographic Cards...	1886	£7.00	–
XF?	Photographic Cards...	1886	£12.50	–
X20	Pretty Athletes	1890	£40.00	–
50	Savage &Semi Barbarous Chiefs &Rulers	1890	£32.00	£1,600.00
L?21	Wellstood Etchings..	1887	£120.00	–
	PRINTED ALBUMS(EXCHANGED FOR COUPONS)			
	Ancient Coins..	1888	–	£375.00
	Ballet Queens	1889	–	£275.00
	Champions Of Games & Sports	1888	–	£1,150.00
	Dancing Girls Of The World	1889	–	£275.00
	Dancing Women	1889	–	£275.00
	Fancy Bathers...	1889	–	£275.00
	Goddesses Of The Greeks & Romans................................	1889	–	£300.00
	Savage & Semi Barbarous Chiefs & Rulers	1890	–	£425.00

N KIMURA & CO (Japan)

Qty		Date	Odds	Sets
?44	Animals & Birds..	1900	£22.50	–
?34	Japanese Uniforms..	1900	£40.00	–
?22	Japanese Warships	1900	£32.50	–

KINNEY BROS. (U.S.A.)

Qty		Date	Odds	Sets
25	Actresses "Set 1"...	1893	£8.00	£200.00
25	Actresses "Set 2"...	1895	£12.50	£315.00
50	Actresses (Group 2)	1891	£7.00	–
75	Actresses (Group 3)	1892	£7.00	–
50	Actresses (Group 4, Coloured)	1893	£7.00	£350.00
?125	Actresses (Group 4, Sepia, Plain Back)...............................	1893	£3.50	–
25	Animals	1890	£21.00	£525.00
10	Butterflies Of The World (White)	1888	£19.00	£190.00
50	Butterflies Of The World (Gold)..	1888	£18.00	£900.00
25	Famous Gems Of The World	1889	£23.00	£575.00
25	Famous Running Horses (American)	1890	£26.00	£650.00
25	Famous Running Horses (English)..	1889	£23.00	£575.00
F45	Famous Ships	1887	£12.50	–
25	Great American Trotters	1890	£27.50	£685.00
52	Harlequin Cards	1888	£25.00	£1,300.00
53	Harlequin Cards, Series 2	1889	£25.00	£1,325.00
L?24	Inaugural Types	1888	£160.00	–
X50	International Cards	1888	£42.00	–
K24	Jocular Oculars (2 Types)	1887	£37.50	–
25	Leaders...	1889	£25.00	£625.00
50	Magic Changing Cards...	1889	£25.00	–
50	Military Series A (Series 7)	1887	£7.00	£350.00
50	Military Series B (Series 8)..	1887	£7.00	£350.00

KINNEY BROS. (U.S.A.) – cont.

Qty		Date	Odds	Sets
30	Military Series C (Series 9)	1887	£7.00	£210.00
50	Military Series D (Coloured Background)	1887	£6.50	£325.00
50	Military Series E (1886)	1887	£6.50	£325.00
18	Military Series F (U.S. Continental)	1887	£6.50	£115.00
3	Military Series F (Vatican)	1887	£65.00	–
5	Military Series F (Decorations)	1887	£48.00	£240.00
51	Military Series G (U.S. Army & Navy)	1887	£6.50	£330.00
85	Military Series H (U.S. State Types)	1887	£6.50	£550.00
60	Military Series I ('I.S.C' In 3 Lines)	1887	£9.50	–
50	Military Series J (England/N.G.S.N.Y.)	1887	£16.00	–
49/50	Military Series K (1853)	1887	£10.00	–
50	Military Series L (Foreign Types)	1887	£7.00	£350.00
15	Military Series M (French Army/Navy)	1887	£7.00	£105.00
5	Military Series M (State Seals)	1887	£55.00	–
50	National Dances (White Border)	1889	£20.00	£1,000.00
25	(No Border)	1889	£24.00	–
25	Naval Vessels Of The World	1889	£23.00	£575.00
50	New Year 1890 Cards	1889	£25.00	£1,250.00
K25	Novelties (Circular, Thick Cards)	1888	£26.00	–
K50	Novelties (Circular, Thin Cards)	1888	£14.00	£700.00
75	Novelties (Die Cut)	1888	£9.00	–
14	Novelties (Oval)	1888	£29.00	–
44	Novelties (Rectangular)	1888	£12.50	£550.00
F?	Photographic Cards	1886	£3.00	–
LF?	Photographic Cards	1886	£6.25	–
50	Surf Beauties	1889	£25.00	£1,250.00
1	Sweet Caporal Calendar	1890	–	£75.00
52	Transparent Playing Cards (3 Types)	1890	£16.00	£830.00
25	Types Of Nationalities (Folders, 4 Types)	1890	£27.00	£675.00

PRINTED ALBUMS (EXCHANGED FOR COUPONS)

		Date	Odds	Sets
	Butterflies	1889	–	£275.00
	Celebrated American & English Running Horses	1890	–	£325.00
	Leaders	1889	–	£240.00
	Liberty Album	1889	–	£210.00
	National Dances	1889	–	£275.00
	Natural History	1890	–	£210.00
	Reigning Beauties	1889	–	£275.00
	Singers & Opera Houses	1889	–	£320.00
	Surf Beauties	1889	–	£275.00

KRAMERS TOB. CO. (PTY) LTD. (S. Africa)

50	Badges Of South African Rugby Football Clubs (Multi-Backed)	1933	£8.00	£400.00

CIE. LAFERME (Germany)

25	Types Of Smokers	1900	£40.00	–

THE LAKE ERIE TOBACCO CO. (U.S.A.)

X?36	State Governors	1888	£100.00	–

B. LEIDERSDORF & CO. (U.S.A.)

T25	Actresses	1895	£50.00	–

I. LEWIS & CO. (U.S.A.)

X?53	Girls And Men In Costumes	1906	£27.50	–

LEWIS & ALLEN CO. (U.S.A.)

Qty		Date	Odds	Sets
X120	Views & Art Studies	1912	£4.50	—

LIGGETT & MYERS TOBACCO CO. (U.S.A.)

?30	Actresses	1890	£65.00	—

LONE JACK CIGARETTE CO. (U.S.A.)

25	Inventors And Inventions	1887	£65.00	—
50	Language Of Flowers (3 Types)	1888	£30.00	—
F?	Photographic Cards	1886	£20.00	—

P. LORILLARD CO. (U.S.A.)

25	Actresses (Coloured)	1888	£30.00	£750.00
M25	Actresses (Irregular Gold Frame)	1889	£29.00	—
M175	Actresses (Fancy Surrounds)	1889	£29.00	—
M75	Actresses (Plain Surround)	1890	£25.00	—
X25	Actresses (Burdick 263)	1889	£30.00	£750.00
X25	Actresses (Burdick 264-1)	1890	£30.00	£750.00
X25	Actresses (Burdick 264-2)	1890	£30.00	£750.00
X25	Actresses (Burdick 264-3, Grey Border)	1890	£30.00	£750.00
X25	Actresses In Opera Roles	1892	£45.00	£1,125.00
M1	Advertisement Card	1890	—	£90.00
T25	Ancient Mythology Burlesqued	1893	£30.00	£750.00
T50	Beautiful Women	1893	£27.50	£1,375.00
X25	Boxing Positions & Boxers	1893	£130.00	—
M?20	Busts Of Girls (Die Cut)	1886	£130.00	—
X25	Circus Scenes	1888	£85.00	£2,125.00
X?15	Everyday Annoyances	1886	£160.00	—
25	National Flags	1888	£29.00	—
T52	Playing Card Inset Girls	1885	£34.00	—
X50	Prizefighters	1888	£135.00	—
X?17	Song Album	1887	£95.00	—
T25	Types Of Flirtation	1892	£55.00	—
T25	Types Of The Stage	1893	£30.00	£750.00

W. C. MACDONALD INC. (Canada)

?350	Aeroplanes & Warships	1940	£1.25	—
53	Playing Cards (Many Printings)	1927	65p	—

B. & J. B. MACHADO (Jamaica)

25	British Naval Series	1916	£22.50	—
F50	Popular Film Stars	1926	£6.00	—
F52	Stars Of The Cinema	1926	£6.00	—
50	The Great War - Victoria Cross Heroes	1916	£24.00	—
F50	The Royal Family At Home And Abroad	1927	£5.00	—
F50	The World Of Sport	1928	£8.00	—

MACLIN-ZIMMER (U.S.A.)

X53	Playing Cards (Actresses)	1890	£24.00	£1,275.00

MALTA CIGARETTE CO

135	Dante's Divine Comedy	1905	£12.50	—
M40	Maltese Families Arms & Letters	1905	£6.50	—
?44	Prominent People	1905	£13.50	—

H. MANDELBAUM (U.S.A.)

Qty		Date	Odds	Sets
20	Comic Types Of People	1890	£62.50	—
36	Flags Of Nations	1890	£40.00	—

MARBURG BROS (U.S.A.)

50	"National Costume" Cards (2 Types)	1887	£55.00	—
X100	Painting Reproductions (Several Printings)	1890	£65.00	—
?X17	Presidents And Other Celebrities	1886	£150.00	—
50	Typical Ships	1887	£60.00	—

MASPERO FRERES LTD. (Palestine)

50	Birds, Beasts & Fishes	1925	£3.50	—

S MATTINNO & SONS (Malta)

X36	Britain Prepared Series	1940	£4.00	—

P. H. MAYO & BROTHER (U.S.A.)

M25	Actresses (Fancy Frame)	1890	£32.00	£800.00
?21	Actresses (Sepia)	1886	£70.00	—
M25	Actresses (Black Border)	1890	£32.00	—
L12	Actresses (Diagonal)	1888	£75.00	—
?50	Actresses (Burdick 488, 2 Types)	1888	£32.00	—
X25	Actresses - Burdick 532 (3 Printings)	1887	£60.00	—
28	Baseball Game (Die Cut)	1890	£90.00	—
40	Baseball Players	1892	£150.00	—
35	College Football Stars	1892	£80.00	—
20	Costumes & Flowers (2 Printings)	1892	£32.50	£650.00
19	Costumes Of Warriors & Soldiers (2 Printings)	1892	£30.00	£570.00
25	Head Dresses Of Various Nations	1890	£35.00	£875.00
48	National Dances (Die Cut)	1890	£50.00	—
M25	National Flowers (Girl & Scene)	1891	£34.00	£850.00
20	Naval Uniforms	1892	£35.00	£700.00
F?	Photographic Cards	1887	£20.00	—
24	Presidents Of The U.S.	1888	£40.00	—
35	Prizefighters (2 Types)	1890	£70.00	—
20	Shakespeare Characters	1891	£35.00	£700.00
X12	The Seasons	1888	£85.00	—
X15	Wings Of Birds Of Plumage	1888	£85.00	—

M. MELACHRINO & CO. (Malta)

52	Peuples Exotiques "1 Serie"	1925	85p	£45.00
52	Peuples Exotiques "2 Serie"	1925	85p	£45.00
52	Peuples Exotiques "3 Serie"	1925	85p	£45.00

MELIA FRERES, ALGERIA

M?	Actresses (Many Groups)	1910	£4.00	—
M?128	Film Stars	1930	£2.75	—

MERCATOR (BELGIUM) (Cigar Bands)

24	British Empire Military Head-Dress	1976	—	£15.00
24	European Military Head-Dress	1976	—	£15.00

MEXICAN PUFFS (U.S.A.)

Qty		Date	Odds	Sets
20	Actresses, Blue Border	1890	£65.00	—

MIFSUD & AZZOPARDI (Malta)

KF59	First Maltese Parliament (2 Types)	1922	£8.50	

MRS. G. B. MILLER & CO. (U.S.A.)

X?7	Actresses & Celebrities	1885	£130.00	—
X?52	Alphabet Cards	1887	£100.00	—
22	Photographs Of All The Presidents	1888	£110.00	—

L. MILLER & SONS (U.S.A.)

49	Animals & Birds	1900	£100.00	—
X25	Battleships	1900	£32.00	£800.00
X100	Beauties "THIBS" (2 Types)	1900	£50.00	—
X25	Generals & Admirals (Spanish War)	1900	£32.00	—
X24	Presidents Of The U.S.	1900	£26.00	£625.00
X50	Rulers Of The World	1900	£24.00	£1,200.00

CHAS. J. MITCHELL (Canada)

26	Actresses "FROGA" (Brown Back)	1900	£38.00	—
26	(Green Back)	1900	£36.00	—
26	Actresses "FROGA" (Playing Card Back)	1900	£60.00	—

MONARCH TOBACCO WORKS (U.S.A.)

X?4	American Indian Chiefs	1890	£135.00	—

MOORE & CALVI (U.S.A.)

X10	Actresses "RAEMA"'	1887	£80.00	—
X53	Beauties, Playing Card Inset, Set 1	1886	£27.00	£1,430.00
X53	Beauties, Playing Card Inset, Set 2	1890	£24.00	£1,270.00
X53	Beauties, Playing Card Inset, Set 3	1890	£24.00	£1,270.00

MURAI BROS. (Japan)

50	Actresses "ALWICS"	1910	£10.00	£500.00
?94	Actresses "MUREG"	1900	£40.00	—
50	Beauties	1902	£14.00	£700.00
24	Beauties "HUMPS"	1900	£35.00	—
100	Beauties, Thick Borders	1902	£35.00	—
50	Chinese Beauties (Stork Back)	1908	£6.50	£325.00
25	Chinese Beauties (Peacock Back)	1912	£4.00	—
25	Chinese Beauties (Peacock, Different)	1912	£5.00	—
50	Chinese Children's Games (White Border)	1911	£3.00	—
20	Chinese Children's Games (Coloured Border)	1911	£3.25	—
M?	Chinese Girls (Various Series)	1905	£7.00	—
25	Chinese Pagodas	1911	£4.00	—
30	Chinese Series	1910	£3.50	—
40	Chinese Trades	1905	£25.00	—
26	Comic Phrases	1900	£35.00	—
50	Dancing Girls Of The World	1900	£40.00	—
32	Flowers	1900	£30.00	—
?125	Japanese Personalities	1900	£40.00	—
?52	Japanese Playing Cards	1900	£45.00	—

MURAI BROS. (Japan) – cont.

Qty		Date	Odds	Sets
50	Wild Animals Of The World	1900	£37.50	—
50	World's Distinguished Personages	1900	£28.00	—
50	World's Smokers	1900	£34.00	—

NATIONAL CIGARETTE & TOB. CO. (U.S.A.)

?12	Actresses	1886	£100.00	—
25	National Types (Sailor Girls)	1890	£30.00	£750.00
F?	Photographic Cards	1888	£7.50	—

NATIONAL CIGARETTE CO. (Australia)

13	English Cricket Team, 1897-8	1897	£325.00	—

NATIONAL TOBACCO WORKS (U.S.A.)

GF?	Actresses, etc. (Newsboy)	1900	£20.00	—
G100	Actresses (Coloured)	1900	£35.00	—

OLD FASHION FINE CUT (U.S.A.)

TF?	Photographic Cards	1890	£15.00	—

OMEGA CIGARETTE FACTORY (Malta)

KF96	Cinema Stars	1936	£3.00	£285.00
F?36	Maltese Footballers	1928	£17.50	—
M?16	Maltese Politicians, Cartoons By 'Mike	1940	£30.00	—
M97	Scenes From Films	1938	£10.00	—
M?4	World War II Leaders, Cartoons By Mike	1940	£30.00	—

OXFORD CIGARETTE CO (Malta)

MF24	Egyptian Scenes (Anonymous)	1926	£8.00	—

M S PACHOLDER (U.S.A.)

10	Actresses (Sub Rosa Cigarettes)	1885	£75.00	—

PENINSULAR TOBACCO CO. LTD. (India)

50	Animals And Birds	1910	£2.50	£125.00
52	Birds Of Brilliant Plumage (P/C Inset)	1916	£3.00	—
25	Birds Of The East, 1st Series	1912	£2.40	£60.00
25	Birds Of The East, 2nd Series	1912	£2.40	£60.00
25	China's Famous Warriors (2 Types)	1912	£3.60	£90.00
25	Chinese Heroes	1913	£3.20	£80.00
50	Chinese Modern Beauties	1912	£6.50	—
50	Chinese Trades, Set 3	1912	£3.00	—
50	Chinese Trades, Set 5	1913	£3.00	—
30	Fish Series	1916	£2.50	£75.00
25	Hindoo Gods	1909	£3.00	—
37	Nautch Girl Series (3 Types)	1910	£6.50	—
25	Products Of The World	1915	£2.00	£50.00

E. T. PILKINTON CO. (U.S.A.)

X48	Fruits & Flowers	1890	£70.00	—

N. PIPERNO, (Egypt)

6	Beauties (Different Colour Backs)	1900	£4.50	—
X?75	Beauties (Different Colour Backs)	1900	£5.00	—

PIZZUTO (Malta)

Qty		Date	Odds	Sets
50	Milton's 'Paradise Lost'	1910	£17.50	—

F. PLANELLES (Algeria)

M?153	Actresses	1905	£5.00	—

THE PLANTERS STORES (India)

50	Actresses "FROGA"..	1900	£37.50	—
25	Beauties "FECKSA"	1900	£40.00	—

POLICANSKY BROS. (South Africa)

50	Aeroplanes Of To-Day (P.O. Box 1006)...................................	1936	£1.80	£90.00
M50	Birds, Beasts & Fishes (Nassa Cigs)....................................	1924	£5.00	—
50	Regimental Uniforms (P.O. Box 1006)...................................	1937	£2.00	£100.00
50	South African Fauna (2 Types)...	1925	£8.50	£425.00

RED MAN CHEWING TOBACCO (U.S.A.)

X40	American Indian Chiefs..	1952	£9.00	£360.00

LA REFORMA (Canary Islands)

X8	Military Uniforms, Serie A-1 (Prussia)	1925	—	£15.00
X8	Military Uniforms, Serie A-3 (France)....................................	1925	—	£15.00
D5	Military Uniforms, Serie A-4 (France)....................................	1925	—	£10.00
D7	Military Uniforms, Serie A-5 (Spain)......................................	1925	—	£15.00
X8	Military Uniforms, Serie A-6 (Prussia)	1925	—	£15.00
D6	Military Uniforms, Serie A-7 (Spain)......................................	1925	—	£11.50
X6	Military Uniforms, Serie B-1 (Shaped)	1925	—	£11.50
X6	Military Uniforms, Serie B-2 (Shaped)	1925	—	£11.50

D. RITCHIE & CO. (Canada)

30	Actresses "RITAN" (Printed Back)	1887	£35.00	—
30	(Plain Back).............................	1887	£32.50	—
?25	Actresses ('Our Production' Back)	1889	£50.00	—
?29	Actresses ('Derby' Front)	1889	£50.00	—
52	Beauties P/C Inset (Several Types)......................................	1888	£30.00	—
36	Flags Of All Nations	1888	£60.00	—
52	Playing Cards...	1888	£35.00	—

D. E. ROSE & CO. (U.S.A.)

G28	Imperial Cards	1890	£65.00	£1,820.00

RUGGIER BROS. (Malta)

M50	The Great Siege Of Malta	1924	£6.50	—

RUMI CIGARETTES (Germany)

M49	Beauties...	1901	£35.00	—

JORGE RUSSO LTD (Gibraltar)

24	Marvels Of The World	1954	£5.00	—

SANTA FE NATURAL LEAF TOBACCO CO (U.S.A.)

Qty		Date	Odds	Sets
36	A Tribute To The Endangered	2001	£1.25	£45.00
36	A Tribute To The Endangered Series 2	2001	£1.25	£45.00
36	Century Of The Great American Spirit	2000	£1.25	—
36	Century Of The Great American Spirit Set 2	2001	£1.25	£45.00
36	Music Of America	2003	£1.25	—
36	Spirit Of The Old West Series 1	1999	£1.50	—
36	Spirit Of The Old West Series 2	2000	£1.50	—

JOHN SCERRI (Malta)

Qty		Date	Odds	Sets
147	Beauties & Children (Black & White)	1930	£1.25	—
180	Beauties & Children (Unicoloured)	1930	£17.50	—
?86	Beauties & Children (Large Numerals)	1930	£15.00	—
45	Beauties & Children (Coloured)	1930	£1.75	—
MF50	Beautiful Women	1931	£3.25	—
MF480	Cinema Artists	1931	£2.40	—
MF180	Cinema Stars	1931	£2.75	—
MF50	Famous London Buildings	1934	£4.00	£200.00
F60	Film Stars (First Serie)	1931	£3.25	—
F60	Film Stars (Second Serie)	1931	£3.25	—
52	Interesting Places Of The World	1934	50p	£26.00
F25	International Footballers	1935	£30.00	—
401	Malta Views	1928	75p	—
MF51	Members Of Parliament-Malta	1928	50p	£25.00
146	Prominent People	1930	£1.40	—
MF100	Scenes From Films	1932	£3.00	—
LF100	Talkie Stars	1932	£3.00	—
M100	World's Famous Buildings	1931	50p	£50.00

J. J. SCHUH TOBACCO CO. (Australia)

Qty		Date	Odds	Sets
60	Australian Footballers A (1/2 Length)	1920	£12.50	—
40	Australian Footballers B (Rays)	1921	£12.50	—
60	Australian Footballers C (Oval Frame)	1922	£22.50	—
60	Australian Jockeys	1921	£7.00	£420.00
F72	Cinema Stars (Black & White)	1924	£2.40	£175.00
60	Cinema Stars (Coloured)	1924	£2.75	—
L40	Maxims Of Success	1917	£40.00	—
F72	Official War Photographs (2 Types)	1918	£3.70	£265.00
F104	Portraits Of Our Leading Footballers	1920	£6.00	—

G. SCLIVAGNOTI (Malta)

Qty		Date	Odds	Sets
50	Actresses & Cinema Stars	1923	£3.00	—
MF71	Grand Masters Of The Order Of Jerusalem	1898	£11.50	—
F102	Opera Singers	1898	£15.00	—
M100	Opera Singers	1898	£15.00	—
72	Scenes With Girls (Black & White)	1905	£35.00	—
M49	Scenes With Girls (Coloured)	1905	£35.00	—

SENATOR (BELGIUM) (Cigar Bands)

Qty		Date	Odds	Sets
24	Decorations And Orders Of Chivalry	1975	—	£5.00

SINSOCK & CO. (China)

Qty		Date	Odds	Sets
?28	Chinese Beauties	1905	£20.00	—

SNIDERS & ABRAHAMS PTY LTD. (Australia)

Qty		Date	Odds	Sets
30	Actresses (Gold Background)	1905	£7.00	£200.00
14	(White Borders)	1905	£7.00	£100.00
20	Admirals & Warships Of The U.S.A. (2 Types)	1908	£8.50	—
2	Advertisement Cards	1905	£35.00	—
60	Animals (Green, Descriptive Back)	1912	£3.75	—
60	Animals & Birds (2 Types)	1912	£3.00	£180.00
15	Australian Cricket Team	1905	£50.00	£750.00
16	Australian Football-Incidents In Play	1906	£16.00	—
72	Australian Footballers-Series A (Full Length)	1904	£22.50	—
76	Australian Footballers-Series B (1/2 Length)	1906	£22.50	—
76	Australian Footballers-Series C (1/2 Length)	1907	£22.50	—
56	Australian Footballers-Series D (Head/Shoulders)	1908	£20.00	—
140	Australian Footballers-Series D (Head/Shoulders)	1909	£20.00	—
60	Australian Footballers-Series E (Head in Oval)	1910	£20.00	—
60	Australian Footballers-Series F (Head in Rays)	1911	£20.00	—
60	Australian Footballers-Series G (With Pennant)	1912	£20.00	—
60	Australian Footballers-Series H (Head in Star) 2 types	1913	£20.00	—
60	Australian Footballers-Series I (Head in Shield) 2 types	1914	£20.00	—
56	Australian Footballers-Series J (1/2-3/4 Length)	1910	£20.00	—
48	Australian Jockeys (Blue Back)	1907	£5.00	£240.00
60	Australian Jockeys (Brown Back)	1908	£5.50	£330.00
56	Australian Racehorses(Horizontal Back)	1906	£5.50	—
56	Australian Racehorses (Vertical Back)	1907	£5.50	—
40	Australian Racing Scenes	1911	£5.50	—
?133	Australian V. C.s And Officers	1917	£7.00	—
?63	Belgian Views	1916	£2.50	—
12	Billiard Tricks	1908	£20.00	—
60	Butterflies & Moths (Captions In Capitals)	1914	£1.75	£105.00
60	(Captions In Mixed Letters)	1914	£1.75	£105.00
60	Cartoons & Caricatures (2 Types)	1907	£6.00	—
12	Coin Tricks	1908	£16.00	—
64	Crests Of British Warships (2 Types)	1915	£5.50	£350.00
40	Cricketers In Action	1906	£65.00	—
12	Cricket Terms	1905	£32.50	£390.00
32	Dickens Series	1909	£5.50	£350.00
16	Dogs (4 Types)	1910	£10.00	£160.00
90	European War Series	1916	£3.50	—
?7	Flags (Shaped Metal)	1915	£6.00	—
?7	Flags (Shaped Card)	1915	£6.50	—
60	Great War Leaders & Warships (3 Types)	1915	£5.00	£300.00
30	How To Keep Fit	1907	£7.00	£210.00
60	Jokes (3 Types)	1906	£4.00	£260.00
12	Match Puzzles	1908	£16.00	—
48	Medals & Decorations	1915	£6.50	—
M48	Melbourne Buildings	1914	£8.50	—
25	Natives Of The World	1904	£18.00	£450.00
12	Naval Terms	1905	£8.50	£100.00
29	Oscar Asche, Lily Brayton & Lady Smokers	1911	£6.50	£190.00
40	Shakespeare Characters	1909	£5.50	£220.00
30	Signalling Series	1916	£7.00	£210.00
14	Statuary	1905	£10.00	£140.00
60	Street Criers In London, 1707	1914	£8.50	—
32	Views Of Victoria In 1857 (2 Types)	1906	£9.00	—
FS?250	Views Of The World	1908	£3.75	—

SOUTH INDIAN TOBACCO MFG. CO.

Qty		Date	Odds	Sets
25	Actresses "ALWICS" And Moslem Personalities	1905	£10.00	–

SPAULDING & MERRICK (U.S.A.)

Qty		Date	Odds	Sets
M24	Actresses And Prizefighters	1888	£75.00	–
M23/24	Animals	1890	£22.00	£500.00

STAR TOBACCO CO. (India)

Qty		Date	Odds	Sets
?66	Beauties '"STARA" (2 Types)	1898	£42.50	–
52	Beauties (P/C Inset) (3 Types)	1898	£27.50	–
52	Heroes Of The Transvaal War (P/C Inset)	1901	£80.00	–
52	Indian Native Types (P/C Inset)	1898	£27.50	£1,500.00

J. W. L. STUBBS (New Zealand)

Qty		Date	Odds	Sets
M50	Barques And Sailing Boats	1926	£25.00	–
F?200	Photographic Cards	1926	£10.00	–

SURBRUG CO. (U.S.A.)

Qty		Date	Odds	Sets
M10	Aeroplane Series No.103	1912	£22.50	£225.00
M10	Prize Dog Series No.102	1911	£22.50	£225.00
M25	Prize Fight Series No.101 (2 Types)	1911	£26.00	£650.00

CIE. DE TABAC TERREBONNE (Canada)

Qty		Date	Odds	Sets
30	Bingo-Puzzle	1924	£5.00	–
30	Bingo-Puzzle, 2nd Series	1925	£5.00	–
30	Bingo-Puzzle, 3rd Series	1926	£5.00	–
30	Bingo-Puzzle, 4th Series	1927	£4.00	–
30	Bingo-Puzzle, 5th Series	1928	£4.00	–

THOMPSON, MOORE & CO (USA)

Qty		Date	Odds	Sets
X10	Rope Knots	1888	£75.00	£750.00

TOBACCO PRODUCTS CORP. (Canada & USA)

Qty		Date	Odds	Sets
48	Canadian Sports Champions	1917	£15.00	–
60	Do You Know?	1918	£6.00	–
60	Hockey Players	1918	£35.00	–
100	Movie Stars (Sepia)	1915	£3.50	–
220	Movie Stars	1915	£2.75	–
120	Movie Stars (Portrait In Oval)	1915	£2.75	–
L?50	Movie Stars	1915	£4.00	–
L?100	Movie Stars, Series No.3	1916	£3.50	–
?180	Movie Stars, Series No.4	1916	£3.50	–
L100	Movie Stars, Series No.5	1916	£3.75	–
18	Ship Picture Letters	1915	£10.00	–

TUCKETT LTD. (Canada)

Qty		Date	Odds	Sets
M52	Aeroplane Series	1930	£4.50	–
M52	Aviation Series (As Above, 3 Types)	1930	£4.50	–
25	Autograph Series (2 Types)	1913	£32.50	–
60	Badges (Regimental)	1917	£12.50	–
?114	Beauties & Scenes (2 Types)	1910	£7.00	–
25	Boy Scout Series	1914	£27.50	–
M8	British Gravures	1923	£13.50	–

TUCKETT LTD. (Canada) – cont.

Qty		Date	Odds	Sets
L8	British Gravures	1923	£13.50	—
F100	British Views Plain Back	1912	£2.00	£200.00
F?224	British Views (3 Types)	1912	£2.00	—
F80	British Warships (2 Types)	1914	£8.50	—
F50	Canadian Scenes	1912	£2.40	£120.00
?51	Card Trick Series	1928	£9.00	—
M48	Delivering Mail (Stamps)	1910	£16.00	—
?110	Girls And Warships	1924	£11.00	—
53	Playing Card Premium Certificates	1930	£7.50	—
M52	Tucketts Auction Bridge Series (2 Types)	1930	£6.50	—

TURCO-AMERICAN TOBACCO CO. (U.S.A.)

M15	Foreign Views	1908	£17.00	—

TURKISH-MACEDONIAN TOBACCO CO (Holland)
ANONYMOUS SILKS

Qty		Date	Odds	Sets
M?43	Animals, Birds And Butterflies	1926	£4.00	—
M18	Arms Of Dutch Colonies	1926	£3.50	—
M21	Arms Of Dutch & European Towns(White)	1926	£3.75	—
?32	Celebrities (White)	1926	£5.00	—
M20	Decorations And Medals	1926	£6.00	—
101	Dutch Celebrities	1934	£4.50	—
M74	Dutch Celebrities, Arms Etc.	1926	£3.50	—
M12	Film Stars	1926	£8.00	—
M249	Flags, Arms And Standards	1926	£1.75	£462.50
D166	Flags And Arms, Series 2	1926	£2.25	—
?31	Flowers	1926	£6.00	—
M34	Flowers	1926	£4.50	—
M20	Flowers (Europa/Afrika)	1926	£5.00	—
M89	Flower Series (A-E)	1926	£4.00	—
M3	Girls Of Many Lands (Black Silk)	1926	£6.50	£19.50
M50	(White Silk)	1929	£4.00	£200.00
M54	Illustrated Initials	1926	£3.50	—
M12	Japanese Series	1926	£7.00	—
M?46	Javanese Figures	1926	£5.00	—
M34	National Costumes	1926	£3.75	£127.50
D62	National Flags (White Silk)	1926	£3.00	—
M141	National Flags (Paper Backs)	1926	£3.50	—
M16	Nature Calendar	1926	£4.50	—
M20	Ships Of All Ages	1926	£8.00	—
?85	Sporting Figures (Series A-E)	1926	£6.00	—
25	Sporting Figures (CA1-25)	1926	£6.50	£162.50
X18	Town Arms Of Holland	1926	£4.00	—
M26	World Celebrities	1926	£6.50	—
M56	Youth Series And Miscellaneous	1926	£4.00	—

U. S. TOBACCO CO. (U.S.A.)

X25	Actresses	1890	£60.00	—

UNITED CIGAR STORES (U.S.A.)

L25	The Aviators (2 Types)	1911	£26.00	£650.00

UNITED TOB. COS. (SOUTH) LTD. (S. Africa)

Qty		Date	Odds	Sets
50	Aeroplanes Of To-Day	1936	£1.80	£90.00
50	African Fish	1937	£1.70	£85.00
48	All Sports Series	1926	£30.00	—
L48	All Sports Series	1926	£35.00	—
50	Animals & Birds(2 Types)	1923	£6.50	—
L24	Arms And Crests Of Universities And Schools Of South Africa	1930	£1.25	£30.00
FS50	Beauties Of Great Britain	1930	£2.50	—
L52	Boy Scout, Girl Guide & Voortrekker Badges	1932	£2.20	£115.00
M50	British Aeroplanes	1933	£1.70	£85.00
L20	British Butterflies (Silk)	1924	£10.00	—
L30	British Roses (Silk)	1924	£11.00	—
L62	British Rugby Tour Of South Africa	1938	£1.85	£115.00
50	Children Of All Nations	1928	80p	£40.00
50	Cinema Stars (Flag Cigarettes)	1922	£2.00	£130.00
X?10	Conundrums	1910	£65.00	—
40	Cricketers & Their Autographs (Plain Back)	1922	£32.50	£1,300.00
28	Dominoes (Rugger Cigarettes)	1938	£3.25	—
60	Do You Know?	1930	50p	£30.00
50	Do You Know?, 2nd Series	1930	50p	£25.00
50	Do You Know?, 3rd Series	1931	50p	£25.00
30	Do You Know? (Different)	1933	60p	£18.00
50	Eminent Film Personalities	1930	£2.00	£100.00
50	English Period Costumes	1932	90p	£45.00
L50	Exercises For Men And Women	1932	£1.20	£60.00
96	Fairy Tales	1926	£1.75	£168.00
24	Fairy Tales (Folders)	1926	£8.50	—
25	Famous Figures From S.A. History	1932	£2.40	£60.00
L100	Famous Works Of Art	1939	30p	£30.00
L120	Farmyards Of South Africa	1934	£1.75	£210.00
L65	Flags Of All Nations (Silk)	1910	£3.00	£195.00
25	Flowers Of South Africa	1932	£1.60	£40.00
FS52	Here There And Everywhere	1930	75p	£37.50
L50	Household Hints	1926	£1.40	—
M50	Humour In Sport	1929	£3.50	£220.00
25	Interesting Experiments	1930	£1.20	£30.00
L100	Medals And Decorations Of The British Commonwealth Of Nations	1941	£1.00	£100.00
50	Merchant Ships Of The World	1925	£1.20	£60.00
30	Merrie England Studies-Female	1914	£7.50	£225.00
52	Miniature Playing Cards (Flag, 2 Sizes)	1938	£1.25	—
53	(Lifeboat)	1938	£2.00	—
53	(Lotus, 2 Colours)	1938	£2.50	—
53	(Needle Point)	1938	£5.00	—
53	(Rugger, 2 Sizes)	1938	£2.50	—
50	Motor Cars	1928	£4.00	£200.00
FS48	Nature Studies	1930	90p	£45.00
X28	1912-13 Springboks	1912	£75.00	—
X?7	Nursery Rhymes	1910	£70.00	—
M25	Old Masters (Silk)	1926	£8.00	—
L100	Our Land	1938	25p	£25.00
M150	Our South African Birds	1942	60p	£90.00
L150	Our South African Birds	1942	40p	£60.00
M100	Our South African Flora	1940	20p	£15.00
L100	Our South African Flora	1940	20p	£15.00

UNITED TOB COS (SOUTH) LTD (S. Africa) – cont.

Qty		Date	Odds	Sets
M100	Our South African National Parks	1941	20p	£15.00
L100	Our South African National Parks	1941	20p	£15.00
L200	Our South Africa-Past & Present (2 Printings)	1938	20p	£40.00
X60	Ozaka's System Of Self Defence (3 Printings)	1911	£60.00	–
L24	Pastel Plates	1930	£1.25	£30.00
L88	Philosophical Sayings	1938	£1.25	£100.00
L50	Pictures Of South Africa's War Effort	1940	30p	£15.00
FS48	Pictures Of The East	1930	75p	£36.00
25	Picturesque People Of The Empire	1929	£1.60	£40.00
L50	Pottery Types (Silk)	1926	£5.50	£275.00
M50	Pottery Types (Silk)	1926	£7.50	–
L50	Race Horses-South Africa (Set 1)	1929	£2.25	£112.50
L52	Race Horses-South Africa (Set 2, 2Types)	1930	£2.25	£115.00
50	Regimental Uniforms	1937	£2.00	£100.00
50	Riders Of The World (Firm's Name)	1931	£1.25	£62.50
50	(C. T. Ltd)	1931	£1.25	£62.50
L52	S A Flora (2 Types)	1935	35p	£20.00
M40	Ships Of All Times	1931	£1.75	£70.00
10	Silhouettes Of M. L. A.'s	1914	£30.00	–
25	South African Birds A Series	1927	£1.60	£40.00
25	South African Birds Second Series	1927	£1.60	£40.00
L52	South African Butterflies	1937	70p	£36.00
L52	South African Coats Of Arms	1931	50p	£26.00
L17	South African Cricket Touring Team	1929	£24.00	–
L17	(Autographed)	1929	£17.50	£300.00
M100	South African Defence	1941	25p	£25.00
L50	South African Flowers (Silk)	1913	£3.75	£187.50
L50	South African Flowers (Second Series)	1913	£4.25	£212.50
L50	South African Places Of Interest	1934	20p	£10.00
L65	South African Rugby Football Clubs	1933	£2.00	£130.00
L52	Sports & Pastimes In South Africa	1936	£2.00	£210.00
L47	Springbok Rugby & Cricket Teams	1931	£3.00	£140.00
FS50	Stereoscopic Photographs	1928	£1.00	£50.00
FS50	Stereoscopic Photographs Of S. Africa	1929	£1.00	£50.00
25	"Studdy" Dogs (Bonzo)	1925	£5.00	£125.00
M50	Tavern Of The Seas	1939	40p	£20.00
50	The Story Of Sand	1934	£1.00	£50.00
50	The World Of Tomorrow	1938	£1.00	£50.00
?98	Transfers (2 Printings)	1925	£5.00	–
X?70	Triangular Test Cricketers 1912	1912	£250.00	–
L40	Views Of South African Scenery	1918	£4.00	£160.00
L36	Views Of S. African Scenery, Second Series	1920	£4.00	£144.00
25	Warriors Of All Nations(Swords Base)	1937	£2.00	£50.00
25	What's This?	1929	£1.60	£40.00
50	Wild Animals Of The World	1932	£1.40	£70.00
25	Wild Flowers Of South Africa, A Series	1925	£1.20	£30.00
25	Wild Flowers Of South Africa, Second Series	1926	£1.20	£30.00
M40	Wonders Of The World	1931	£1.00	£40.00
M100	World-Famous Boxers	1939	£6.00	–

UNIVERSAL TOBACCO CO. (India)

F50	Actresses (Plain Back)	1900	£27.50	–
F50	(Printed Back)	1900	£30.00	–

154

UNIVERSAL TOBACCO CO. (PTY.) LTD (S. Africa)

Qty		Date	Odds	Sets
835	Flags Of All Nations	1935	£1.25	—
M?368	Park Lane Fashions	1934	£8.50	—

S. W. VENABLE TOBACCO CO.(U.S.A.)

X?56	Actresses (Multi-Backed)	1888	£40.00	—
X12	Baseball & Seashore Scenes (7 Backs)	1888	£85.00	—

R. WHALEN & CO. (U.S.A.)

L25	Actresses	1890	£60.00	—
M25	Actresses (Names Only)	1890	£30.00	—

WYNEN ZIGARETTEN (Germany)

?46	Tanzerinnen Aller Welt	1900	£37.50	—

GEO. F. YOUNG (U.S.A.)

X?76	Actresses	1889	£35.00	—
X12	Baseball & Seashore Scenes	1888	£85.00	—
X10	National Sports-Girls	1887	£100.00	—
X?	Photographic Cards	1886	£10.00	—

Part 3

NON-TOBACCO
ISSUES

INDEX OF BRANDS (Non-Tobacco)

156

A-1 DAIRIES LTD.

Qty		Date	Odds	Sets
25	Birds And Their Eggs	1965	£1.60	£40.00
25	Butterflies And Moths	1964	–	£4.00
25	The Story Of Milk	1967	£1.00	–

A-1 DOLLISDALE TEA

Qty		Date	Odds	Sets
25	Do You Know About Shipping & Trees?	1963	–	£2.50

A.B.C. (Cinemas)

Qty		Date	Odds	Sets
10	Animals	1952	£2.00	£20.00
10	An Adventure In Space	1950	£3.25	–
10	Birds	1958	£1.00	£10.00
10	Birds & Bird-Watching	1953	£2.75	£27.50
10	British Athletes	1955	£1.75	–
20	British Soldiers (Black Back)	1949	£0.45	£9.00
20	(Brown Back)	1949	£0.35	£7.00
10	Colorstars	1962	£0.65	£6.50
10	Colorstars (2nd Series)	1962	£3.75	£37.50
10	Colorstars (3rd Series)	1962	£2.00	£20.00
10	Dogs	1957	£2.50	£25.00
L16	Film Stars	1935	£5.00	–
10	Film Stars	1948	£3.00	£30.00
10	Horses	1958	£1.75	–
10	Interesting Buildings	1956	£0.50	£5.00
10	Journey By Land	1954	£2.75	£27.50
10	Journey By Water	1954	£2.75	£27.50
10	Journey To The Moon	1955	£2.75	–
10	Parliament Buildings	1957	£1.00	–
10	Railway Engines	1951	£5.00	£50.00
10	Scenes From The Films	1953	£4.50	–
10	Sea Exploration	1957	£1.25	–
10	Sea Scenes	1958	£0.60	£6.00
10	Sports On Land	1956	–	£7.00
12	Star Series	1936	£5.00	–
10	Travel Of The Future	1956	£0.80	–
10	Water Sports	1956	£0.75	£7.50

A.& B.C. GUM

Qty		Date	Odds	Sets
M120	All Sport Series	1954	£5.00	£650.00
P17	Banknotes	1971	£4.00	£65.00
X55	Batman (Pink Back, Fan Club Panel)	1966	£2.75	£150.00
X55	(Pink Back, No Panel)	1966	£2.00	£110.00
X55	Batman (Numbered On Front)	1966	£2.75	£150.00
X44	Batman (1A-44A)	1966	£3.50	£155.00
X44	Batman (1B-44B)	1966	£4.75	–
X38	Batman (Black Back)	1966	£4.75	£180.00
X38	(Black Back, Dutch)	1966	£7.00	–
M1	Batman Secret Decoder	1966	–	£14.00
X73	Battle Cards	1966	£1.75	£135.00
X66	Battle Of Britain	1970	£1.75	£115.00
X60	Bazooka Joe And His Gang	1968	£4.30	–
X60	Beatles (Black & White)	1964	£4.85	£290.00
X45	Beatles, 2nd Series	1965	£8.00	–
X40	Beatles (Coloured)	1965	£11.00	–
K114	Car Stamps	1971	£3.00	–

Qty		Date	Odds	Sets
X21	Car Stamps Albums	1971	£6.00	£125.00
L?56	Christian Name Stickers	1967	£3.75	–
X15	Civil War Banknotes	1965	£3.75	–
X88	Civil War News	1965	£3.50	£350.00
X43	Comic Book Foldees	1968	£2.20	£95.00
P24	Crazy Disguises	1970	£9.00	–
X48	Cricketers	1959	£2.50	£120.00
X48	Cricketers 1961 Test Series 94 x 68mm	1961	£3.25	£156.00
X48	90 x 64mm	1961	£2.90	£140.00
X66	Elvis Presley Series	1956	£12.00	–
X36	Exploits Of William Tell	1960	£2.25	£80.00
M22	Famous Indian Chiefs	1968	£6.00	–
X54	Fantastic Twisters	1972	£6.50	–
M48	Film & TV Stars	1953	£3.50	£168.00
M48	Film & TV Stars No.2 Series (49-96)	1953	£3.75	£180.00
M48	Film & TV Stars No.3 Series (97-144)	1953	£3.75	£180.00
X48	Film Stars (Plain Back)	1954	£3.00	£165.00
X73	Flags (Cut-Outs)	1971	£0.80	–
L80	Flags Of The World	1960	£1.30	£105.00
X80	Flags Of The World	1959	£1.40	£110.00
40	Flag Stickers	1966	£5.50	–
X46	Footballers (Planet, 1-46)	1958	£3.20	£145.00
X46	(Without "Planet" 1-46)	1958	£3.50	£160.00
X46	Footballers (Planet, 47-92)	1958	£6.40	£295.00
X46	(Without "Planet" 47-92)	1958	£9.20	–
X49	Footballers (Football Quiz, 1-49)	1959	£4.00	£200.00
X49	Footballers (Football Quiz, 50-98)	1959	£7.25	–
X42	Footballers (Black Back, 1-42)	1960	£4.00	–
X42	Footballers (Black Back, 43-84)	1960	£7.50	–
XF64	Footballers (Plain Back)	1961	£6.00	–
XF44	Footballers (Plain Back, Scottish)	1962	£13.50	–
X82	Footballers (Bazooka)	1962	£8.00	–
X55	Footballers (Make-A-Photo, 1-55)	1963	£4.90	£270.00
X55	Footballers (Make-A-Photo, 56-110)	1963	£4.85	–
X81	Footballers (Make-A-Photo, Scottish)	1963	£13.00	–
X58	Footballers (Quiz, 1-58)	1964	£4.30	£250.00
X45	Footballers (Quiz, 59-103)	1964	£10.75	–
X46	Footballers (Quiz, 104-149)	1964	£13.00	–
X81	Footballers (Quiz, Scottish)	1964	£11.00	–
X55	Footballers (In Pairs, 1-110)	1966	£5.00	–
X55	Footballers (In Pairs, 111-220)	1966	£7.50	£410.00
X55	Footballers (In Pairs, Scottish)	1966	£11.00	–
X55	Footballers (Star Players)	1967	£4.00	£220.00
P12	Footballers	1967	£8.75	£105.00
X45	Footballers (Football Quiz, Scottish)	1968	£9.25	–
X54	Footballers (Yellow, 1-54)	1968	£4.50	£245.00
X47	Footballers (Yellow, 55-101)	1968	£3.75	£175.00
M20	Football Team Emblems	1968	£7.00	–
E26	Football Team Pennants	1968	£8.75	–
X65	Footballers (Football Facts, 1-64)	1969	£2.15	£140.00
X54	Footballers (Football Facts, 65-117)	1969	£2.15	£115.00
X55	Footballers (Football Facts, 117-170)	1969	£2.50	£135.00
MF36	Footballers	1969	£2.75	£100.00
X42	Footballers (Football Facts, Scottish, 1-41)	1969	£7.50	–
X35	Footballers (Football Facts, Scottish, 42-75)	1969	£9.25	–

A.& B.C. GUM – cont.

Qty		Date	Odds	Sets
MF15	Footballers (Scottish)	1969	£6.00	£90.00
X85	Footballers (Orange Back, 1-85)	1970	£1.90	£160.00
X85	Footballers (Orange Back, 86-170)	1970	£1.35	£120.00
X85	Footballers (Orange Back, 171-255)	1970	£4.50	£380.00
72	Football Colour Transparencies	1970	£7.50	–
P14	Footballers, Pin-Ups	1970	£7.00	£100.00
X85	Footballers (Green Back, Scottish, 1-85)	1970	£4.75	–
X86	Footballers (Green Back, Scottish, 86-171)	1970	£4.50	–
P28	Footballers, Pin-Ups (Scottish)	1970	£8.75	–
X109	Footballers (Did You Know, 1-109)	1971	£3.00	–
X110	Footballers (Did You Know, 110-219)	1971	£2.75	£300.00
X71	Footballers (Did You Know, 220-290)	1971	£5.45	£385.00
X73	Footballers (Did You Know, Scottish, 1-73)	1971	£2.70	£195.00
X71	Footballers (Did You Know, Scottish, 74-144)	1971	£7.50	–
23	Football Club Crests	1971	£2.20	£50.00
16	Football Club Crests (Scottish)	1971	£2.80	£45.00
X109	Footballers (Orange/Red, 1-109)	1972	£3.25	£355.00
X110	Footballers (Orange/Red, 110-219)	1972	£4.00	£440.00
M22	Football Card Game	1972	£1.35	£30.00
M23	Footballers, Superstars	1972	£8.00	–
X89	Footballers (Rub Coin, Scottish, 1-89)	1972	£5.40	£480.00
X89	Footballers (Orange/Red, Scottish, 90-179)	1972	£7.50	–
M32	Footballers (Autographed Photos)	1973	£3.50	£110.00
X131	Footballers (Blue Back, 1-131)	1973	£4.75	–
X130	Footballers (Blue Back, 132-263)	1973	£5.40	£700.00
X90	Footballers (Red Back, Scottish, 1-90)	1973	£5.40	–
X88	Footballers (Red Back, Scottish, 91-178)	1973	£6.25	–
E16	Football Giant Team Posters	1973	£10.75	–
X132	Footballers (Red Back, Rub Coin)	1974	£2.00	£265.00
X132	Footballers (Green Back, Scottish, Rub Coin)	1974	£4.25	–
X40	Fotostars	1961	£3.75	–
X66	Funny Greetings	1961	£1.20	£80.00
X66	Funny Valentines	1961	£3.75	–
X36	Golden Boys (Matt)	1958	£5.50	–
XF40	(Glossy)	1958	£6.50	–
L27	Grand Prix	1970	£0.45	£12.00
D200	Hip Patches	1968	£2.75	–
X55	Huck Finn	1968	£3.25	–
X60	Kung Fu	1974	£1.90	£115.00
X55	Land Of The Giants	1969	£4.75	£260.00
X55	Lotsa Laffs	1970	£3.75	£210.00
X84	Love Initials	1970	£2.15	–
X36	Magic	1967	£4.25	–
L1	Magic Circle Club Application	1969	–	£10.00
X74	Man On The Moon	1969	£3.80	£280.00
X55	Mars Attacks	1965	£27.00	–
X52	Mickey Takers	1970	£3.50	–
M24	Military Emblem Stickers	1966	£4.50	–
X55	Monkees (Black & White)	1967	£1.65	£90.00
X55	Monkees (Coloured)	1967	£3.00	£165.00
X30	Monkees Hit Songs	1967	£4.00	£120.00
E16	Monster Tattoos	1970	£4.75	–
X49	Nutty Initial Stickers	1968	£4.75	–
E16	Olympic Posters	1972	£3.50	£55.00
X36	Olympics	1972	£4.25	–

A.& B.C. GUM – cont.

Qty		Date	Odds	Sets
X50	Outer Limits	1966	£5.90	£295.00
X55	Partridge Family	1972	£2.20	£120.00
X120	Planes (88 x 64mm)	1960	£2.15	–
X120	Planes (94 x 67mm)	1960	£1.90	–
X44	Planet Of The Apes	1968	£5.50	–
M96	Pop Stars Fab. Photo Stamps	1965	£6.50	–
X33	Put-On Stickers	1969	£3.25	–
X48	Railway Quiz	1958	£1.00	£48.00
X72	Railway Quiz	1959	£2.75	–
M24	Royal Portraits	1953	£2.70	£65.00
M34	Silly Stickers	1966	£3.00	–
X25	Sir Francis Drake	1961	£4.50	–
X88	Space Cards	1958	£5.50	–
X44	Stacks Of Stickers	1971	£4.50	–
X55	Star Trek	1969	£9.00	£500.00
X66	Superman In The Jungle	1968	£2.15	–
X16	Superman In The Jungle (Jig-Saw)	1968	£3.75	£60.00
X45	The Champions	1969	£4.05	–
M1	The Champions Secret Decoder	1969	–	£18.00
X25	The Girl From U.N.C.L.E.	1965	£3.50	£88.00
X36	The High Chaparral	1969	£2.60	£94.00
X54	The Legend Of Custer	1968	£2.50	£135.00
L55	The Man From U.N.C.L.E.	1965	£1.20	£65.00
X40	The Rolling Stones	1965	£11.00	–
X50	Top Stars	1964	£3.70	£185.00
X40	Top Stars (Different)	1964	£5.40	£220.00
E16	T.V.Cartoon Tattoos	1972	£8.75	–
X56	TV Westerns	1959	£2.85	£160.00
X44	Ugly Stickers	1967	£3.25	–
P88	Wacky Plaks	1962	£2.75	–
E16	Walt Disney Characters Tattoos	1973	£12.00	–
E16	Wanted Posters	1968	£5.50	–
X70	Who-Z-At Star?	1958	£3.00	£210.00
X55	Winston Churchill Cards	1965	£1.20	£65.00
X37	World Cup Footballers	1970	£6.50	–
50	World Cup Football Stickers	1966	£9.75	–
E16	World Cup Posters	1970	£5.50	–
X66	You'll Die Laughing (Creature Feature)	1974	£1.75	£115.00
X48	You'll Die Laughing (Purple Back)	1967	£1.35	£65.00

A.H.C. (Confectionery)

25	Tropical Birds (Anon.)	1955	–	£10.00
25	Wonders Of The Universe	1955	–	£3.50

A & P PUBLICATIONS

24	British Classic Cars	1992	–	£4.00

ABBEY GRANGE HOTEL

15	Fighting Vessels	1986	–	£2.50

ACE (Commercial)

X33	Sporting Greats - Motor Racing	1988	–	£5.00
X33	Sporting Greats - Tennis	1988	–	£8.50

ACTIVE MARKETING INTERNATIONAL INC. (U.S.A.)

Qty		Date	Odds	Sets
X50	The James Dean Gallery	1992	—	£20.00

ADIDAS (Sportswear)

Qty		Date	Odds	Sets
X30	World's Leading Soccer Stars	2002	—	£12.50

P.A. ADOLPH ('Subbuteo')

Qty		Date	Odds	Sets
F50	Famous Footballers	1954	£10.00	—
24	Famous Footballers Second Series	1954	£1.75	£42.00

A.W. ALLEN (Confectionery, Australia)

Qty		Date	Odds	Sets
32	Bradman's Records	1931	£37.00	—
72	Butterflies & Moths	1920	£2.25	—
36	Cricketers (Brown Front)	1932	£13.00	£470.00
36	Cricketers (Brown Front, Different)	1933	£14.00	—
36	Cricketers (Flesh Tinted, Frame Back)	1934	£11.75	£420.00
36	Cricketers (Flesh Tinted, No Frame)	1936	£11.75	£420.00
36	Cricketers (Coloured)	1938	£10.50	£380.00
M24	Fliers	1926	£7.25	—
48	Footballers (Action)	1939	£11.00	—
144	Footballers (Striped Colours)	1933	£7.50	—
72	Footballers (Pennants)	1934	£7.00	—
49	Kings & Queens Of England	1937	£1.75	£85.00
36	Medals	1938	£2.35	£85.00
36	Soldiers Of The Empire	1938	£2.35	—
36	Sports & Flags Of Nations	1936	£3.50	£125.00
M24	Wrestlers	1926	£7.00	£190.00

ALMA CONFECTIONERY

Qty		Date	Odds	Sets
48	James Bond 007 Moonraker	1980	£4.00	£190.00

JAMES ALMOND & SONS (Confectionery)

Qty		Date	Odds	Sets
25	Sports And Pastimes	1925	£9.00	£250.00

AMABILINO PHOTOGRAPHIC (Commercial)

Qty		Date	Odds	Sets
L30	Display Fireworks	1988	—	£6.50

AMALGAMATED PRESS LTD.

Qty		Date	Odds	Sets
24	Aeroplanes (Plain Back)	1933	£3.75	£90.00
32	Aeroplanes & Carriers	1932	£3.50	£110.00
M32	Australian & English Cricket Stars	1932	£12.50	£400.00
M12	Catchy Tricks And Teasers	1933	£5.00	£60.00
M16	England's Test Match Cricketers	1928	£11.50	£185.00
M22	English League (Div.1) Footer Captains	1926	£4.25	£90.00
M16	Exploits Of The Great War	1929	£2.75	£44.00
16	Famous Aircraft	1927	£3.75	£60.00
M16	Famous Australian Cricketers	1928	£12.50	£200.00
16	Famous Film Stars	1927	£6.25	£100.00
M24	Famous Footer Internationals	1926	£5.25	£125.00
F8	Famous Screen Stars (Anon., Film Fun)	1930	£5.75	—
M22	Famous Shipping Lines	1926	£6.25	—
M32	Famous Test Match Cricketers	1926	£6.75	£215.00
24	Famous Trains & Engines	1932	£3.75	—
16	Fighting Planes Of The World	1934	£4.50	—

AMALGAMATED PRESS LTD. – cont.

Qty		Date	Odds	Sets
32	Football Fame Series	1936	£4.25	£135.00
M16	Great War Deeds	1927	£3.40	£55.00
M32	Great War Deeds (Different)	1928	£3.50	–
M16	Heroic Deeds Of The Great War	1927	£3.40	£55.00
32	Makes Of Motor Cars And Index Marks	1923	£2.75	£88.00
32	Mechanical Wonders Of 1935	1935	£2.65	£85.00
32	Modern Motor Cars	1926	£6.75	–
24	Motors (Plain Back)	1933	£4.00	£100.00
X15	Prominent Football Teams	1938	£6.50	£95.00
24	Ships Of The World (Champion)	1924	£2.70	£65.00
33	Ships Of The World (Different, Anon.)	1935	£3.75	–
MF66	Sportsmen	1922	£1.70	£120.00
32	Sportsmen Of The World	1934	£3.50	£110.00
M12	Sports "Queeriosities"	1933	£4.00	£48.00
X40	Test Match Favourites	1934	£10.00	£400.00
M24	The Great War 1914-1918	1928	£3.25	£78.00
M16	The Great War 1914-1918 New Series	1929	£3.00	£50.00
M16	The R.A.F. At War (Plain Back)	1940	£5.50	–
M32	Thrilling Scenes From The Great War	1927	£3.50	£110.00
M16	Thrills Of The Dirt Track	1929	£9.50	£150.00
M16	Tip-Top Tricks & Teasers	1927	£4.00	£65.00
M14	V.C.s & Their Deeds Of Valour (Plain Back)	1939	£4.25	£60.00
M24	Wonderful London	1926	£4.20	£125.00

AMANDA'S FLOWERS

Qty		Date	Odds	Sets
L12	Flower Children	1990	–	£4.00

AMARAN TEA

Qty		Date	Odds	Sets
25	Coins Of The World	1964	£0.50	–
25	Dogs Heads	1965	£1.00	£25.00
25	Do You Know	1969	£0.50	–
25	Flags And Emblems	1964	£0.40	£10.00
25	Naval Battles	1971	£0.50	–
25	Old England	1969	–	£2.50
25	Science In The 20th Century	1966	–	£2.50
25	The Circus	1966	£0.50	£12.50
25	Veteran Racing Cars	1965	£0.80	£20.00

AMATEUR PHOTOGRAPHER (Periodical)

Qty		Date	Odds	Sets
P4	Advertising Postcards	1990	–	£2.00

THE ANGLERS MAIL (Periodical)

Qty		Date	Odds	Sets
E3	Terminal Tackle Tips	1976	–	£3.00

ANGLING TIMES (Magazine)

Qty		Date	Odds	Sets
X15	Baits	1980	–	£5.00
X24	Collect-A-Card (Floats)	1986	–	£5.00
M24	Collect-A-Card (Fish)	1988	–	£5.00
X15	Floats	1980	–	£5.00
X15	Sea Fish	1980	–	£5.00
X15	Species	1980	–	£5.00

ANGLO-AMERICAN CHEWING GUM LTD.

Qty		Date	Odds	Sets
L36	Kidnapped (Thriller Chewing Gum)	1935	£5.00	—
X66	The Horse	1966	£0.65	£43.00
40	Underwater Adventure	1966	—	£5.00
50	Zoo Stamps Of The World	1966	£0.90	£45.00

ANGLO CONFECTIONERY LTD.

Qty		Date	Odds	Sets
X66	Captain Scarlet And The Mysterons	1968	£3.00	£200.00
L12	Football Hints (Folders)	1970	£1.35	£16.00
L84	Football Quiz	1969	£1.50	£125.00
X66	Joe 90	1968	£4.00	£265.00
L56	National Team Colours (Soccer)	1970	£3.50	£195.00
X84	Railway Trains & Crests	1974	£0.80	£67.50
X66	Space	1967	£2.20	£145.00
X66	Tarzan	1967	£1.60	£105.00
X66	The Beatles - Yellow Submarine	1968	£13.00	—
X66	The Horse	1966	£3.00	—
L56	The New James Bond 007	1970	£13.50	—
L64	U F O	1971	£4.85	£310.00
M24	Vintage Cars Series	1970	£3.50	£84.00
L78	Walt Disney Characters	1971	£5.50	£430.00
L66	Wild West	1970	£2.20	£145.00
L48	World Cup 1970	1970	£2.25	£108.00

ANONYMOUS – TRADE ISSUES

Qty		Date	Odds	Sets
50	Animals Of The World	1954	—	£3.00
29	Boy Scouts Signalling	1910	£6.50	—
25	Bridges Of The World	1958	—	£2.50
25	British Uniforms Of The 19th Century			
25	(Black Back)	1957	—	£6.00
25	(Blue Back)	1957	—	£4.00
20	Budgerigars	1950	£0.60	£12.00
25	Cacti	1961	—	£2.00
25	Careless Moments	1922	£1.00	£25.00
M56	Caricatures Of Cricketers By Durling	1959	—	£18.00
M50	Caricatures Of Cricketers By Mac	1959	—	£16.00
M164	Caricatures Of Cricketers	1959	—	£50.00
25	Children Of All Nations	1958	—	£2.50
25	Cinema And TV Stars (Barbers Tea Reprint)	1993	—	£15.00
MF12	Cinema Stars	1929	£5.00	£60.00
F6	Cinema Stars (Name In Black)	1930	£6.00	—
F6	Cinema Stars (Name In White)	1930	£6.00	—
25	Dogs	1958	—	£15.00
25	Do You Know?	1963	—	£2.50
25	Evolution Of The Royal Navy	1957	£0.80	—
25	Family Pets	1964	—	£5.00
25	Flags & Emblems	1961	—	£5.00
25	Flowers	1971	—	£3.00
25	Football Clubs & Badges	1962	—	£6.00
40	Greats From The States (Golf)	1994	—	£20.00
25	Jockeys And Owners Colours	1963	£0.50	£12.50
25	Medals Of The World	1960	—	£7.50
100	Miscellaneous Subjects (Gum)	1965	—	£12.50
25	Modern Aircraft	1958	—	£2.50
X12	Motor Cycles (Collectors Series)	1987	—	£2.50

ANONYMOUS – TRADE ISSUES – cont.

Qty		Date	Odds	Sets
25	Musical Instruments...	1971	–	£2.50
25	Pigeons...	1971	–	£5.00
25	Pond Life...	1963	–	£2.00
50	Prize & Game Chickens (Allen & Ginter Reprint)...................	2000	–	£10.00
M24	R.A.F. Badges..	1985	–	£16.00
1	Soldier - Bugler...	1965	–	£2.50
25	Sports Of The Countries	1967	–	£17.50
25	The Circus..	1966	–	£10.00
25	The Wild West..	1960	–	£15.00
25	Train Spotters	1962	–	£5.00
1	Venice In London..	1965	–	£1.00

SILK ISSUES

M1	Field-Marshal Earl Kitchener..................................	1915	–	£3.00
P1	Field-Marshal Earl Kitchener..................................	1915	–	£6.00
M4	Great War Incidents..	1916	£15.00	£60.00
M1	King Of Belgium...	1915	–	£2.00
P1	King Of Belgium...	1915	–	£2.50
M10	Review Titles Travestied	1915	£15.00	£150.00
M4	Warships..	1915	£17.50	£70.00

BELGIAN ISSUES

X90	Belgian Military Uniforms..	1970	–	£22.50
X26	Cartouche (Film)..	1960	–	£10.00
X38	Sindbad The Sailor (Film).......................................	1960	–	£15.00

U.S. ISSUES ('STRIP CARDS')

10	Film Stars "A"	1926	–	£20.00
10	Film Stars "B"	1926	–	£20.00
10	Film Stars "C"	1926	–	£20.00
10	Film Stars "D"	1926	–	£20.00
T60	Pinocchio (Bread Issue)	1939	–	£70.00
10	Presidents "A"	1926	–	£35.00
10	Presidents "B"	1926	–	£35.00
10	Western Pioneers...	1926	–	£35.00

SPANISH ISSUES

X40	Footballers (P/C Backs)	1930	£1.75	£70.00

APLIN & BARRETT (Cheese)

X25	Whipsnade...	1937	£1.30	£32.50

ARBUCKLE COFFEE CO. (U.S.A.)

P50	Animals	1890	£7.00	£350.00
P50	Cooking Subjects	1889	£6.50	–
P100	General Subjects (Unnumbered).............................	1890	£8.00	–
P50	General Subjects (51-100)	1890	£7.50	–
P50	History Of Sports & Pastimes Of World..................	1893	£10.00	£500.00
P50	History Of United States & Territories.....................	1892	£9.00	£450.00
P50	Illustrated Atlas Of U.S. (51-100)	1889	£8.50	£425.00
P100	Illustrated Jokes..	1890	£8.50	–
P50	Principal Nations Of The World (51-100)	1889	£7.00	£350.00
P50	Views From A Trip Around The World	1891	£7.00	£350.00

ARDMONA (Tinned Fruit, Australia)

Qty		Date	Odds	Sets
X50	International Cricket Series III	1980	—	£10.00

ARMITAGE BROS. LTD. (Pet Foods)

25	Animals Of The Countryside	1964	—	£2.50
25	Country Life	1968	—	£2.50

ARMY CAREERS INFORMATION OFFICE

M24	British Regiments	1991	—	£7.50
M24	British Regiments 2nd Series	1992	—	£7.50

ARROW CONFECTIONERY CO.

13	Conundrums	1904	£32.50	—
12	Shadowgraphs	1904	£32.50	—

ASKEY'S (Biscuits)

25	People & Places	1971	—	£2.50
25	Then And Now	1971	—	£4.00

AUSTIN MOTOR CO. LTD

L13	Famous Austin Cars	1953	£12.00	—

AUSTRALIAN DAIRY CORPORATION

X63	Kanga Cards (Cricket)	1985	—	£15.00
X54	Super Cricket Card Series 1982-3	1983	—	£15.00
X50	Super Cricket Card Series 1983-4	1984	—	£15.00

AUSTRALIAN LICORICE PTY. LTD.

?27	Australian Cricketers	1930	£14.50	—
24	Australian Cricketers	1931	£14.75	£350.00
24	English Cricketers (Blue Back)	1928	£14.50	£350.00
24	English Cricketers (Black Back)	1930	£14.50	—
18	English Cricketers ('18 In Set')	1932	£14.50	£260.00
12	South African Cricketers	1931	£15.00	£180.00

AUTOBRITE (Car Polish)

25	Vintage Cars	1965	£1.00	£25.00

AUTOMATIC MACHINE CO.

25	Modern Aircraft	1958	—	£10.00

AUTOMATIC MERCHANDISING CO.

X25	Adventure Twins And The Treasure Ship	1958	—	£22.50

AVON RUBBER CO. LTD.

30	Leading Riders Of 1963	1963	£2.50	£75.00

B.B.B. PIPES

25	Pipe History	1926	£12.00	£300.00

B.J.B. CARDS (Commercial, Canada)

L25	Famous Golfers Of The 40's And 50's 1st Series	1992	—	£12.50

B.P. OIL UK.

Qty		Date	Odds	Sets
25	England '98 (Soccer)	1998	£0.25	£6.50
1	Album For Above	1998	—	£1.25

B.T. LTD. (Tea)

Qty		Date	Odds	Sets
25	Aircraft	1961	£0.80	£20.00
25	British Locomotives	1961	£1.00	—
25	Do You Know?	1967	£0.40	£10.00
25	Holiday Resorts	1963	—	£3.00
25	Modern Motor Cars	1962	£1.60	—
25	Occupations	1962	—	£5.00
25	Pirates And Buccaneers	1961	£1.50	—
25	The West	1964	—	£7.50

BADSHAH TEA CO.

Qty		Date	Odds	Sets
25	British Cavalry Uniforms Of The 19th Century	1963	—	£7.50
25	Butterflies And Moths	1971	—	£2.50
25	Fish And Bait	1971	—	£7.50
25	Fruits Of Trees And Shrubs	1965	—	£10.00
25	Garden Flowers	1963	—	£7.50
25	Naval Battles	1971	£0.50	£12.50
25	People & Places	1970	—	£2.50
25	Regimental Uniforms Of The Past	1971	—	£3.50
25	Romance Of The Heavens	1968	£1.20	£30.00
24	The Island Of Ceylon	1955	£4.00	—
25	Wonders Of The World ("Series Of 50")	1970	£0.40	£10.00

BAILEY'S (Toffee)

Qty		Date	Odds	Sets
25	War Series (Ships)	1916	£20.00	—

BAKE-A-CAKE LTD.

Qty		Date	Odds	Sets
56	Motor Cars	1952	£5.00	£280.00

BAKER, WARDELL & CO (Tea)

Qty		Date	Odds	Sets
25	Animals In The Service Of Man	1964	£2.50	£62.50
36	Capital Tea Circus Act	1964	£4.00	£144.00
25	Do You Know? 1st Series	1962	£3.50	—
25	Do You Know? 2nd Series	1962	£3.50	—
25	Irish Patriots	1962	£10.00	—
25	The History Of Flight 1st Series	1963	£10.00	—
25	The History Of Flight 2nd Series	1963	£6.50	—
25	They Gave Their Names	1963	£2.40	£60.00
25	Transport Present And Future	1962	£5.50	—
25	World Butterflies	1964	£6.50	—

BARBERS TEA LTD.

Qty		Date	Odds	Sets
1	Advertising Card - Cinema & T.V. Stars	1955	—	£5.00
1	Advertising Card - Dogs	1956	—	£0.60
1	Advertising Card - Railway Equipment	1958	—	£5.00
25	Aeroplanes	1956	£0.60	£15.00
24	Cinema And Television Stars	1955	£2.00	£90.00
24	Dogs	1961	—	£5.00
5	Ferry To Hong Kong	1957	£12.00	—
25	Locomotives	1956	£1.80	£45.00
24	Railway Equipment	1958	£0.60	£15.00

BARCLAYS BANK

Qty		Date	Odds	Sets
X21	Sunderland A.F.C..	1990	–	£12.00

JOHN O. BARKER (IRELAND) LTD. (Gum)

Qty		Date	Odds	Sets
X24	Circus Scenes...	1970	£3.00	£72.00
X24	Famous People	1970	£2.00	£48.00
25	The Wild West...	1970	£4.00	–

BARRATT & CO. LTD. (Confectionery)

Qty		Date	Odds	Sets
M30	Aircraft (Varnished)..	1941	£5.50	£165.00
M30	Aircraft (Unvarnished, Different).....................................	1943	£6.50	–
25	Animals In The Service Of Man.......................................	1964	–	£2.75
16	Australian Cricketers, Action Series	1926	£16.00	£260.00
15	Australian Test Players	1930	£30.00	–
45	Beauties - Picture Hats	1911	£20.00	–
25	Birds..	1960	£0.65	£16.00
50	Botany Quest..	1966	£1.90	£95.00
25	British Butterflies..	1965	£2.60	£65.00
25	Butterflies And Moths	1969	–	£2.75
25	Cage & Aviary Birds..	1960	–	£7.50
50	Captain Scarlet And The Mysterons	1967	£3.75	£185.00
50	Cars Of The World	1965	£1.90	£95.00
M122	Characters From Film Cartoons	1940	£9.50	–
K4	Coronation & Jubilee Medallions....................................	1902	£23.50	–
25	Coronation, 1911	1911	£21.00	–
20	Cricket Team Folders..	1933	£23.50	–
?284	Cricketers, Footballers & Football Team	1925	£16.00	–
L60	Disneyland 'True Life'	1956	£1.75	£105.00
P6	Europe's Best (Soccer)...	1992	–	£7.50
L50	F.A. Cup Winners..	1935	£26.00	–
25	Fairy Stories..	1926	£3.40	£85.00
12	Famous British Constructions, Aircraft...........................	1925	£18.50	–
25	Famous Cricketers (Numbered)......................................	1931	£12.50	–
50	Famous Cricketers (Unnumbered).................................	1932	£13.50	–
X9	Famous Cricketers (Folders)..	1932	£23.00	–
X34	Famous Cricketers (Folders)..	1934	£17.00	–
M7	Famous Cricketers (Unnumbered)..................................	1936	£17.00	–
M60	Famous Cricketers (Unnumbered)..................................	1937	£11.50	–
M40	Famous Cricketers (Numbered)......................................	1938	£11.50	–
35	Famous Film Stars	1961	£3.25	£115.00
M100	Famous Footballers (Unnumbered, Black)	1935	£12.50	–
M98	Famous Footballers (Unnumbered, Sepia)	1936	£12.50	–
M110	Famous Footballers (Numbered)	1937	£12.50	–
M20	Famous Footballers (Numbered)	1938	£12.75	–
M110	Famous Footballers (Numbered)	1939	£12.00	–
M79	Famous Footballers (Non-Descriptive)	1947	£11.75	–
M50	Famous Footballers, New Series....................................	1950	£7.75	–
M50	Famous Footballers, New Series (diff.)	1952	£7.50	–
M50	Famous Footballers Series A.1.......................................	1953	£6.50	£325.00
M50	Famous Footballers Series A.2.......................................	1954	£5.80	£290.00
M50	Famous Footballers Series A.3.......................................	1955	£6.00	–
60	Famous Footballers Series A.4.......................................	1956	£4.75	£285.00
60	Famous Footballers Series A.5.......................................	1957	£6.75	–
60	Famous Footballers Series A.6.......................................	1958	£6.00	–
60	Famous Footballers Series A.7.......................................	1959	£7.00	–

BARRATT & CO. LTD. (CONFECTIONERY) – cont.

Qty		Date	Odds	Sets
50	Famous Footballers Series A.8	1960	£5.75	—
50	Famous Footballers Series A.9	1961	£5.75	—
50	Famous Footballers Series A.10	1962	£2.00	£100.00
50	Famous Footballers Series A.11	1963	£5.25	—
50	Famous Footballers Series A.12	1964	£5.25	—
50	Famous Footballers Series A.13	1965	£5.25	—
50	Famous Footballers Series A.14	1966	£5.75	—
50	Famous Footballers Series A.15	1967	£1.70	£85.00
50	Famous Sportsmen	1971	£1.85	—
M45	Fastest On Earth	1953	£1.90	£85.00
32	Felix Pictures	1930	£27.50	—
50	Film Stars (No Company Name)	1934	£7.75	—
50	Film Stars (With Company Name)	1936	£7.75	—
25	Fish And Bait	1962	—	£16.00
P6	Football Action	1991	—	£8.00
12	Football Action Caricatures	1928	£27.00	—
100	Football Stars	1930	£27.00	—
50	Football Stars	1974	£7.00	—
X156	Football Team Folders	1933	£27.00	—
M66	Football Teams-1st Division	1930	£16.00	—
48	Giants In Sport	1959	£6.50	—
P12	Gold Rush (Packets)	1960	£6.50	—
P6	Great Defenders (Soccer)	1992	—	£8.00
P6	Great Goalkeepers	1991	—	£8.00
P6	Great Grounds (Soccer)	1991	—	£7.50
P6	Great Managers (Soccer)	1991	—	£8.00
P6	Great Managers, Series 2	1992	—	£8.00
25	Head-Dresses Of The World	1962	—	£5.00
25	Historical Buildings	1960	—	£2.75
48	History Of The Air (English Text)	1959	£1.25	£60.00
32	History Of The Air (Bi-Lingual)	1959	£4.75	—
25	History Of The Air (different)	1960	—	£5.00
25	Interpol	1964	£3.60	£90.00
40	Knight Rider	1987	£0.50	£20.00
50	Leaders Of Sport	1927	£16.00	—
30	Looney Tunes Cartoons	1997	—	£7.50
35	Magic Roundabout	1968	£1.40	—
25	Merchant Ships Of World (Black Back)	1962	—	£10.00
25	(Blue Back)	1962	—	£7.50
P6	Midfield Dynamos (Soccer)	1992	—	£7.50
L40	Modern Aircraft	1957	£2.50	£100.00
M45	Modern British Aircraft	1959	£4.00	£180.00
13	National Flags	1914	£21.00	—
64	Natural History (Plain Back)	1940	£5.75	—
M24	Naval Ships (Plain Back)	1939	£8.00	—
M6	Our King & Queen (Plain Back)	1940	£9.00	£54.00
25	People & Places	1965	—	£2.50
25	Pirates And Buccaneers	1960	£0.80	£20.00
P25	Pop Stars	1980	£1.00	£25.00
12	Prominent London Buildings	1920	£21.00	£250.00
30	Robin Hood	1961	£3.00	£90.00
36	Sailing Into Space	1959	£2.75	£100.00
50	Soccer Stars	1973	£3.70	£185.00
50	Soldiers Of The World	1966	£0.70	£35.00
16	South African Cricketers	1929	£21.00	—

Although there have been tens of thousands of card sets issued, there are comparatively few books about the hobby. Foremost among the works of reference are those published by the Cartophilic Society. These include a number of books on individual firms, such as Ogden and Wills. Most important, however, are the revised edition of the "World Tobacco Index" and the new British Trade Index and British Trade Handbook. Each of these builds on the previous volumes, and records new issues, old series that have recently been discovered, and additional subjects to those sets that had been only partially seen. Because it is published annually, our catalogue is often more advanced in its information, and we always welcome news about additions and amendments, which will always be passed on to the Society's research Editor.

A number of dedicated collectors have made their own contributions by compiling lists of a more specialised nature, and we have indeed published many of these ourselves. Among works currently available are one on cricket and one on tennis, a work on tobacco football cards, and one each on all known golf and boxing cards and a superb book on all tobacco and trade silk issues.

For general work on the hobby we recommend "The Story of Cigarette Cards". This book is superbly illustrated, well written and offers excellent value. Details of all the books we stock are given in the first few pages of the Catalogue.

TYPE COLLECTING

There are now many collectors who concentrate on types either exclusively or in addition to their main collections. This involves keeping one or two cards from every series issued. Limitations of space and money make this a good compromise for many people, since they can have a limited goal, yet still providing a sufficient challenge to maintain their interest.

The advent of modern albums has eased one problem for type collectors, since they can now limit themselves to just one card per series, and still be able to see both front and back of that type. Further limitations may also be self-imposed by collecting the issues of just one country, or commodity. One collector 'only' collects one card from each manufacturer, while a lifetime could be spent just in trying to collect the different types issued by the tobacco firm of Wills!

The general collector can also acquire types as a method of identifying those series of which he wishes to obtain complete sets—and those that he wishes to avoid. It is also a useful idea to obtain type cards of all the varieties of one series, so that one can have a complete set of all the pictures and also a specimen of all the different backs that could be found with that front.

BARRATT & CO. LTD. (Confectionery) – cont.

Qty		Date	Odds	Sets
25	Space Mysteries	1965	£0.80	£20.00
L20	Speed Series	1930	£8.50	–
50	Tarzan	1967	–	£25.00
35	Test Cricketers Series A	1956	£6.25	£220.00
48	Test Cricketers Series B	1957	£7.75	£375.00
12	The Magic Sword Quest For Camelot	1998	–	£1.50
50	The Secret Service	1970	£2.00	£100.00
24	The Wild West	1961	–	£8.00
25	The Wild West (Different)	1963	–	£10.00
50	The Wild Wild West	1969	£1.70	£85.00
P6	The World's Greatest Teams (Soccer)	1991	–	£8.00
25	The Young Adventurer	1965	£2.60	£65.00
50	Thunderbirds	1967	£3.80	£190.00
50	Thunderbirds Second Series	1968	£1.00	£50.00
50	Tom & Jerry	1971	£0.85	£42.00
P6	Top Strikers (Soccer)	1991	–	£8.00
P6	Top Strikers 2	1992	–	£8.00
50	Trains	1970	£0.25	£12.50
50	Trains Of The World	1964	–	£12.50
35	T.V.'s Huckleberry Hound & Friends	1961	£1.70	£60.00
35	T.V.'s Sea Hunt	1961	£2.50	£90.00
35	T.V.'s Yogi Bear	1969	£4.75	–
35	T.V.'s Yogi Bear & Friends	1971	£0.75	£25.00
70	U F O	1971	£1.25	–
1	Victory V Sign	1940	–	£11.50
M35	Walt Disney Characters	1956	£5.30	£185.00
50	Walt Disney Characters, 2nd Series	1957	£5.75	–
36	Walt Disney's Robin Hood	1957	£2.10	£75.00
35	Walt Disney's True Life	1962	£1.25	£45.00
25	Warriors Through The Ages	1962	£0.80	–
25	What Do You Know?	1964	–	£2.75
X72	Wild Life	1972	£0.85	£60.00
M50	Wild Animals By George Cansdale	1954	£1.70	£85.00
36	Wild West Series No.1	1959	£2.00	£72.00
25	Willum	1961	£6.50	–
50	Wisecracks	1970	–	£6.50
50	Wisecracks 2nd Series	1970	£0.50	£25.00
50	Wisecracks 3rd Series	1971	£0.40	£20.00
50	Wonders Of The World	1962	–	£5.00
P6	World Beaters (World Cup Action)	1994	–	£7.50
P6	World Beaters (World's Greatest Players	1994	–	£8.00
25	World Locomotives	1961	£0.60	–
50	Wunders Der Welt	1968	–	£6.00
50	Zoo Pets	1964	£1.30	£65.00

GEO. BASSETT & CO. LTD. (Confectionery)

Qty		Date	Odds	Sets
30	Adventure Game Cards	2001	–	£5.00
25	Looney Tunes Cartoons	1999	–	£6.00
25	Motor Cars-Vintage & Modern	1968	£1.60	£40.00
25	Nursery Rhymes	1966	£1.60	£40.00
25	Popular Dogs	1967	£1.00	£25.00
70	U F O	1974	–	£25.00
25	Victoria Cross Heroes In Action	1970	£1.20	£30.00

GEO. BASSETT & CO. LTD. (Confectionery) – cont.

Qty		Date	Odds	Sets
	BARRATT DIVISION			
50	Age Of The Dinosaurs	1979	£1.20	£60.00
40	Ali Cat Magicards	1978	£2.00	—
50	Asterix In Europe	1977	£0.60	£30.00
50	Athletes Of The World	1980	£0.25	£12.50
48	Bananaman	1986	—	£4.50
M20	Battle (Packets)	1985	£2.50	£50.00
50	Cricket First Series	1978	£9.50	—
50	Cricket Second Series	1979	£3.75	£185.00
48	Dandy-Beano Collection (Black Back)	1989	—	£8.50
48	Dandy-Beano Collection (Blue Back, Different)	1990	—	£8.50
50	Disney-Health & Safety	1977	—	£25.00
50	Football Action	1977	£4.75	—
50	Football Action	1978	£4.75	—
50	Football 1978-79	1979	£3.00	—
50	Football 1979-80	1980	£0.50	£25.00
50	Football 1980-81	1981	£0.50	£25.00
50	Football 1981-82	1982	£3.75	—
50	Football 1982-83	1983	£2.75	—
50	Football 1983-84	1984	£0.20	£10.00
50	Football 1984-85	1985	£1.30	£65.00
48	Football 1985-86	1986	£0.50	£24.00
48	Football 1986-87	1987	£0.50	£24.00
48	Football 1987-88	1988	£1.00	£50.00
48	Football 1988-89	1989	—	£10.00
48	Football 1989-90	1990	—	£10.00
48	Football 1990-91	1991	—	£12.50
50	Football Stars	1974	£2.00	£100.00
50	Football Stars 1975-6	1975	£3.70	£185.00
M50	Guinness Book Of Records	1990	—	£13.00
48	Hanna Barbera's Cartoon Capers	1984	£1.60	£75.00
24	Holograms (Plain Backs)	1986	£0.30	£7.50
24	(Red Backs)	1986	—	£7.00
50	House Of Horror	1982	£1.50	—
50	Living Creatures Of Our World	1979	£0.20	£10.00
50	Play Cricket 1980	1980	£0.30	£15.00
25	Pop Stars	1974	—	£5.00
35	Secret Island	1976	£1.50	£50.00
40	Secret Island Second Series	1976	—	£3.50
M20	Sky Fighters (Packets)	1986	£1.75	£35.00
49/50	Space 1999	1976	£1.60	£80.00
50	Super Heroes	1984	£0.85	£42.00
50	Survival On Star Colony 9	1979	£0.65	£32.00
40	Swim & Survive	1983	£0.45	£18.00
M20	The A Team	1986	—	£10.00
50	The Conquest Of Space	1980	£0.55	£27.50
50	Tom & Jerry	1974	£2.40	—
50	World Cup Stars	1974	—	£12.00
40	World Of The Vorgans	1978	£2.35	—
50	World Record Breakers	1983	£1.30	£65.00
49/50	Yogi's Gang	1976	£1.85	—

BATTLEAXE TOFFEE

24	British And Empire Uniforms	1915	£27.50	—

BAYTCH BROS. (Commercial)

Qty		Date	Odds	Sets
64	Fighting Favourites	1951	£11.50	—

BEANO LTD. (Gum)

Qty		Date	Odds	Sets
1	Bang-O Spacesuit Coupon	1950	—	£0.50
25	Fascinating Hobbies	1950	£4.00	—
50	Modern Aircraft (Beano)	1951	£1.20	£60.00
50	(British Educational)	1951	—	£7.50
50	Ships Of The Royal Navy	1955	£0.80	£40.00
50	The Conquest Of Space	1956	—	£7.00
50	This Age Of Speed No.1 (Aeroplanes)	1954	£0.60	£30.00
50	This Age Of Speed No.2 (Buses & Trams)	1954	£2.00	—
50	Wonders Of Modern Transport (Aircraft)	1955	—	£35.00
25	Wonders Of The Universe (Foto Gum)	1960	—	£2.50

BEANSTALK (Commercial)

Qty		Date	Odds	Sets
15	Saturday Afternoon Heroes	2003	—	£5.50
15	Vintage Football Stars	2003	—	£5.50

BEATALL'S (Rubber Goods)

Qty		Date	Odds	Sets
F?24	Beauties	1924	£25.00	—

S.N. BEATTIE & CO. (Commercial)

Qty		Date	Odds	Sets
24	Safety Signs	1955	£3.50	—

J.J. BEAULAH (Canned Goods)

Qty		Date	Odds	Sets
1	Boston Stump	1953	—	£0.60
25	Coronation Series	1953	£1.40	£35.00
24	Marvels Of The World	1954	—	£3.00
24	Modern British Aircraft	1953	—	£6.50

THE BEAUTIFUL GAME LIMITED

Qty		Date	Odds	Sets
X50	Football Greats	1999	—	£20.00

T.W. BECKETT & CO. LTD. (South Africa)

Qty		Date	Odds	Sets
M50	Animals Of South Africa, Series 3	1966	£0.30	£15.00

THE BEEHIVE STORES

Qty		Date	Odds	Sets
25	British Uniforms Of The 19th Century	1959	—	£17.50

BELLS SCOTCH WHISKY

Qty		Date	Odds	Sets
42	Other Famous Bells (Shaped)	1975	—	£24.00
40/42	Other Famous Bells (Shaped)	1975	£0.50	£20.00

J. BELLAMY & SONS LTD. (Confectionery)

Qty		Date	Odds	Sets
25	Vintage & Modern Trains Of The World	1975	—	£6.50

BILLY BEMBO (Commercial)

Qty		Date	Odds	Sets
X54	Vanity Fair 1st Edition (Playing Cards)	1995	—	£10.00
X54	Vanity Fair 2nd Edition (Playing Cards)	1995	—	£10.00

BENSEL WORK FORCE LTD

Qty		Date	Odds	Sets
20	Occupations	1991	—	£3.50

VAN DEN BERGHS LTD. (Margarine Etc.)

Qty		Date	Odds	Sets
P8	Birds..	1974	–	£4.00
70	Countryside Cards	1975	£0.65	£45.00
X24	Pirates	1965	£3.00	£72.00
M12	Recipes From Round The World	1958	£2.25	£27.00
M12	Regional Recipes	1958	£2.25	£27.00
X24	This Modern World	1965	£2.25	£54.00

DE BEUKELAER (Biscuits)

Qty		Date	Odds	Sets
KF100	All Sports	1932	£1.00	£100.00
M125	Dumbo	1940	£1.50	–
KF900	Film Stars (101-1000)......................	1932	£1.25	–
KF100	Film Stars (1001-1100).....................	1937	£1.25	£125.00
KF100	Film Stars (B1-100).........................	1935	£1.25	£125.00
K160	Film Stars (Gold Background)...............	1936	£1.75	–
132	Film Stars (Gold Background)...............	1938	£1.60	–
M125	Gulliver's Travels	1940	£1.20	£150.00
M125	Pinocchio Series	1940	£1.25	£156.00
M60	Sixty Glorious Years	1940	£1.50	–
M100	Snow White Series..........................	1940	£1.50	£150.00

J. BIBBY & SONS LTD. (Cooking Fat)

Qty		Date	Odds	Sets
L25	Don't You Believe It	1955	£1.00	£25.00
L25	Good Dogs	1955	£2.80	£70.00
L25	How What And Why..........................	1955	£1.20	£30.00
L25	Isn't It Strange	1955	£1.00	£25.00
L25	They Gave It A Name........................	1955	£2.00	£50.00
L25	This Wonderful World	1955	£1.20	£30.00

BIRCHGREY LTD. (Sporting Promotions)

Qty		Date	Odds	Sets
L25	Panasonic European Open..................	1989	–	£15.00
L15	The Ryder Cup...............................	1988	–	£15.00

ALFRED BIRD & SONS (Custard)

Qty		Date	Odds	Sets
K48	Happy Families	1938	£1.50	£72.00

BIRDS EYE FOODS LTD.

Qty		Date	Odds	Sets
X6	Birds Eye Book Of Record Breakers	1970	£3.25	£20.00
T12	England's Football Team	1980	–	£40.00
30	Wonders Of The Seven Seas................	1978	£1.00	£30.00

BIRKUM (Cheese, Denmark)

Qty		Date	Odds	Sets
25	Motor Cars...................................	1956	£1.20	£30.00

BISHOPS STORTFORD DAIRY FARMERS (Tea)

Qty		Date	Odds	Sets
25	Dogs Heads..................................	1967	£1.50	–
25	Freshwater Fish	1964	£1.50	–
25	Historical Buildings	1964	–	£6.00
25	History Of Aviation..........................	1964	–	£15.00
25	Passenger Liners	1965	–	£3.50
25	Pond Life.....................................	1966	–	£3.00
25	Science In The 20th Century	1966	–	£3.00
25	The Story Of Milk	1966	–	£3.00

BLACKPOOL PROGRAMME & MEMORABILIA COLLECTORS CLUB

Qty		Date	Odds	Sets
13	Blackpool Legends (Numbered Limited Edition Of 300)	2004	—	£10.00

BLACK CAT (Commercial)

15	Sunderland - Cup Kings Of '73...	2003	—	£6.00

BLAKEY'S BOOT PROTECTORS LTD.

72	War Series	1916	£6.50	—

BLUE BAND SERIES (Stamps)

24	History Of London's Transport 1st Series - Black Front	1954	£1.00	£24.00
24	- Blue Front	1954	£1.00	£24.00
24	- Orange Front....	1954	£0.70	£17.00
24	History Of London's Transport 2nd Series	1955	£2.50	£60.00
16	See Britain By Coach..	1999	—	£6.00

BLUE BIRD (Periodical)

T10	Famous Beauties Of The Day	1923	£8.00	—

BLUE BIRD STOCKINGS

P12	Exciting Film Stars	1963	£2.75	£33.00
M24	Star Cards...	1963	£7.00	—

BLUE CAP LTD. (Cheese)

K144	Flixies...	1952	£0.85	£120.00

PACKAGE SERIES

12	Animal Series D	1953	£1.50	—
12	Animal Series E..	1953	£2.50	—
12	Farm Series A	1953	£1.50	£18.00
12	Farm Series B	1953	£1.50	£18.00
12	Farm Series C	1953	£1.50	£18.00
12	Sports Series D	1953	£2.50	£30.00
12	Sports Series E	1953	£3.00	—

E. H. BOOTH & CO. LTD. (Tea)

25	Badges & Uniforms Of Famous British Regiments And Corps..	1967	—	£3.00
25	Ships And Their Workings	1971	£1.20	£30.00
24	The Island Of Ceylon	1955	£4.00	—

BOW BELLS (Periodical)

MF6	Handsome Men On The British Screen	1922	£8.00	£48.00

BOY'S CINEMA (Periodical)

MF6	Cinema Stars (Anon)..	1931	£4.50	£27.00
MF6	Famous Film Heroes..	1922	£5.00	£30.00
M24	Famous Heroes	1922	£4.50	—
F7	Film Stars (Anon)..	1932	£3.50	£24.50
MF8	Film Stars (Brown Front)	1930	£4.50	£36.00
MF8	Film Stars (Black Front, Different)..	1931	£4.50	£36.00

BOYS COMIC LIBRARY

4	Heroes Of The Wild West	1910	£17.50	—

BOYS FRIEND (Periodical)

Qty		Date	Odds	Sets
3	Famous Boxers Series	1911	£16.00	–
3	Famous Flags Series	1911	£8.00	£24.00
3	Famous Footballers Series	1911	£20.00	£60.00
3	Famous Regiments Series	1911	£10.00	£30.00
MF4	Footballers (1/2 Length)	1923	£6.25	£25.00
MF5	Footballers (2 Per Card)	1922	£6.00	£30.00
MF15	Rising Boxing Stars	1922	£4.50	£67.50

BOYS MAGAZINE (Periodical)

Qty		Date	Odds	Sets
M8	Boxers	1922	£9.00	–
M8	Coloured Studies-Famous Internationals	1922	£6.50	£52.00
M10	Cricketers	1922	£10.00	£100.00
F10	Famous Cricketers Series	1929	£6.00	£75.00
F12	Famous Footballers Series	1929	£6.00	£72.00
MF10	Football Series	1922	£4.50	£45.00
X9	Football Teams	1929	£12.50	–
M30	Footballers (Picture 49 x 39mm)	1922	£6.00	£180.00
M64	Footballers & Sportsmen (Picture 56 x 35)	1922	£5.00	£320.00
12	Zat Cards (Cricketers)	1930	£8.50	£100.00
M11	Zat Cards (Cricketers)	1930	£10.00	£110.00

BOYS REALM (Periodical)

Qty		Date	Odds	Sets
MF15	Famous Cricketers	1922	£3.50	£52.50
MF9	Famous Footballers	1922	£5.00	£45.00

C. & T. BRIDGEWATER LTD. (Biscuits)

Qty		Date	Odds	Sets
KF48	Coronation Series	1937	£0.20	£8.00
KF96	Film Stars 1st ("CE" Over No.)	1932	£0.25	£25.00
KF96	Film Stars 2nd ("E" Below No.)	1933	£1.00	–
KF96	Film Stars 3rd (Black & White)	1934	£1.00	£96.00
KF48	Film Stars 4th	1935	£0.50	£24.00
KF48	Film Stars 5th	1937	£1.75	£84.00
KF48	Film Stars 6th ("F" Before No.)	1938	£2.00	–
F48	Film Stars 7th	1939	£1.75	£84.00
KF48	Film Stars 8th	1940	£0.75	£36.00
KF48	Radio Stars 1st (Black & White)	1935	£1.50	£72.00
KF48	Radio Stars 2nd (Coloured)	1936	£0.40	£20.00

JOHN M. BRINDLEY (Printers)

Qty		Date	Odds	Sets
30	Australian Cricketers	1986	–	£12.50
12	Bob Hoare Cricket Charies	1992	–	£4.00
20	Car Badges And Emblems	1987	–	£5.00
30	Cricketers, A Series	1985	–	£12.50
30	Cricketers, 2nd Series	1985	–	£20.00
X16	Cricketers, Howzat, 3rd Series	1985	–	£10.00
30	Cricketers, 4th Series	1986	–	£10.00
X20	Cricketers, 5th Series (Sketches)	1986	–	£10.00
30	Cricket, The Old School	1987	–	£10.00
30	Famous Operatic Roles	1992	–	£6.50
20	Golf	1987	–	£12.00
20	Horse Racing	1987	–	£5.00
30	London, Brighton & South Coast Railway	1986	–	£6.50
20	Military	1987	–	£4.00
25	Old Golfing Greats	1988	–	£20.00

174

JOHN M. BRINDLEY (PRINTERS) – cont.

Qty		Date	Odds	Sets
L6	World Boxers	1992	–	£3.50
L6	World Boxers Part 2 (7-12)	1993	–	£3.00

BRISTOL-MYERS CO LTD (Toothpaste)

Qty		Date	Odds	Sets
50	Speed	1964	£4.00	£200.00

BRITISH AUTOMATIC CO. (Weight)

Qty		Date	Odds	Sets
24	British Aircraft	1950	£1.75	£42.00
24	British Birds	1950	£2.25	–
24	British Locomotives	1948	£1.30	£31.50
36	British Motor Cars	1950	£3.25	£117.00
44	Coronation Information	1953	£1.00	£44.00
32	Dogs, A Series	1953	£0.65	£21.00
32	Dogs (A Series, No "Weigh Daily", As 2nd)	1953	£0.90	£28.00
32	Dogs, Second Series	1953	£0.85	£27.00
24	Famous Trains Of The World A Series	1952	£1.60	£38.50
24	Famous Trains Of The World Second Series	1952	£1.80	–
37	Fortunes, 1st Series	1950	£1.00	–
32	Fortunes, 2nd Series	1953	£0.50	£16.00
32	Fortunes, 3rd Series	1954	£0.75	£24.00
24	Fresh Water Fish	1950	£1.75	£42.00
24	History Of Transport	1948	£0.30	£7.50
44	Jokes	1951	£0.40	£18.00
24	Olympic Games	1952	£5.00	–
37	Quotations	1951	£0.75	–
24	Racing & Sports Cars	1957	£3.20	£75.00
24	Space Travel	1955	£2.00	£48.00
24	Speed	1949	£0.35	£8.50
24	Sportsmen	1955	£3.00	£72.00
20	Twenty Questions	1952	£2.50	–
24	Warships Of The World	1954	£1.50	£36.00
1	Watch Your Weight	1950	–	£0.75

BRITISH GAS

Qty		Date	Odds	Sets
X20	Leeds RLFC Season 1988-89	1988	£0.20	£4.00
X20	Leeds RLFC Season 1989-90	1989	£0.20	£4.00
X20	Leeds RLFC Season 1990-91	1990	£0.20	£4.00
X20	Leeds RLFC	1991	£0.20	£4.00
X20	Leeds RLFC Season 1992-93	1992	£0.20	–

C. BRITTON PUBLISHING (Commercial)

Qty		Date	Odds	Sets
L24	Golf Courses Of The British Isles	1993	–	£7.50

BROOKE BOND & CO. LTD. (Tea)

Qty		Date	Odds	Sets
50	Adventurers & Explorers	1973	£0.20	£5.00
50	African Wild Life	1962	£0.25	£12.50
25	A Journey Downstream	1990	£0.20	£2.50
L25	A Journey Downstream (Double Cards)	1990	£0.60	£15.00
50	Asian Wild Life	1962	£0.25	£12.50
50	Bird Portraits (No Address)	1957	£2.00	£100.00
50	(With Address)	1957	£0.70	£35.00
20	British Birds	1954	£3.50	£70.00
50	British Butterflies	1963	£0.50	£25.00

BROOKE BOND & CO. LTD. (Tea) – cont.

Qty		Date	Odds	Sets
50	British Costume	1967	£0.20	£6.00
50	British Wild Life (Brooke Bond Great Britain Ltd.)	1958	£1.25	£62.50
50	(Brooke Bond Tea Ltd.)........................	1958	£0.65	£32.50
50	(Brooke Bond & Co. Ltd.)........................	1958	£1.40	£70.00
50	Butterflies Of The World	1964	£0.20	£8.50
12	Chimp Stickers	1986	£1.00	£12.00
12	Chimp Stickers (Tak Tic Backs)........................	1986	£4.50	–
M24	Creatures Of Legend	1994	£0.50	£12.00
X12	Creatures Of Legend (Double Cards)	1994	£1.00	£12.00
50	Discovering Our Coast...........................	1989	£0.20	£5.00
L25	Discovering Our Coast (Double Cards)...................	1989	£0.40	£10.00
50	Famous People.................................	1969	£0.20	£6.00
50	Features Of The World...........................	1984	£0.20	£5.00
L25	Features Of The World (Double Cards)....................	1984	£0.40	£10.00
50	Flags And Emblems Of The World....................	1967	£0.20	£6.00
X40	40 Years Of The Chimps TV Advertising	1996	£0.30	£12.00
50	Freshwater Fish	1960	£0.90	£45.00
M40	Going Wild	1994	£0.20	£6.00
X20	Going Wild (Doubles)	1994	–	£7.50
50	History Of Aviation	1972	£0.20	£6.50
50	History Of The Motor Car	1968	£0.30	£15.00
40	Incredible Creatures (Last Line Sheen Lane)......................	1985	£0.20	£8.00
40	(Last Line Walton...)........................	1986	£0.20	£8.00
40	(Last Line PO Box...)........................	1986	£0.20	£4.00
40	(Thick Cards, Stickers)........................	1987	£6.00	–
40	(Green Back, Irish)........................	1986	£3.50	£140.00
L20	Incredible Creatures (Double, Sheen)........................	1986	£1.20	£24.00
L20	(Double, Walton)........................	1986	£2.20	–
L20	(Double, PO Box)........................	1986	£0.80	£16.00
X20	International Soccer Stars	1998	£0.70	£14.00
50	Inventors & Inventions	1975	£0.20	£5.00
40	Natural Neighbours...........................	1992	£0.50	£20.00
L20	Natural Neighbours (Double Cards).....................	1992	£0.50	£10.00
40	Olympic Challenge 1992...........................	1992	£0.40	£16.00
L20	Olympic Challenge 1992 (Double Cards).....................	1992	£0.60	£12.00
40	Olympic Greats................................	1979	£0.40	£16.00
50	Out Into Space ("Issued With...")........................	1956	£7.50	£375.00
50	("Issued In...")	1958	£1.20	£60.00
40	Play Better Soccer..................................	1976	£0.20	£4.00
40	Police File	1977	£0.20	£4.00
P10	Poly Filla Modelling Cards	1974	£6.00	–
50	Prehistoric Animals	1972	£0.20	£7.50
X45	Pyramid Power (Black Back)	1998	–	£18.00
X45	(Red Back)........................	1996	£0.50	£22.50
50	Queen Elizabeth I-Queen Elizabeth II	1982	£0.20	£5.00
L25	Queen Elizabeth I-II (Double Cards).........................	1982	£1.25	–
40	Small Wonders..................................	1981	£0.20	£4.00
12	Teenage Mutant Hero Turtles	1990	£0.20	£2.00
L6	Teenage Mutant Hero Turtles (Doubles).....................	1990	£0.85	£5.00
20	The Dinosaur Trail (Postcode BB11PG)......................	1993	£0.50	£10.00
20	(Postcode BB111PG)...........................	1993	£0.20	£3.00
L10	The Dinosaur Trail (Doubles) (Postcode BB11PG)	1993	£1.00	£10.00
L10	(Postcode BB111PG)	1993	£0.40	£4.00
12	The Language Of Tea	1988	£0.20	£2.50
25	The Magical World Of Disney	1989	£0.20	£5.00

BROOKE BOND & CO. LTD. (Tea) – cont.

Qty		Date	Odds	Sets
L25	The Magical World Of Disney (Doubles)	1989	£0.60	£15.00
50	The Race Into Space	1971	£0.20	£10.00
50	The Saga Of Ships	1970	£0.20	£5.00
50	The Sea-Our Other World	1974	£0.20	£5.00
X50	The Secret Diary Of Kevin Tipps	1995	£0.20	£10.00
X30	The Wonderful World Of Kevin Tipps	1997	£0.60	–
50	Transport Through The Ages	1966	£0.20	£6.00
50	Trees In Britain	1966	£0.20	£6.00
50	Tropical Birds	1961	£0.20	£8.00
40	Unexplained Mysteries Of The World	1987	£0.20	£4.00
L20	Unexplained Mysteries Of The World (Double Cards)	1988	£0.40	£8.00
40	Vanishing Wildlife	1978	£0.20	£4.00
50	Wild Birds In Britain	1965	£0.20	£5.00
50	Wild Flowers A Series	1955	£1.70	£85.00
50	Wild Flowers Series 2 ('Issued By')	1959	£0.25	£12.50
50	(No Issued By)	1959	£1.75	£87.50
50	Wild Flowers Series 3	1964	£0.20	£6.00
50	Wildlife In Danger	1963	£0.20	£5.00
50	Wonders Of Wildlife	1976	£0.20	£5.00
40	Woodland Wildlife	1980	£0.20	£4.00
X50	Zena Skinner International Cookery	1974	£12.50	–

BLACK BACK REPRINTS

Qty		Date	Odds	Sets
50	African Wild Life	1973	–	£5.00
50	British Butterflies	1973	–	£5.00
50	British Costume	1973	–	£5.00
50	Discovering Our Coast	1994	–	£7.50
50	Famous People	1973	–	£5.00
50	Flags And Emblems Of The World	1973	–	£15.00
50	Freshwater Fish	1973	–	£20.00
50	History Of The Motor Car	1974	–	£10.00
40	Olympic Greats	1988	–	£12.00
50	Queen Elizabeth I-Queen Elizabeth II	1987	–	£12.50
40	Small Wonders	1988	–	£4.00
50	The Race Into Space	1974	–	£5.00
50	The Saga Of Ships	1973	–	£5.00
50	Transport Through The Ages	1973	–	£15.00
50	Trees In Britain	1973	–	£5.00
50	Tropical Birds	1974	–	£5.00
40	Vanishing Wildlife	1988	–	£6.00
50	Wild Birds In Britain	1973	–	£5.00
50	Wild Flowers Series 2	1973	–	£5.00
50	Wildlife In Danger	1973	–	£5.00
40	Woodland Wildlife	1988	–	£7.50

CARD GAMES BASED ON REGULAR SERIES

Qty		Date	Odds	Sets
L36	British Costume Snap Game	1974	–	£25.00
L36	Flags & Emblems Snap Game	1974	–	£25.00
L36	Motor History Snap Game	1974	–	£25.00

CANADIAN ISSUES

Qty		Date	Odds	Sets
48	African Animals	1964	£0.20	£6.50
48	Animals And Their Young ('Products')	1972	£0.20	£10.00
48	(Tea/Coffee)	1972	£7.50	–

BROOKE BOND & CO. LTD. (Tea) – cont.

Qty		Date	Odds	Sets
48	Animals Of North America			
	('Roland' Back) (2 Printings)............................	1960	£3.00	—
	('Rolland' Back)............................	1962	£2.50	£120.00
48	Birds Of North America............................	1965	£1.25	£60.00
48	Butterflies Of North America............................	1966	£1.00	£48.00
48	Canadian/American Songbirds............................	1963	£2.50	£120.00
48	Dinosaurs............................	1971	£2.75	£132.00
48	Exploring The Ocean............................	1974	—	£6.00
48	Indians Of Canada............................	1970	£1.25	£60.00
48	North American Wildlife In Danger............................	1959	—	£7.00
48	Songbirds Of North America (Red Rose/Blue Ribbon).......	1959	£1.25	£60.00
48	Songbirds Of North America (Red Rose Only,			
	'Albums Available')............................	1959	£3.50	£168.00
48	The Arctic............................	1973	£0.30	£15.00
48	The Space Age............................	1969	£0.50	£24.00
48	Transportation Through The Ages (Top Line Black)..........	1967	£0.50	£24.00
48	(Top Line Red).............	1967	£6.00	—
48	Trees Of North America............................	1968	£0.50	£24.00
48	Tropical Birds (Top Line Black)............................	1964	£0.75	£36.00
48	(Top Line Red)............................	1964	£6.00	—
48	Wild Flowers Of North America............................	1961	£0.70	£35.00

RHODESIAN ISSUES

Qty		Date	Odds	Sets
50	African Birds............................	1965	£5.00	£250.00
50	African Wild Life............................	1963	£6.00	—
50	Asian Wild Life............................	1963	£6.00	—
50	Butterflies Of The World............................	1966	£5.00	—
50	Tropical Birds............................	1962	£4.00	£200.00
50	Wildlife In Danger............................	1964	£5.00	—

SOUTH AFRICAN ISSUES

Qty		Date	Odds	Sets
50	Our Pets............................	1967	£6.00	—
50	Out Into Space............................	1966	£5.00	£250.00
50	Wild Van Afrika (Bilingual)............................	1965	£6.00	—
50	(One Language)............................	1965	£9.00	—

U.S.A. ISSUES

Qty		Date	Odds	Sets
48	Animals Of North America (Black Back)............................	1960	£12.00	—
48	(Blue Back)............................	1960	£9.00	£450.00
48	Birds Of North America............................	1962	£7.00	—
48	Butterflies Of North America............................	1964	£4.00	£200.00
48	Canadian/American Songbirds............................	1966	£2.75	£132.00
48	Dinosaurs............................	1963	£9.00	—
48	Tropical Birds............................	1964	£4.00	£200.00
48	Wild Flowers Of North America (Dark Blue)............................	1961	£4.00	£200.00
48	(Light Blue)............................	1961	£20.00	—

BROOK MOTORS

Qty		Date	Odds	Sets
G12	Motor Cycles (Cut From Calendars)............................	1975	—	£8.00
P12	Steam Engines............................	1961	—	£36.00
P12	Steam Engines (Different)............................	1973	—	£18.00
P12	The Traction Engine............................	1967	—	£33.00
P12	Veteran Cars............................	1961	—	£25.00

BROOKFIELD SWEETS (Ireland)

Qty		Date	Odds	Sets
50	Animals Of The World	1956	£3.75	—
25	Aquarium Fish 1st Series	1957	£4.00	—
25	Aquarium Fish 2nd Series	1957	£4.00	—
25	Motor Cars	1954	£4.50	—
50	The Conquest Of Space	1956	£4.00	—

BROOKS DYE WORKS LTD.

P4	Interesting Shots Of Old Bristol	1950	—	£4.00

DAVID BROWN (Tractors)

XF3	Is Your Slip Showing?	1954	£3.00	£9.00

BROWN & POLSON (Custard)

X25	Recipe Cards	1925	£4.00	—

BROWNE BROS. LTD. (Tea)

25	Birds	1964	£1.50	£37.50
25	British Cavalry Uniforms Of The 19th Century	1964	£0.65	—
25	Garden Flowers	1965	£2.00	—
25	History Of The Railways 1st Series	1964	—	£12.50
25	History Of The Railways 2nd Series	1964	—	£12.50
25	Passenger Liners	1966	£2.00	—
25	People & Places	1965	—	£2.50
24	The Island Of Ceylon	1955	£4.00	—
25	Tropical Birds	1966	—	£3.00
25	Wonders Of The Deep	1965	—	£3.00
25	Wonders Of The World	1970	—	£5.00

BRYANT & MAY LTD. (Matches)

50	Kings & Queens (Player Reprint)	1991	—	£12.50
50	Life In The Hedgerow (Wills Reprint)	1991	—	£12.50
L12	The Thirties	1992	—	£12.00

BUCHANAN'S (Jam)

24	Birds And Their Eggs	1924	£8.50	£204.00

JOHNNY BUNNY (Medicines)

25	Football Clubs And Badges	1958	£3.00	£75.00

BUNSEN CONFECTIONERY CO.

?199	Famous Figures Series	1925	£17.50	—

BURDALL & BURDALL (Gravy Salt)

30	Wild Animals	1924	£7.00	—

BURTON'S WAGON WHEELS (Biscuits)

25	Indian Chiefs	1972	£0.60	£15.00
L7	Pictures Of The Wild West	1983	£7.00	£49.00
25	The West	1972	—	£4.00
25	Wild West Action	1972	—	£5.00

179

BUTTAPAT DAIRIES

Qty		Date	Odds	Sets
25	People Of The World	1915	£20.00	—

BUTTERCUP BREAD CO (Australia)

L24	Alan Border Tribute..	1994		
L24	Border's Ashes Heroes..	1993	—	£10.00
L24	1993-94 World Series All Stars............................	1993	—	£10.00

C. & G. CONFECTIONERY CO.

25	Box Of Tricks 1st Series	1965	£4.50	—
25	Box Of Tricks 2nd Series	1965	£4.50	—

CBS IRONMONGERY LTD.

30	Glamorgan Cricketers...	1984	—	£15.00

CMK PUBLICATIONS INC. (U.S.A.)

X26	Cars Of The World	1992	—	£4.00

CADBURY BROS. LTD. (Chocolate)

12	Age Of The Dinosaur..	1971	£1.25	£15.00
T12	Antarctic Series..	1913	£30.00	—
X6	Bay City Rollers..	1975	£1.50	—
L12	Birds In Springtime	1983	—	£3.00
6	Bournville Series B..	1906	£20.00	£120.00
P3	Bournville Views (Script At Side)...........................	1906	£3.50	£10.50
P6	Bournville Views (Block At Side)	1906	£3.50	£21.00
P6	Bournville Views (White Borders)..........................	1906	£3.50	£21.00
P8	Bournville Views (Gravure)...................................	1906	£4.00	—
6	Bournville Village Series.......................................	1906	£20.00	—
P25	British Birds (Reward Cards)	1910	£9.00	—
12	British Birds & Eggs...	1910	£12.00	—
P12	British Birds & Their Eggs (Reward Cards)	1910	£11.00	—
P32	British Butterflies & Moths (Reward Cards)	1910	£6.00	£192.00
6	British Colonies, Maps & Industries......................	1908	£20.00	£120.00
120	British Marvels	1932	£1.50	—
120	British Marvels Album No. 2	1933	£1.60	—
12	British Trees Series (2 Printings)..........................	1911	£6.50	£78.00
80	Cadbury's Picture Making	1936	£1.40	—
12	Cathedral Series...	1913	£7.50	£90.00
6	Colonial Premiers Series.......................................	1908	£20.00	£120.00
12	Constellations Series	1912	£8.00	£95.00
24	Copyright (Inventors) Series	1914	£13.50	—
1	Coronation	1911	—	£30.00
48	Dangerous Animals...	1970	£0.75	£36.00
6	Dog Series	1908	£37.50	—
P12	English Industries...	1908	£35.00	—
25	Fairy Tales..	1924	£3.60	£90.00
27	Famous Steamships	1923	£3.50	£95.00
12	Fish	1910	£12.50	—
P6	Fish & Bait Series...	1909	£35.00	—
12	Flag Series	1912	£3.75	£45.00
P6	Flag Series (Joined Pairs)	1912	£7.00	£42.00
P12	Flag Series (Different)...	1910	£27.50	—
X12	Flight (Birds)...	1982	£0.50	£6.00

CADBURY BROS. LTD. (Chocolate) – cont.

Qty		Date	Odds	Sets
32	Happy Families	1950	£3.50	—
?X5	Knotty Problems	1910	£27.50	—
1	Largest Steamers In The World	1912	—	£100.00
6	Locomotive Series	1906	£32.50	—
12	Match Puzzles	1906	£35.00	—
6	Old Ballad Series	1906	£22.50	—
X6	Panama Series	1910	£30.00	—
X5	Pop Stars	1975	£1.00	£5.00
1	Poster Series	1910	—	£35.00
X8	Prehistoric Monsters	1975	—	£6.00
P1	Puzzle Card	1910	—	£20.00
P6	Rivers Of British Isles (Reward Cards)	1910	£16.00	£96.00
24	Shadow Series	1914	£15.00	—
6	Shipping Series (4 Sizes)	1910	£12.00	—
T6	Sports Series	1906	£50.00	—
24	Strange But True	1970	—	£2.50
G1	The Magic Bournville Cocoa Tins	1910	—	£20.00
25	Transport	1925	£0.90	£22.50
L6	Wildlife Stickers	1986	—	£3.00

CADET SWEETS

Qty		Date	Odds	Sets
25	Arms And Armour	1961	—	£2.50
50	Buccaneers	1957	—	£15.00
50	Buccaneers (Different)	1959	—	£15.00
25	Daktari	1969	—	£10.00
50	Doctor Who And The Daleks	1965	£3.50	—
25	Dogs 1st Series	1958	—	£22.50
25	Dogs 2nd Series	1958	—	£22.50
25	Evolution Of The Royal Navy	1959	—	£3.50
M22	Famous Explorers (Packets)	1960	£8.00	—
50	Fifty Years Of Flying	1953	£0.80	£40.00
50	Footballers	1956	—	£21.00
50	Footballers (Different) Large Wording	1959	—	£26.50
50	Small Wording	1959	—	£25.00
25	How?	1969	—	£10.00
50	Motor Cars	1954	£1.75	—
25	Prehistoric Animals	1961	—	£20.00
50	Railways Of The World (Cadet)	1956	—	£8.00
50	(Paramount Laboratories)	1956	£0.80	£40.00
50	(Paramount Sweets)	1956	£0.50	£25.00
50	Record Holders Of The World	1956	—	£15.00
50	Stingray	1965	—	£30.00
48	The Adventures Of Rin Tin Tin	1960	£0.80	£40.00
50	The Conquest Of Space	1957	—	£8.50
25	Treasure Hunt	1964	—	£2.50
50	U.N.C.L.E. (Line Drawings)	1966	£2.20	£110.00
50	U.N.C.L.E. (Photos)	1966	£1.30	£65.00
25	What Do You Know?	1965	—	£12.50

A.J. CALEY & SON (Confectionery)

Qty		Date	Odds	Sets
K24	Film Stars	1930	£8.00	£192.00
10	Passenger Liners	1939	£12.00	—
48	Wisequacks (Mickey Mouse Weekly)	1939	£10.00	—

CALTEX OIL (Australia)

Qty		Date	Odds	Sets
P6	Stargazer (Haley's Comet)	1986	—	£1.50

F. C. CALVERT & CO. LTD. (Toothpaste)

25	Dan Dare Series	1954	£6.50	—

CANDY GUM (Italy)

50	Autosprint I Serie (Printed Back)	1975	—	£6.00
50	(Plain Back)	1975	—	£7.50
30	Autosprint II Serie (Printed Back)	1975	—	£6.00
30	(Plain Back)	1975	—	£7.50

CANDY NOVELTY CO.

25	Animals Of The Countryside	1964	£5.00	—
50	Animals Of The World	1964	£4.00	—
M25/50	Dog Series - A1 Set	1953	—	£4.00
32	Motor Car Series	1953	£6.00	—
25	Ships Through The Ages 2nd Series	1957	£5.50	—
32	Western Series	1953	£6.50	—

CANNINGS (Jam)

25	Types Of British Soldiers	1914	£15.00	—

F. CAPERN (Bird Seed)

12	Cage Birds	1924	£12.50	—
P54	Cage Birds	1926	£4.50	—
24	Picture Aviary	1964	—	£20.00
1	Picture Aviary Introductory Card	1964	—	£0.25

CAPEZIO (BALLET SHOES, U.S.A.)

XF12	Famous Dancers Gallery	1950	—	£36.00

CARD COLLECTORS SOCIETY (Reprints)

25	A.B.C. Of Sport (Ogdens)	2002	—	£6.50
50	A Gallery Of 1935 (Mitchell)	1999	—	£10.00
50	Air-Raid Precautions (Ogdens)	1999	—	£10.00
50	Allied Army Leaders (Wills)	2000	—	£10.00
50	Animals Of The Countryside (Player)	1999	—	£10.00
50	Arms Of Companies (Wills)	1999	—	£10.00
50	Boxers (Ogdens)	2001	—	£10.00
50	Boy Scout And Girl Guide (Player)	2001	—	£10.00
50	British Birds (Ogdens)	2000	—	£10.00
50	British Empire Series (Player)	1999	—	£10.00
50	Builders Of The Empire (Wills)	1999	—	£10.00
50	Butterflies & Moths (Player)	2000	—	£10.00
50	By The Roadside (Ogdens)	2000	—	£10.00
50	Celebrated Gateways (Player)	2001	—	£10.00
50	Champions Of 1936 (Ogdens)	2000	—	£10.00
50	Cities Of The World (Player)	1999	—	£10.00
50	Colour In Nature (Ogdens)	2001	—	£10.00
25	Common Fallacies (Lambert & Butler)	2001	—	£6.50
50	Construction Of Railway Trains (Ogdens)	1999	—	£10.00
25	Coronation Series, 1911 (Salmon & Gluckstein)	2000	—	£6.50
50	Countries Arms And Flags (Player)	2001	—	£10.00

CARD COLLECTORS SOCIETY (Reprints) – cont.

Qty		Date	Odds	Sets
50	Cricketers (Churchman)	1999	–	£10.00
50	Cricketers 1938 (Player)	2000	–	£10.00
50	Dogs (Wills)	2001	–	£10.00
50	Dogs By Wardle (Full Length) (Player)	2002	–	£10.00
50	Dogs (Scenic Background) (Player)	1997	–	£10.00
50	Double Meaning (Wills)	1999	–	£10.00
50	Do You Know, 2nd Series (Wills)	1998	–	£10.00
25	Eastern Proverbs, A Series (Churchman)	2001	–	£6.50
25	Egyptian Kings & Queens And Classical Deities (Player)	2001	–	£6.50
50	Empire Air Routes (Lambert & Butler)	2000	–	£10.00
50	Engineering Wonders (Wills)	1999	–	£10.00
50	Famous Irish-Bred Horses (Player)	2001	–	£10.00
50	Famous Scots (Mitchell)	1999	–	£10.00
50	Film Stars (Player)	2000	–	£10.00
50	Film Stars, 2nd Series (Player)	2001	–	£10.00
50	First Aid (Mitchell)	2001	–	£10.00
50	First Aid (Wills)	1999	–	£10.00
50	Flower Culture In Pots (Wills)	2000	–	£10.00
50	Football Caricatures (Ogdens)	2002	–	£10.00
50	Foreign Birds (Ogdens)	2001	–	£10.00
50	Fowls, Pigeons & Dogs (Smith)	2000	–	£10.00
50	Game Birds And Wild Fowl (Player)	1999	–	£10.00
50	Gardening Hints (Wills)	2003	–	£10.00
50	Gems Of Belgian Architecture (Wills)	2001	–	£10.00
50	Gems Of French Architecture (Wills)	2003	–	£10.00
25	Greetings Of The World (Hignett)	2000	–	£6.50
50	History Of Naval Dress (Player)	2001	–	£10.00
25	Holiday Resorts (Smith)	2000	–	£6.50
50	Household Hints (1927) (Wills)	1999	–	£10.00
50	Humorous Drawings (Mitchell)	1999	–	£10.00
50	Interesting Buildings (Hignett)	2001	–	£10.00
25	Interesting Door-Knockers (Churchman)	2000	–	£6.50
50	Interesting Sidelights On The Work Of The G.P.O. (Lambert & Butler)	1999	–	£10.00
50	International Air Liners (Player)	2001	–	£10.00
50	In Town To-Night (Churchman)	1999	–	£10.00
50	Irish Industries (Wills)	2001	–	£10.00
50	Life In The Royal Navy (Wills)	1999	–	£10.00
50	Medals (Wills)	2002	–	£10.00
50	Military Head-Dress (Player)	1999	–	£10.00
50	Modern British Pottery (Ogdens)	1999	–	£10.00
25	Money (Mitchell)	2000	–	£6.50
50	Motor Cars, 2nd Series (Player)	2000	–	£10.00
50	Motor Cars, 3rd Series (Lambert & Butler)	2001	–	£10.00
50	Nature Series (Player)	2000	–	£10.00
25	Optical Illusions (Faulkner)	2000	–	£6.50
50	Overseas Dominions (Australia) (Wills)	2003	–	£10.00
50	Overseas Dominions (Canada) (Wills)	2002	–	£10.00
50	Phil May Sketches (Churchman)	2002	–	£10.00
25	Pipes Of The World (Churchman)	2000	–	£6.50
25	Pirates & Highwaymen (Lambert & Butler)	2001	–	£6.50
25	Players Past & Present (Player)	2002	–	£6.50
25	Prehistoric Animals (Edwards, Ringer & Bigg)	2000	–	£6.50
50	Products Of The World (Player)	1999	–	£10.00
50	Prominent Racehorses Of 1933 (Hignett)	2000	–	£10.00

CARD COLLECTORS SOCIETY (Reprints) – cont.

Qty		Date	Odds	Sets
50	Safety First (Wills)	2000	–	£10.00
50	School Arms (Wills)	2000	–	£10.00
50	Scotland's Story (Mitchell)	2000	–	£10.00
50	Sea Fishes (Player)	2002	–	£10.00
50	Shakespeare Series (Numbered) (Ogdens)	2000	–	£10.00
50	Ships' Badges (Wills)	2000	–	£10.00
50	Smugglers And Smuggling (Ogdens)	1999	–	£10.00
50	Speed (1930) (Wills)	2001	–	£10.00
50	Speedway Riders (Player)	2000	–	£10.00
25	Sports & Games In Many Lands (Edwards, Ringer & Bigg)	2001	–	£6.50
50	Strange Craft (Wills)	2001	–	£10.00
50	Swimming, Diving And Life-Saving (Ogdens)	2000	–	£10.00
50	Tennis (Player)	1999	–	£10.00
25	The Inns Of Court (Churchman)	2002	–	£6.50
50	The King's Coronation (Churchman)	2001	–	£10.00
50	The Story Of Navigation (Churchman)	1999	–	£10.00
50	The Story Of Sand (Ogdens)	2001	–	£10.00
50	Trick Billiards (Ogdens)	2001	–	£10.00
50	Vanity Fair, 2nd Series (Wills)	2002	–	£10.00
25	Warriors Of All Nations (Churchman)	2001	–	£6.50
50	Warships (Wills)	2002	–	£20.00
50	Wild Flowers (1923) (Wills)	1999	–	£10.00
50	Wonders Of The Deep (Player)	2001	–	£10.00
50	Wonders Of The Sea (Wills)	2000	–	£10.00

CARD INSERT LTD.

Qty		Date	Odds	Sets
1	Famous Footballers (J. Logie)	1953	–	£7.50

CARDLYNX (Commercial)

Qty		Date	Odds	Sets
L6	Butterflies	2007	–	£3.00
L6	Eagles	2007	–	£3.00
L6	Gangsters	2004	–	£3.00
L6	Golfers	2006	–	£3.00
L6	Horses	2007	–	£3.00
L6	Jazz Greats	2004	–	£3.00
L6	Lighthouses	2008	–	£3.00
L6	Owls	2004	–	£3.00
L6	Parrots	2004	–	£3.00
L6	Poultry Breeds	2007	–	£3.00
L6	Poultry	2004	–	£3.00
L6	Sea Shells	2008	–	£3.00
L6	Space Firsts	2004	–	£3.00
L6	Victorian Poultry	2007	–	£3.00

CARD PROMOTIONS (Commercial)

Qty		Date	Odds	Sets
50	Aeroplanes (B.A.T. Reprint)	2000	–	£8.50
48	Army Badges (Gallaher Reprint)	2001	–	£8.50
25	Battleships & Crests (Hill Reprint)	1995	–	£6.25
50	British Sea Dogs (John Sinclair Reprint)	1997	–	£8.50
50	British Warriors (Cope Reprint)	1996	–	£8.50
25	Conan Doyle Characters (Boguslavsky Reprint)	1996	–	£6.25
75	Cricketers Series (Pattrieouex Reprint)	1997	–	£13.50
25	Days Of Nelson (Fry Reprint)	2003	–	£6.25
25	Days Of Wellington (Fry Reprint)	2003	–	£6.25

THE SIX-EIGHT
THE SIDE STEP 5TH STEP

BOOT & SHOE
MANUFACTURE. 1837 & 1937

RUDOLPH VALENTINO

JESSE OWENS

main problem regarding the
e of cigarette cards lies in the
to strike a balance between being
o maintain them in as good
on as possible and yet being able
nine them. If the reader is simply
stor there is no problem—he can
ach set carefully in paper, put it
ox, and thence into a bank vault.
only way to enjoy cigarette cards
k at them. The modern method
use cards in transparent pages,
an accommodate most sizes of
nd can be stored in loose leaf
The entire card may be viewed,
ck and front, yet will not
te through sticky fingers or spilt
Care should be taken to use a
de from a suitable material—
e on the market now many
y cheap pages which contain
unts of plasticiser, a substance
uld adversely affect certain
d details of our own Nostalgia
on albums are given on pages
7 of this book.
method of storage which is
nore popular is to mount cards
which can then be hung on
wall. Several framing systems
ailable which hold the cards

"THERE WAS AN OLD WOMAN WHO LIVED IN A SHOE"

GERMAN INFANTRY IN BRUSSELS

IMPERIAL TOBACCO COMPANY

This huge Company was founded on 2nd November 1901 in order to combat the spreading influence in Britain of the American Tobacco Co. The founder members were headed by Wills, and included such well known card issuers as Player, Smith, Hignett and Lambert & Butler. During the next few years they were to acquire a number of other well known companies such as Churchman and Faulkner. However their most important acquisitions were probably those of Ogden at the conclusion of the Tobacco war, and Mardon Son & Hall, the printers who became responsible for the production of most of their cigarette cards.

The formation date is most important to cartophilists, because from that time onward the card issues of the constituent firms bore the message "Branch of the Imperial Tobacco Co. (of Great Britain and Northern Ireland) Ltd." in addition to the individual firm's name. Because, for example, there are two printings of Wills Locomotives and Faulkner Our Gallant Grenadiers, one with and one without the "I.T.C. clause" as it is popularly known, it is safe to say that each of these was issued around 1901-2; or that Vanity Fair came a little earlier and Borough Arms a little later.

Cards issued abroad (including the Channel Islands) which mentioned the I.T.C. member's names did NOT include the I.T.C. clause, since they were always issued by the British Americ Tobacco Co. which was partly owned I.T.C.

A cartophilic consequence of t formation of the I.T.C. was the pract of issuing identical card series unc several of the firm's, or indeed B.A.T. Hence Garden Life was issued Edwards Ringer & Bigg, Lambert Butler and Wills; Angling by Faulkn Mitchell and B.A.T.; Boy Scouts Churchman, Ogden and I.T.C. (Canad It is always likely that series issued I.T.C. firms with the same series ti will be the same basic set, such as Raid Precautions by Churchma Hignett, Mitchell, Ogden and Wills.

CARD PROMOTIONS (Commercial) – cont.

Qty		Date	Odds	Sets
32	Drum Horses (B.A.T. Reprint)	2000	–	£6.25
50	Famous Airmen & Airwomen (Carreras Reprint)	1996	–	£8.50
25	Famous Jockeys (Taddy Reprint)	1996	–	£6.25
25	Famous Running Horses (Engish)(Kinney Reprint)	1996	–	£6.25
50	Flowers To Grow (Lea Reprint)	1997	–	£8.50
75	Footballers (Carreras Reprint)	1997	–	£13.50
60	Football Captains 1907-8 (Cohen Weenen Reprint)	1998	–	£10.00
30	Generals Of The American Civil War (Duke Reprint)	1995	–	£6.25
40	Home & Colonial Regiments (Cohen Weenen Reprint)	1998	–	£8.50
50	Indian Regiment Series (B.A.T. Reprint)	2000	–	£8.50
50	Lawn Tennis Celebrities (Gallaher Reprint)	1997	–	£8.50
25	Military Uniforms, C (American Tobacco Co. Reprint)	2003	–	£6.25
25/24	Motor Cars (Gallaher Reprint)	1995	–	£6.25
24	Past & Present - The Army (Teofani Reprint)	2001	–	£6.25
24	Past & Present - Weapons Of War (Teofani Reprint)	2001	–	£6.25
50	Pirates Of The Spanish Main (Allen &Ginter Reprint)	1996	–	£8.50
48	Poultry (C.W.S. Reprint)	1996	–	£8.50
25	Railway Engines (G.Phillips Reprint)	1997	–	£6.25
50	Regimental Colours & Standards (Gallaher Reprint)	1995	–	£8.50
30	Regimental Nicknames (Hustler Reprint)	1997	–	£6.25
33	Regimental Pets (B.A.T. Reprint)	1998	–	£6.25
25	Royalty Series (Taddy Reprint)	1998	–	£6.25
50	Signed Portraits of Famous Stars(Gallaher Reprint)	1997	–	£8.50
50	Star Artistes (Cohen Weenen Reprint)	1998	–	£8.50
25	Territorial Regiments (Taddy Reprint)	1995	–	£6.25
25	Territorial Series (Godfrey Phillips Reprint)	2000	–	£6.25
25	Thames Series (Taddy Reprint)	1996	–	£6.25
50	The Great War Series (1-50) (Gallaher Reprint)	2001	–	£8.50
50	The Great War Series (51-100) (Gallaher Reprint)	2003	–	£8.50
25	The Great War V.C. Heroes, 1st Series (Gallaher Reprint)	2001	–	£6.25
25	The Great War V.C. Heroes, 2nd Series (Gallaher Reprint)	2001	–	£6.25
25	The Great War V.C. Heroes, 3rd Series (Gallaher Reprint)	2001	–	£6.25
25	The Great War V.C. Heroes, 4th Series (Gallaher Reprint)	2001	–	£6.25
25	The Great War V.C. Heroes, 5th Series (Gallaher Reprint)	2003	–	£6.25
25	The Great War V.C. Heroes, 7th Series (Gallaher Reprint)	2003	–	£6.25
25	The Great War V.C. Heroes, 8th Series (Gallaher Reprint)	2003	–	£6.25
50	The South African Series (101-150) (Gallaher Reprint)	2000	–	£8.50
50	The South African Series (151-200) (Gallaher Reprint)	2000	–	£8.50
25	Types Of British Soldiers (G.Phillips Reprint)	1997	–	£6.25
50	Types Of The British Army (Gallaher Reprint)	1995	–	£8.50
50	Types Of The British Army 51-100 (Gallaher Reprint)	1996	–	£8.50
20	Types Of The British Army (Hill Reprint)	2000	–	£6.25
25	Types Of Volunteer & Yeomanry (Woods Reprint)	1996	–	£6.25
25	Uniforms (Cope Reprint)	1996	–	£6.25
50	Victoria Cross Heroes (Cohen Weenen Reprint)	1998	–	£8.50
20	Victoria Cross Heroes (1-20) (Taddy Reprint)	1996	–	£6.25
20	Victoria Cross Heroes (21-40) (Taddy Reprint)	1996	–	£6.25
20	Victoria Cross Heroes (41-60) (Taddy Reprint)	1997	–	£6.25
20	Victoria Cross Heroes (61-80) (Taddy Reprint)	1997	–	£6.25
20	Victoria Cross Heroes (81-100) (Taddy Reprint)	1997	–	£6.25
25	Victoria Cross Heroes (101-125) (Taddy Reprint)	1996	–	£6.25
15	War Series K (Murray Reprint) (Leaders)	1999	–	£5.00
20	War Series K (Murray Reprint) (Uniforms)	1999	–	£6.00
25	Winners On The Turf (Boguslavsky Reprint)	1995	–	£6.25

CARDS TO COLLECT (Commercial)

Qty		Date	Odds	Sets
50	Deep Sea Diving	1996	—	£12.50

CARDTOON CREATIONS

| M25 | Championship Champions 2005-2006 (Reading F. C.) | 2006 | — | £8.00 |

CARR'S BISCUITS

| M30 | Animals Of The World | 1930 | £8.50 | — |
| G20 | Cricketers | 1967 | £7.00 | £140.00 |

CARSON'S CHOCOLATE

| 72 | Celebrities | 1902 | £16.50 | — |

CARTER'S LITTLE LIVER PILLS

| 28 | Dominoes | 1911 | £1.25 | £35.00 |

F. C. CARTLEDGE (Razor Blades)

X48	Epigrams "A"	1939	£0.25	£12.00
X64	Epigrams "B"	1939	£0.25	£16.00
X96	Epigrams "C"	1941	£0.25	£24.00
50	Famous Prize Fighters	1938	£3.70	£210.00

CARTOPHILIC SOCIETY

| 16 | London Branch Personalities | 1980 | — | £5.00 |
| 20 | London Branch Personalities, 2nd Series | 1995 | — | £4.00 |

CASH & CO. (Shoes)

| 20 | War Series | 1916 | £16.00 | — |

CASSELLS (Periodical)

| M6 | British Engines | 1923 | £11.00 | — |
| M12 | Butterflies & Moths Series | 1923 | £6.50 | £78.00 |

CASTROL OIL

| X18 | Famous Riders | 1956 | £5.00 | £90.00 |
| X24 | Racing Cars | 1955 | £4.00 | £96.00 |

CAVE AUSTIN & CO. LTD. (Tea)

| 20 | Inventors Series | 1923 | £11.00 | — |

CCC LTD.

L15	Arsenal Cup Winners 1992-1993	1993	—	£6.00
L20	Doctor Who	1993	—	£12.50
L1	Promotional Card	1993	—	£0.50
L6	Wild Cats	1994	—	£3.00

CECIL COURT COLLECTORS CENTRE

L25	Ashes Winning Captains	1993	—	£8.50
L20	Christopher Columbus	1992	—	£6.50
L1	Promotional Card	1992	—	£0.50
L12	Class Of '66 (Soccer)	2002	—	£7.50
L20	Famous Film Directors	1992	—	£6.50
L1	Promotional Card (Hitchcock)	1992	—	£0.50

CEDE LTD.

Qty		Date	Odds	Sets
25	Coins Of The World	1956	—	£4.00

CENTRAL ELECTRICITY AUTHORITY

M10	Interesting Careers	1961	—	£2.00

CEREBOS (Salt)

100	Sea Shells	1925	£2.50	£250.00

CEYLON TEA CENTRE

24	The Island Of Ceylon	1955	—	£2.00

CHANNEL 4/CHEERLEADER PRODUCTIONS (TV)

L20	All Time Great Quarterbacks	1989	—	£35.00

H. CHAPPEL & CO. (Confectionery)

10	British Celebrities..	1905	£32.50	—

CHARTER TEA & COFFEE CO. LTD.

25	Prehistoric Animals, First Series	1962	—	£25.00
25	Prehistoric Animals, Second Series....................................	1962	—	£25.00
25	Strange But True, First Series..	1961	£1.00	£25.00
25	Strange But True, Second Series..	1961	—	£15.00
25	Transport Through The Ages, First Series...........................	1961	£1.00	£25.00
25	Transport Through The Ages, Second Series......................	1961	£0.70	£17.50

CHEF & BREWER

L20	Historic Pub Signs	1984	—	£10.00

CHIVERS & SONS LTD. (Preserves)

L125	Firm Favourites	1932	£2.00	—
K53	Miniature Playing Cards..	1965	£1.40	—
P6	Studies Of English Fruits Series 1	1924	£6.50	£39.00
P6	Studies Of English Fruits Series 2	1924	£6.50	£39.00
24	Wild Wisdom...	1964	£3.25	£78.00
48	Wild Wisdom In Africa..	1964	£3.25	£156.00
48	Wild Wisdom, River And Marsh	1964	£3.25	£156.00

PACKAGE ISSUES

L15	Children Of Other Lands..	1952	£0.90	£13.50
L15	Chivers British Birds	1951	£1.20	£18.00
L20	On Chivers Farms	1951	£0.85	£17.00

CHIX CONFECTIONERY CO. LTD.

M12	Batman (Packets)..	1990	—	£6.00
X50	Famous Footballers	1960	£7.00	—
X48	Famous Footballers No.1 Series	1953	£4.75	£228.00
X48	Famous Footballers No.2 Series	1956	£5.75	£276.00
X48	Famous Footballers No.3 Series	1958	£6.75	£324.00
X50	Famous Last Words..	1970	£1.50	—
X24	Footballers (Portrait & Action) 1-24	1960	—	£30.00
X24	Footballers (Portrait & Action) 25-48	1960	—	£60.00
L50	Funny Old Folk...	1970	—	£12.50

CHIX CONFECTIONERY CO. LTD. – cont.

Qty		Date	Odds	Sets
L50	Happy Howlers	1970	£0.80	£40.00
L50	Krazy Kreatures From Outer Space	1970	£1.80	£90.00
T36	Looney Tunes (Packets)	1990	–	£8.50
L6	Looney Tunes (Packets)	1990	–	£2.50
L50	Military Uniforms	1970	–	£20.00
L50	Moon Shot	1966	£2.40	£120.00
X50	Popeye	1960	£3.20	£160.00
X24	Scottish Footballers	1960	£8.50	£200.00
X50	Ships Of The Seven Seas	1968	£1.70	£85.00
X50	Soldiers Of The World	1962	£1.25	£62.50
X50	Sport Through The Ages	1968	£3.40	£170.00
L6	The Joker (Batman Packets)	1989	–	£8.00
P52	The Real Ghostbusters (Package Slides)	1990	–	£25.00
96	T.V. And Radio Stars	1954	£4.00	–
X50	Wild Animals	1960	£1.50	£75.00

CHUMS (Periodical)

Qty		Date	Odds	Sets
MF23	Cricketers	1923	£5.50	£125.00
MF20	Football Teams	1922	£4.50	£90.00
F8	Football Teams New Series	1923	£4.50	£36.00
X10	Real Colour Photos (Footballers)	1922	£8.00	£80.00

CHURCH & DWIGHT (Baking Soda, U.S.A.)

Qty		Date	Odds	Sets
M60	Beautiful Birds, New Series	1896	£4.00	£240.00
60	Beautiful Birds, New Series (Miniature)	1896	£5.00	–
60	Beautiful Birds, New Series (Standard)	1896	£6.00	–
M60	Beautiful Birds Of America	1894	£5.50	£330.00
60	Beautiful Birds Of America	1894	£6.50	–
M60	Beautiful Flowers	1895	£3.50	£210.00
60	Beautiful Flowers	1895	£4.50	–
X10	Birds Of Prey	1976	–	£25.00
M30	Champion Dog Series	1902	£10.00	–
30	Champion Dog Series	1902	£10.00	–
M30	Dairy Animals	1895	£10.00	£300.00
30	Dairy Animals	1895	£10.00	–
M30	Fish Series	1900	£3.75	£112.50
30	Fish Series	1900	£5.00	–
M30	Game Bird Series	1904	£4.00	£120.00
30	Game Bird Series	1904	£5.00	–
M60	Interesting Animals	1897	£4.50	£270.00
60	Interesting Animals (Miniature)	1897	£6.00	–
60	Interesting Animals (Standard)	1897	£7.00	–
M30	Interesting Animals (Re-Issue)	1915	£6.00	–
30	Interesting Animals (Re-Issue)	1915	£8.00	–
M30	Mother Goose Series	1900	£6.50	–
30	Mother Goose Series	1900	£8.00	–
M30	New Series Of Birds	1908	£3.00	£90.00
30	New Series Of Birds	1908	£4.00	–
M30	New Series Of Dogs	1910	£8.50	–
30	New Series Of Dogs	1910	£9.00	–
M30	Useful Birds Of America	1915	£2.50	£75.00
30	Useful Birds Of America	1915	£3.50	–
M30	Useful Birds Of America, 2nd Series	1918	£2.50	£75.00
30	Useful Birds Of America, 2nd Series	1918	£3.00	–

CHURCH & DWIGHT (Baking Soda, U.S.A.) – cont.

Qty		Date	Odds	Sets
M30	Useful Birds Of America, 3rd Series	1922	£2.50	£75.00
30	Useful Birds Of America, 3rd Series	1922	£2.50	£75.00
M30	Useful Birds Of America, Series 4	1924	£3.00	£90.00
30	Useful Birds Of America, Series 4	1924	£2.50	£75.00
M15	Useful Birds Of America, Series 5	1924	£3.00	£45.00
M15	Useful Birds Of America, Series 6	1924	£3.00	£45.00
M15	Useful Birds Of America, Series 7	1924	£3.00	£45.00
M15	Useful Birds Of America, Series 8	1924	£3.00	£45.00
M15	Useful Birds Of America, Series 9	1926	£0.60	£9.00
M15	Useful Birds Of America, Series 10	1926	£1.00	£15.00

CIBA PHARMACEUTICAL PRODUCTS (U.S.A.)

P12	Medicine Men	1960	–	£20.00

CLARNICO (Confectionery)

30	Colonial Troops (Many Backs)	1900	£30.00	–
25	Great War Leaders	1915	£22.00	–
29	Wolf Cubs Signalling	1910	£35.00	–

CLASSIC GAMES INC. (U.S.A.)

X100	Deathwatch 2,000	1993	–	£13.00

THE CLASSIC MOTOR CYCLE

16	Motor Races 1931 (Ogden Reprint)	1989	–	£3.00

CLEVEDON CONFECTIONERY LTD.

50	British Aircraft	1958	£3.20	£160.00
25	British Orders Of Chivalry & Valour	1960	£5.50	–
50	British Ships	1959	£3.50	£175.00
M50	British Trains And Engines	1958	£8.00	–
25	Dan Dare	1961	£8.00	–
40	Did You Know?	1963	£5.50	–
40	Famous Cricketers	1959	£12.00	–
25	Famous Cricketers (Different)	1962	£12.00	–
50	Famous Football Clubs	1964	£4.50	–
50	Famous Footballers	1961	£7.00	–
50	Famous International Aircraft	1963	£1.70	£85.00
M50	Famous Screen Stars	1959	£4.50	£225.00
40	Film Stars	1958	£4.50	£180.00
50	Football Club Managers	1959	£12.50	–
50	Hints On Association Football	1961	£3.75	£187.50
50	Hints On Road Safety	1962	£3.00	£150.00
50	International Sporting Stars	1960	£4.50	–
M50	Regimental Badges	1959	£3.75	–
X25	Sporting Memories	1962	£10.00	–
50	The Story Of The Olympics	1961	£2.80	£140.00
50	Trains Of The World	1962	£2.75	–
M60	Wagon Train	1963	£6.50	–

CLEVELAND (Petrol)

P20	Golden Goals	1970	£1.20	£24.00

CLIFFORD (Commercial)

50	Footballers	1950	£25.00	–

CLOVER DAIRIES LTD.

Qty		Date	Odds	Sets
25	Animals And Reptiles	1970	—	£3.00
25	British Rail	1973	—	£3.00
25	People & Places	1972	—	£2.50
25	Prehistoric Animals	1965	—	£4.00
25	Science In The 20th Century	1971	—	£2.50
25	Ships And Their Workings	1971	—	£3.00
25	The Story Of Milk	1970	—	£3.00
25	Transport Through The Ages	1971	—	£3.00

COCA COLA (Drinks)

X49	FIFA World Cup	2002	—	£15.00
M100	Our Flower Paradise (S. Africa)	1960	—	£60.00
X96	The World Of Nature (U.S.A.)	1960	—	£70.00

COFTON COLLECTIONS (Shop)

L7	Alice In Wonderland	2002	—	£3.00
25	Dogs, 1st Series	1988	—	£4.50
25	Dogs, 2nd Series	1988	—	£4.50
25	Dogs, 3rd Series	1988	—	£4.50
L25	Nursery Rhymes	1992	—	£7.50
L20	Worcestershire County Cricket Club	1989	—	£6.50

CECIL COLEMAN LTD. (Confectionery)

24	Film Stars	1935	£8.00	—

COLGATE-PALMOLIVE (Toiletries)

M24	Famous Sporting Trophies	1979	—	£12.00
P4	Royal Britain	1953	£2.00	£8.00

COLINVILLE LTD. (Gum)

M56	Look' N See	1958	£5.00	—
X25	Prairie Pioneers	1959	£5.00	—
M28	Space Fantasy, 1st Series (1-28)	1959	£8.50	—
M28	Space Fantasy, 2nd Series (29-56)	1959	£9.00	—

COLLECT-A-CARD CORPORATION (U.S.A)

X100	Harley-Davidson Series 2	1992	—	£20.00
X100	Harley-Davidson Series 3	1993	—	£20.00
X109	Vette Set (Corvette Cars, Inc H, Gram)	1991	—	£22.00

COLLECTABLE PICTURES (Commercial)

L13	England v Australia - Ashes Series 2005	2005	—	£8.50
L20	Liverpool FC European Champions - 2005	2005	—	£7.50

COLLECTABLES OF SPALDING (Shop)

25	British Cavalry Uniforms	1987	—	£5.00
25	Military Maids	1987	—	£5.00
25	Warriors Through The Ages	1987	—	£5.00

COLLECTOR & HOBBYIST (Periodical)

25	Fascinating Hobbies	1950	—	£2.50

COLLECTORS' CORNER

Qty		Date	Odds	Sets
L20	Halifax As It Was..	1989	—	£4.50

COLLECTORS FARE

Qty		Date	Odds	Sets
16	Reading F.C. Simod Cup Winners......................................	1990	—	£2.50
X16	Reading F.C. Simod Cup Winners......................................	1990	—	£3.00

COLLECTORS SHOP

Qty		Date	Odds	Sets
25	Bandsmen Of The British Army	1960	—	£12.50
3	Bonus Cards...	1961	£1.50	—
2	Bonus Cards 1961-62..	1961	—	£3.00

COLMAN'S MUSTARD

Qty		Date	Odds	Sets
X8	Boer War Celebrities..	1900	£30.00	—

COLT 45 (Drink)

Qty		Date	Odds	Sets
X5/6	Advertising Slogans (Silk)	1976	£4.00	—
P4	American Scenes (Beer Mats)	1975	—	£5.00

COMET SWEETS ('C.S')

Qty		Date	Odds	Sets
25	A. & M. Denis On Safari, 1st Series	1961	—	£2.50
25	A. & M. Denis On Safari, 2nd Series	1961	—	£2.50
50	Footballers And Club Colours................................	1963	£1.25	—
25	Modern Wonders (Black Back).............................	1961	—	£3.00
25	(Blue Back)..	1961	—	£15.00
25	Olympic Achievements, 1st Series	1960	£1.20	£30.00
25	Olympic Achievements, 2nd Series........................	1960	£1.20	£30.00
M22	Olympic Achievements (Package)	1960	£10.00	—
25	Record Holders Of The World	1962	—	£12.50
25	Ships Through The Ages, 1st Series	1963	£1.20	£30.00
25	Ships Through The Ages, 2nd Series	1963	£1.20	£30.00

COMIC LIFE (Periodical)

Qty		Date	Odds	Sets
MF4	Sports Champions..	1922	£6.50	£26.00

COMMODEX (Gum)

Qty		Date	Odds	Sets
L88	Operation Moon..	1969	£2.40	£210.00
L120	Super Cars...	1970	£2.00	£240.00

COMMONWEALTH SHOE & LEATHER CO (U.S.A)

Qty		Date	Odds	Sets
M12	Makes Of Planes..	1930	£4.00	£48.00

COMO CONFECTIONERY PRODUCTS LTD.

Qty		Date	Odds	Sets
M52	Adventures Of Fireball XL5	1965	£16.00	—
L25	History Of The Wild West Series No.1...................	1963	£5.50	—
L25	History Of The Wild West Series No.2...................	1963	—	£15.00
50	Lenny's Adventures	1961	£1.50	£75.00
50	Noddy And His Playmates	1962	£2.25	—
M25	Noddy's Adventures	1958	£7.00	—
L25	Noddy's Adventures, 1st Series	1958	£3.25	—
L25	Noddy's Adventures, 2nd Series	1958	£3.75	—
25	Noddy's Budgie & Feathered Friends 1st Series.................	1964	£3.50	—
25	Noddy's Budgie & Feathered Friends 2nd Series	1964	£2.75	—

COMO CONFECTIONERY PRODUCTS LTD. – cont.

Qty		Date	Odds	Sets
M25	Noddy's Friends Abroad	1959	£7.00	–
L50	Noddy's Friends Abroad	1959	£2.80	£140.00
M25	Noddy's Nursery Rhyme Friends	1959	£6.75	–
L50	Noddy's Nursery Rhyme Friends	1959	£1.90	£95.00
L50	Sooty's Adventures	1960	£2.00	–
L50	Sooty's New Adventures, Second Series	1961	£2.00	–
50	Sooty's Latest Adventures, 3rd Series	1963	£2.00	–
25	Speed, 1st Series	1962	£2.00	£50.00
25	Speed, 2nd Series	1962	£0.80	£20.00
25	Supercar, 1st Series	1962	£6.75	–
25	Supercar, 2nd Series	1962	£4.75	–
25	Top Secret, 1st Series	1965	£2.60	£65.00
25	Top Secret, 2nd Series	1965	£2.40	£60.00
L26	XI5, 1st Series	1965	£21.00	–
L26	XI5, 2nd Series	1966	£21.00	–

COMPTON'S GRAVY SALT

Qty		Date	Odds	Sets
22	Footballers, Series A (Black)	1924	£25.00	–
22	Footballers, Series A (Coloured)	1924	£25.00	–
22	Footballers, Series B (Black)	1924	£25.00	–
22	Footballers, Series B (Coloured)	1924	£27.50	–
22	Footballers, Series C	1924	£27.50	–
22	Footballers, Series D	1924	£27.50	–

COOPER & CO. LTD. (Tea)

Qty		Date	Odds	Sets
50	Do You Know?	1962	–	£6.00
25	Inventions & Discoveries, 1st Series	1962	£1.80	£45.00
25	Inventions & Discoveries, 2nd Series	1962	£1.60	£40.00
25	Mysteries & Wonders Of The World, 1st Series	1961	£1.00	£25.00
25	Mysteries & Wonders Of The World, 2nd Series	1961	£0.60	£15.00
25	Prehistoric Animals, First Series	1962	–	£32.50
25	Prehistoric Animals, Second Series	1962	–	£32.50
25	Strange But True, First Series	1961	–	£3.50
25	Strange But True, Second Series	1961	–	£4.00
24	The Island Of Ceylon	1955	£3.50	–
25	Transport Through The Ages, 1st Series	1961	–	£7.50
25	Transport Through The Ages, 2nd Series	1961	£0.40	£10.00

CO-OPERATIVE SOCIETIES (Shops)

Qty		Date	Odds	Sets
D306	Espana '82. Complete With Album	1982	–	£26.00
D306	Special Poster For Above (only if ordered at the same time)	1982	–	£1.00
M48	World Cup Teams & Players (Complete With Poster)	1982	–	£8.50

CORNERSTONE COMMUNICATIONS INC (U.S.A.)

Qty		Date	Odds	Sets
X110	Doctor Who	1994	–	£20.00
X110	Doctor Who, Series 3	1996	–	£20.00
X90	Doctor Who, Series 4	1996	–	£20.00
X81	The Avengers	1992	–	£30.00
X99	The Avengers In Colour, Series 2	1993	–	£30.00
X86	The Avengers Return, Series 3	1995	–	£30.00

COUNTY PRINT SERVICES (Commercial)

Qty		Date	Odds	Sets
M25	Australian Test Cricketers	1993	–	£10.00
X48	County Cricket Teams 1900-1914	1992	–	£9.00

COUNTY PRINT SERVICES (Commercial) – cont.

Qty		Date	Odds	Sets
20	Cricket Pavilions	1991	—	£10.00
X24	Cricket Teams 1884 - 1900	1990	—	£7.00
50	Cricketers 1890	1989	—	£8.00
50	Cricketers 1896	1989	—	£8.00
50	Cricketers 1900	1990	—	£8.00
50	Cricketers 1906	1992	—	£8.00
20	Cricketers (Murray Reprint)	1991	—	£7.50
25	Cricketers (Reeves Ltd Reprint)	1993	—	£8.00
M25	Cricket's Golden-Age	1991	—	£9.00
X12	Cricket's Pace Partners	1995	—	£8.00
X12	Cricket's Spin Twins	1995	—	£8.00
L25	Derbyshire Test Cricketers	1994	—	£10.00
M27	Famous Cricket Crests	1992	—	£12.50
M25	Famous Cricket Ties	1992	—	£9.00
X12	First Knock (Cricket's Opening Pairs)	1994	—	£9.00
L25	Glamorgan Test Cricketers	1993	—	£10.00
L25	Gloucestershire Test Cricketers	1994	—	£10.00
L25	Hampshire Test Cricketers	1995	—	£10.00
L25	Kent Test Cricketers	1993	—	£10.00
L25	Lancashire Test Cricketers	1993	—	£10.00
L25	Leicestershire Test Cricketers	1995	—	£10.00
L25	Middlesex Test Cricketers	1994	—	£10.00
M24	1920's Test Cricketers	1994	—	£10.00
M24	1920's Test Cricketers, 2nd Series	1995	—	£10.00
25	1995 England Cricket Characters	1995	—	£10.00
L25	Northamptonshire Test Cricketers	1993	—	£10.00
L25	Nottinghamshire Test Cricketers	1994	—	£10.00
L25	Somerset Test Cricketers	1994	—	£10.00
15	S. African Cricket Team 1907 (Taddy Reprint)	1993	—	£7.50
L25	Surrey Test Cricketers	1994	—	£10.00
L25	Sussex Test Cricketers	1994	—	£10.00
14	The England Cricket Team 1903-1904	1991	—	£4.00
15	The England Cricket Team 1907-1908	1992	—	£10.00
17	The England Cricket Team 1932-33	1995	—	£6.00
16	The England Cricket Team 1990-91	1990	—	£6.00
16	The South African Cricket Team 1894	1990	—	£8.00
M15	The South African Cricket Team 1965	1994	—	£6.00
M30	Vic Lewis Cricket Club 1952-1992	1992	—	£6.00
L25	Warwickshire Test Cricketers	1994	—	£10.00
L25	Worcestershire Test Cricketers	1995	—	£10.00

COW & GATE (Baby Food)

X24	Advertisement Cards	1928	£2.50	£60.00
X48	Happy Families	1928	£1.25	£60.00

COWANS (Confectionery, Canada)

24	Dog Pictures	1930	£7.50	£180.00
24	Horse Pictures	1930	£7.00	£168.00
24	Learn To Swim	1929	£7.50	£180.00
24	Noted Cats	1930	£7.50	£180.00

CRESCENT CONFECTIONERY CO.

100	Sportsmen	1928	£40.00	—

CRICKET MEMORABILIA SOCIETY

Qty		Date	Odds	Sets
X50	Memorabilia Through The Ages...................................	2000	—	£9.00

CROMWELL STORES

Qty		Date	Odds	Sets
25	Do You Know?..	1963	—	£6.50
25	Racing Colours	1963	—	£10.00

CROSBIE (Preserves)

Qty		Date	Odds	Sets
K54	Miniature Playing Cards.....................................	1938	£1.00	—

JOSEPH CROSFIELD & SONS LTD. (Soap)

Qty		Date	Odds	Sets
36	Film Stars..	1924	£9.00	—

THE CROXLEY CARD COMPANY LIMITED

Qty		Date	Odds	Sets
L20	British Lions	1999	—	£12.00
X20	Saracens (Rugby)...	2000	—	£10.00

CRYSELCO ELECTRIC LAMPS

Qty		Date	Odds	Sets
X25	Beautiful Waterways..	1939	£1.20	£30.00
X25	Buildings Of Beauty..	1938	£1.20	£30.00
X12	Interesting Events Of Sixty Years Ago......................	1955	—	£25.00

CRYSTAL CAT CARDS (Commercial)

Qty		Date	Odds	Sets
X6	Attitude (By Louis Wain)....................................	2005	—	£3.00
X6	Cats In Black (By Louis Wain)..............................	2005	—	£3.00
X6	Cats - Prizewinners (By Louis Wain)........................	2004	—	£3.00
X6	Diabolo (By Louis Wain)....................................	2005	—	£3.00
X6	Happy Days (By Louis Wain).................................	2005	—	£3.00
X6	Purr-Fect Reaction (By Louis Wain).........................	2005	—	£3.00
X6	Sports & Leisure Series (By Louis Wain)....................	2004	—	£3.00

D. CUMMINGS & SON (Commercial)

Qty		Date	Odds	Sets
64	Famous Fighters..	1949	£4.25	£270.00

D&V (Commercial)

Qty		Date	Odds	Sets
25	Famous Boxers (Hudden Reprint)	1992	—	£6.00
35	Famous Boxers (Singleton/Cole Reprint)	1992	—	£6.00

DAILY HERALD (Newspaper)

Qty		Date	Odds	Sets
32	Cricketers	1954	£4.25	£136.00
32	Footballers	1954	£4.25	£136.00
32	Turf Personalities	1955	£1.60	£50.00

DAILY ICE CREAM CO.

Qty		Date	Odds	Sets
24	Modern British Locomotives	1954	£3.50	£84.00

DAILY MAIL (Newspaper)

Qty		Date	Odds	Sets
P176	War Photographs	1916	£3.00	—

DAILY MIRROR (Newspaper)

Qty		Date	Odds	Sets
M100	Star Soccer Sides	1972	£0.70	£70.00

DAILY SKETCH (Newspaper)

Qty		Date	Odds	Sets
40	World Cup Souvenir	1970	£3.25	£130.00

DAILY STAR (Newspaper)

Qty		Date	Odds	Sets
D412	Football	1981	—	£30.00

THE DAILY TELEGRAPH (Newspaper)

Qty		Date	Odds	Sets
26	England Rugby World Cup 1995	1995	—	£5.00
26	Ireland Rugby World Cup 1995	1995	—	£5.00
26	Scotland Rugby World Cup 1995	1995	—	£5.00
26	Wales Rugby World Cup 1995	1995	—	£5.00

DAINTY NOVELS

Qty		Date	Odds	Sets
10	World's Famous Liners	1922	£12.50	—

DANDY GUM

Qty		Date	Odds	Sets
M200	Animal Fables (Black Back)	1971	£0.40	—
M200	(Red Back)	1971	£0.50	—
M200	Birds (F1-200)	1968	£0.60	—
K50	Bird Series (Transfers)	1950	£2.00	—
M160	Cars And Bikes	1977	£1.10	£176.00
M97	Film & Entertainment Stars (Serie G)	1968	£1.25	£125.00
M116	Flag Parade	1965	—	£35.00
M55	Football World Cup (P/C Inset)	1986	—	£25.00
M72	Motor Cars	1966	£1.40	—
M53	Our Modern Army (P/C Inset)	1958	—	£60.00
M43/53	Our Modern Army (as above)	1958	£0.25	£10.00
M53	Pin Ups (P/C Inset)	1956	£2.00	£105.00
M70	Pop Stars (Serie P)	1977	£1.00	—
M100	Soldier Parade	1970	£0.65	—
M200	Struggle For The Universe	1970	£0.30	£60.00
M72	Veteran & Vintage Cars (V1-72)	1966	£1.50	£108.00
K48	Wiggle Waggle Pictures	1969	£2.60	£125.00
M100	Wild Animals (H1-100)	1969	—	£25.00
M200	Wonderful World (Y1-200)	1978	—	£40.00

DART FLIPCARDS INC (Commercial, Canada)

Qty		Date	Odds	Sets
X90	Pepsi Cola Premium Trading Cards	1996	—	£15.00
X100	Pepsi Cola Trading Cards	1994	—	£13.00
X72	The Frighteners	1996	—	£15.00

LIAM DEVLIN & SONS LTD. (Confectionery)

Qty		Date	Odds	Sets
L36	Coaching Gaelic Football	1960	£11.00	—
48	Corgi Toys	1971	£2.50	—
50	Do You Know?	1964	—	£6.50
M50	Famous Footballers (New Series)	1952	£18.00	—
M50	Famous Footballers, Series A.1	1953	£16.00	—
M50	Famous Footballers, Series A.2	1954	£16.00	—
50	Famous Footballers, Series A.3	1955	£16.00	—
M54	Famous Speedway Stars	1960	£17.00	—
M45	Fastest On Earth	1953	£5.00	—
36	Flags Of The Nations	1960	£5.00	—
48	Gaelic Sportstars	1960	£10.00	—
48	Irish Fishing	1962	£3.00	—
L36	Irish Theatre And Showland Stars	1965	£8.75	—
50	Modern Transport	1966	—	£8.00
48	Our Dogs	1963	£10.00	—
48	Right Or Wrong? (Sports)	1963	£6.50	—
M35	Walt Disney Characters	1956	£7.50	—
M48	Wild Animals By George Cansdale	1954	£6.00	—
48	Wild Wisdom	1970	£3.25	—
50	Wonders Of The World	1972	—	£7.00
100	World Flag Series	1970	£6.00	—

DIAMOND COLLECTION (Commercial)

Qty		Date	Odds	Sets
L20	Rock N Roll	1997	—	£6.00

DICKSON ORDE & CO. (Confectionery)

Qty		Date	Odds	Sets
50	Footballers	1960	—	£22.50
25	Ships Through The Ages	1961	£3.50	—
25	Sports Of The Countries	1962	—	£40.00

DINKIE PRODUCTS LTD. (Hair Grips)

Qty		Date	Odds	Sets
L24	Films (Plain Backs)	1952	£3.50	—
L20	Gone With The Wind, Fifth Series	1948	£6.25	£125.00
X20	M.G.M. Films, Third Series	1948	£3.00	£60.00
L24	M.G.M. Films, Ninth Series	1950	£6.50	—
L24	M.G.M. Films, Tenth Series	1951	£6.00	£144.00
L24	M.G.M. Stars, Seventh Series	1949	£4.00	£96.00
L24	Paramount Pictures, Eighth Series	1950	£4.00	£96.00
X24	Stars & Starlets, First Series	1947	£3.00	£72.00
X20	Stars & Starlets, Second Series	1947	£3.00	£60.00
L24	United Artists Releases, Eleventh Series	1951	£6.00	£144.00
L24	Warner Bros. Artists, Fourth Series	1948	£5.00	£120.00
L24	Warner Bros. Films, Sixth Series	1949	£4.00	£96.00

DIRECT ACCESS (Commercial)

Qty		Date	Odds	Sets
L8	British Sporting Stars	1992	—	£7.00

DIRECT TEA SUPPLY CO.

Qty		Date	Odds	Sets
25	British Uniforms Of The 19th Century	1958	—	£20.00

F.M.DOBSON (Confectionery)

Qty		Date	Odds	Sets
X144	Flags Of The World	1980	£0.25	—
100	Newcastle & Sunderland's 100 Greatest Footballers	1982	—	£15.00
2	Error Cards	1982	—	£1.00

PETER DOMINIC (Vintner)

Qty		Date	Odds	Sets
P17	Cricket Badges	1990	—	£17.00

A. & J. DONALDSON LTD. (Commercial)

64	Golden Series (Soccer)	1955	£25.00	—
?507	Sports Favourites	1953	£9.00	—

DONRUSS (Gum, U.S.A.)

X59	B.M.X. Card Series	1984	—	£15.00
X66	1980 P.G.A. Tour	1981	—	£50.00
X66	1981 P.G.A. Tour	1982	—	£60.00
X66	Sgt. Peppers Lonely Hearts Club Band	1978	—	£25.00
X74	Tron	1983	—	£7.50

DORMY COLLECTION (Commercial)

25	Golf - The Modern Era	1994	—	£10.00

DOUBLE DIAMOND (Beer)

P5	Puzzle Pictures (Beer Mats)	1976	—	£2.50

DRYFOOD LTD. (Confectionery)

50	Animals Of The World	1956	—	£5.00
K50	Zoo Animals	1955	—	£4.50

DUCHESS OF DEVONSHIRE DAIRY CO. LTD.

L25	Devon Beauty-Spots	1936	£4.00	£100.00

DUNHILLS (Confectionery)

25	Ships And Their Workings	1962	—	£6.00

DUNKIN (Confectionery, Spain)

X88	Martial Arts	1976	£1.00	£88.00
M50	Motor Cycles Of The World	1976	£2.40	£120.00

DUNN'S (Chocolate)

60	Animals	1924	£8.50	—
48	British Birds & Their Eggs	1924	£7.50	—

DUOCARDS (U.S.A.)

X90	Gone With The Wind	1996	—	£15.00
X72	The Beatles Yellow Submarine	1999	—	£17.50

DUTTON'S BEER

12	Team Of Sporting Heroes	1981	—	£2.50

THE EAGLE (Periodical)

16	Wallet Of Soccer Stars	1965	£3.50	£56.00

EAST KENT NATIONAL BUS CO

X8	British Airways Holidays	1984	—	£1.50

J. EDMONDSON & CO. (Confectionery)

26	Actresses 'FROGA'	1901	£55.00	—
4	Aeroplane Models	1939	£16.50	—
50	Art Picture Series	1914	£14.00	—
15	Birds & Their Eggs	1924	£12.50	—

J. EDMONDSON & CO. (CONFECTIONERY) – cont.

Qty		Date	Odds	Sets
?22	Boy Scout Proficiency Badges	1924	£35.00	–
25	British Army Series	1914	£25.00	–
20	British Ships	1925	£3.25	£65.00
20	Dogs	1924	£8.50	£170.00
20	Famous Castles	1925	£7.50	£150.00
30	Flags & Flags With Soldiers	1905	£17.50	–
40	Flags Of All Nations	1923	£10.00	–
24	Pictures From The Fairy Stories	1930	£6.25	£150.00
24	Popular Sports	1930	£12.00	–
25	Sports & Pastimes Series	1916	£16.00	–
12	Throwing Shadows On The Wall	1937	£4.50	£54.00
25	War Series	1916	£15.00	–
12	Woodbine Village	1936	£3.75	£45.00
26	Zoo Alphabet	1935	£8.00	

EDWARDS & SONS (Confectionery)

Qty		Date	Odds	Sets
27	Popular Dogs	1954	£5.00	–
12	Products Of The World	1957	–	£1.50
25	Transport Present And Future (Descriptive)	1956	–	£3.00
25	(Non-Descriptive)	1955	–	£3.00
25	Wonders Of The Universe	1956	–	£3.00

ELECTROLUX (Leisure Appliances)

Qty		Date	Odds	Sets
P16	Weekend Tours	1990	–	£5.75

ELKES BISCUITS LTD.

Qty		Date	Odds	Sets
25	Do You Know?	1964	–	£3.50

ELY BREWERY CO. LTD.

Qty		Date	Odds	Sets
M24	Royal Portraits	1953	£2.50	£60.00

EMAP LTD. (Magazines)

Qty		Date	Odds	Sets
X14/15	World Class Winners (Sport)	1997	–	£11.50

EMPIRE MARKETING BOARD

Qty		Date	Odds	Sets
12	Empire Shopping	1926	£3.25	£39.00

H.E. EMPSON & SONS LTD. (Tea)

Qty		Date	Odds	Sets
25	Birds	1962	£0.60	£15.00
25	British Cavalry Uniforms Of The 19th Century	1963	£0.50	£12.50
25	Garden Flowers	1966	£1.00	£25.00
25	History Of The Railways, 1st Series	1966	£1.40	£35.00
25	History Of The Railways, 2nd Series	1966	£1.40	£35.00
25	Passenger Liners	1964	£1.50	£37.50
24	The Island Of Ceylon	1955	£4.00	–
25	Tropical Birds	1966	£0.50	£12.50
25	Wonders Of The Deep	1965	–	£3.50

ENGLISH & SCOTTISH C.W.S. (Shops)

Qty		Date	Odds	Sets
50	British Sport Series	1904	£37.50	–
25	Humorous Peeps Into History (1-25)	1927	£3.25	£81.50
25	Humorous Peeps Into History (26-50)	1928	£5.00	£125.00
25	In Victoria's Days	1930	£3.20	£80.00

ENGLISH & SCOTTISH C.W.S. (Shops) – cont.

Qty		Date	Odds	Sets
X12	The Rose Of The Orient, Film Series	1925	£0.50	£6.00
X12	The Rose Of The Orient, 2nd Film Series	1925	£0.50	£6.00
X12	The Story Of Tea (Blue Back)	1925	£1.25	£15.00
X12	The Story Of Tea (Brown Back, Different)	1925	£0.90	£11.00

ENSIGN FISHING TACKLE

Qty		Date	Odds	Sets
L6	Birds Of Prey	1996	—	£3.00
L6	"Fisherman's Lore"	2002	—	£3.00
L20	Freshwater Fish	1995	—	£7.50
L6	Game Birds	1995	—	£3.00
L6	Garden Birds	1996	—	£3.00
L6	"It's A Dog's Life"	2002	—	£3.00
L6	Lifeboats	2002	—	£3.00
L6	Lighthouses	2002	—	£3.00
L6	Norman Neasom's Rural Studies, Series 1	2002	—	£3.00
L6	Norman Neasom's Rural Studies, Series 2	2002	—	£3.00
L6	Owls	1996	—	£3.00
L25	Salmon Flies	1994	—	£7.50
L6	Sea Fish	2002	—	£3.00
L6	Sharks	2002	—	£3.00
L6	The Art Of Angling, A Series	1996	—	£3.00
L6	The Art Of Angling, 2nd Series	1996	—	£3.00
L6	The Art Of Angling, 3rd Series	2002	—	£3.00
L6	Water Loving Birds	2002	—	£3.00

EPOL (South Africa)

Qty		Date	Odds	Sets
M30	Dogs	1974	£1.50	£45.00

JOHN E. ESSLEMONT LTD. (Tea)

Qty		Date	Odds	Sets
25	Before Our Time	1966	—	£7.50
25	Into Space	1966	£1.20	£30.00
24	The Island Of Ceylon	1961	£5.00	—

ESSO PETROLEUM CO.

Qty		Date	Odds	Sets
P20	Olympics	1972	£2.25	£45.00
M16	Squelchers (Football)	1970	£1.75	£28.00

ESTA MEDICAL LABORATORIES INC. (U.S.A.)

Qty		Date	Odds	Sets
E6	Curiosa Of Conception	1960	—	£12.50

EVERSHED & SON LTD. (Soap)

Qty		Date	Odds	Sets
25	Sports And Pastimes	1914	£17.00	—

EVERY GIRL'S PAPER

Qty		Date	Odds	Sets
MF17	Film Stars	1924	£5.00	—

EWBANKS LTD. (Confectionery)

Qty		Date	Odds	Sets
25	Animals Of The Farmyard	1960	£0.40	—
25	British Uniforms	1956	—	£4.50
25	Miniature Cars & Scooters	1960	—	£8.00
50	Ports And Resorts Of The World	1960	—	£6.00
25	Ships Around Britain	1961	—	£3.00

EWBANKS LTD. (Confectionery) – cont.

Qty		Date	Odds	Sets
25	Sports And Games	1958	–	£5.00
25	Transport Through The Ages (Black Back)	1957	-	£3.00
25	(Blue Back)	1957	–	£12.50

EXPRESS WEEKLY (Periodical)

25	The Wild West (No Overprint)	1958	–	£12.50
25	(Red Overprint)	1958	–	£6.00
L25	(Doubles)	1958	–	£12.50

EXTRAS

24	Prehistoric Monsters And The Present	1979	£2.75	£66.00

F1 SPORTSCARD MARKETING INC. (Canada)

X200	Formula 1 Racing Cards	1992	–	£20.00

F.A.I. INSURANCE GROUP (Australia)

X24	Australian Cricket Team 1989/90	1989	–	£10.00

FACCHINO'S CHOCOLATE WAFERS

100	Cinema Stars	1936	£0.85	£85.00
50	How Or Why!	1937	£0.90	£45.00
50	People Of All Lands	1937	£2.00	–
50	Pioneers	1937	£2.00	£100.00

FAITH PRESS (Commercial)

10	Boy Scouts (LCC)	1928	£7.50	£75.00

FAMILY STAR (Periodical)

MF4	Film Stars (Pairs)	1956	£5.00	£20.00
K52	Fortune Telling Cards	1952	£0.80	–

FARM-TO-DOOR SUPPLIES (Luton) LTD.

25	Castles Of Great Britain	1965	£4.50	–
25	Cathedrals Of Great Britain	1964	£4.50	–

FARROWS (Sauces)

50	Animals In The Zoo	1925	£8.00	£400.00

FASHODA (Commercial)

50	Motor Races 1931 (Ogdens Reprint)	1993	–	£8.50

FAULDER'S CHOCOLATES

10	Ancient v. Modern Sports	1924	£7.50	–
10	Birds And Nests	1924	£6.00	–
10	Fruits	1924	£6.00	–
10	Game	1924	£6.00	–

FAX-PAX (Commercial)

X36	ABC And Numbers	1987	–	£4.00
X36	Animal Spelling	1988	–	£4.00
X40	Cathedrals & Minsters	1989	–	£4.00
X36	Fables	1987	–	£4.00
X40	Famous Golfers	1993	–	£8.50
X36	Football Greats	1989	–	£7.00
X36	Football Stars	1989	–	£6.00

FAX-PAX (Commercial) – cont.

Qty		Date	Odds	Sets
X40	Historic Houses	1990	—	£4.50
X36	London	1987	—	£4.50
X40	Ringlords	1991	—	£6.00
X40	Scotland's Heritage	1990	—	£4.00
X38	Tennis	1987	—	£10.00
X40	World Of Sport	1993	—	£8.50

ALEX FERGUSON (Confectionery)

41	V.C. Heroes	1916	£20.00	—

THE FESTIVAL OF 1000 BIKES COMMITTEE

L24	The Vintage Motor Cycle Club	1993	—	£6.00

FIELD GALLERIES

L7	Racehorses & Jockeys, A Series	1997	—	£3.00
L7	Racehorses & Jockeys, 2nd Series	1997	—	£3.00

FILM PICTORIAL (Periodical)

P2	Film Stars(Silk)	1923	£32.50	£65.00

JOHN FILSHILL LTD. (Confectionery)

24	Birds & Their Eggs	1924	£8.50	£200.00
25	Footballers	1924	£22.00	£550.00
25	Types Of British Soldiers	1914	£25.00	—

FINDUS (Frozen Foods)

20	All About Pirates	1967	—	£7.50

FINE FARE TEA

25	Inventions & Discoveries, 1st Series	1965	£0.80	£20.00
25	Inventions & Discoveries, 2nd Series	1965	£0.80	£20.00
12	Your Fortune In A Tea-Cup	1966	—	£3.00

FISH MARKETING BOARD

18	Eat More Fish	1930	£3.50	—

FITCHETT'S LTD (Soap)

27	Advertisement Series	1910	£27.50	—

FIZZY FRUIT (Confectionery)

25	Buses And Trams	1959	—	£25.00

FLEER GUM INC. (U.S.A.)

X72	Here's Bo!	1980	—	£6.50
E12	Here's Bo Posters	1980	—	£3.50

FLEETWAY PUBLICATIONS LTD.

P1	Billy Fury (June)	1960	—	£1.00
P28	Football Teams 58/59	1959	£3.50	£98.00
P28	Football Teams 59/60	1960	£3.50	£98.00
P2	Pop Stars (Roxy)	1961	—	£2.50
50	Star Footballers Of 1963	1963	£1.75	£87.50

FLORENCE CARDS (Commercial)

Qty		Date	Odds	Sets
24	Luton Corporation Tramways	1983	—	£2.00
T20	Tramway Scenes	1985	—	£2.00

FORD MOTOR CO. LTD.

L50	Major Farming	1955	£8.00	—

FOSTER CLARK PRODUCTS (Malta)

50	The Sea-Our Other World	1974	—	£20.00

FOSTER'S LAGER

P4	How To Order Your Foster's (Beer mats)	1988	—	£1.50

FRAMEABILITY (Commercial)

L17	British Police Vehicles	2002	—	£6.00
L17	British Steam Locomotives	2002	—	£6.00
L10	England World Cup Winners 1966	2002	—	£4.00
L17	Fire Engines	1996	—	£5.00
L17	Fire Engines, 2nd Series	1998	—	£6.00
L10	Highwaymen	2003	—	£4.00
L6	Traction Engines	1999	—	£2.50

A. C. W.FRANCIS (Confectionery, Grenada)

25	Football Clubs And Badges	1967	—	£27.50
25	Pond Life	1967	—	£10.00
25	Sports Of The Countries	1967	—	£22.50

LES FRERES (Shop)

25	Aircraft Of World War II	1964	—	£30.00

J. S. FRY & SONS LTD. (Confectionery)

3	Advertisement Cards	1910	£27.50	—
50	Ancient Sundials	1924	£3.20	£160.00
50	Birds & Poultry	1912	£3.00	£150.00
24	Birds And Their Eggs	1912	£4.50	£108.00
15	China & Porcelain	1907	£13.00	£195.00
P2	Coronation Postcards	1911	£12.00	—
25	Days Of Nelson	1906	£12.50	£312.50
25	Days Of Wellington	1906	£12.00	£300.00
25	Empire Industries	1924	£8.50	—
50	Exercises For Men & Women	1926	£6.00	£300.00
48	Film Stars	1934	£3.25	£156.00
50	Fowls, Pigeons & Dogs	1908	£4.50	£225.00
P12	Fun Cards	1972	—	£2.00
25	Match Tricks	1921	£32.50	—
15	National Flags	1908	£7.00	£105.00
50	Nursery Rhymes	1917	£4.00	£200.00
50	Phil May Sketches	1905	£4.00	£200.00
25	Red Indians	1927	£8.00	£200.00
25	Rule Britannia!	1915	£6.00	£150.00
50	Scout Series	1912	£8.00	£400.00
48	Screen Stars	1936	£3.50	£168.00
120	This Wonderful World	1935	£1.75	—
50	Time & Money In Different Countries	1908	£3.50	£175.00

J. S. FRY & SONS LTD. (Confectionery) – cont.

Qty		Date	Odds	Sets
50	Tricks And Puzzles (Black Back)	1924	£4.20	£210.00
50	Tricks & Puzzles (Blue Back)	1918	£3.80	£190.00
L1	Vinello Advertisement Card	1922	–	£30.00
6	War Leaders ("Campaign" Packets)	1915	£27.50	–
25	With Captain Scott At The South Pole	1913	£13.00	£325.00

CANADIAN ISSUES

Qty		Date	Odds	Sets
50	Children's Nursery Rhymes	1912	£12.50	–
25	Hunting Series	1912	£20.00	–
25	Radio Series	1912	£12.50	–
50	Scout Series-Second Series	1913	£13.50	–
50	Treasure Island Map	1912	£8.00	–

FUTERA (Commercial)

Qty		Date	Odds	Sets
X90	Arsenal-Fans Selection	1997	–	£15.00
X108	Arsenal-Fans Selection (Inc. Embossed Cards)	1998	–	£18.00
X108	Arsenal-Fans Selection (Inc. Embossed Cards)	1999	–	£14.00
X108	Aston Villa-Fans Selection (Inc. Embossed Cards)	1998	–	£18.00
X108	Aston Villa-Fans Selection (Inc. Embossed Cards)	1999	–	£14.00
X108	Celtic-Fans Selection (Inc. Embossed Cards)	1998	–	£18.00
X108	Celtic-Fans Selection (Inc. Embossed Cards)	1999	–	£14.00
X108	Chelsea-Fans Selection (Inc. Embossed Cards)	1998	–	£18.00
X108	Chelsea-Fans Selection (Inc. Embossed Cards)	1999	–	£14.00
X108	Leeds United-Fans Selection (Inc. Embossed Cards)	1998	–	£18.00
X108	Leeds United-Fans Selection (Inc. Embossed Cards)	1999	–	£14.00
X99	Liverpool	1998	–	£24.00
X90	Liverpool-Fans Selection	1998	–	£14.00
X108	Liverpool-Fans Selection (Inc. Embossed Cards)	1999	–	£14.00
X100	Man. United	1997	–	£20.00
X90	Man. United-Fans Selection	1997	–	£15.00
X99	Man. United	1998	–	£22.00
X108	Man. United-Fans Selection (Inc. Embossed Cards)	1998	–	£18.00
X108	Newcastle Utd.-Fans Selection (Inc. Embossed Cards)	1999	–	£14.00
X24	World Stars 3D Football Cards	2002	–	£7.00

G.B. & T.W. (Commercial)

Qty		Date	Odds	Sets
L20	Golfing Greats	1989	–	£10.00

GALBRAITH'S STORES LTD.

Qty		Date	Odds	Sets
25	Animals In The Service Of Man	1960	£6.00	–

GALLERY OF LEGENDS

Qty		Date	Odds	Sets
71	The British Open Golf Collection	1998	–	£12.00

GAMEPLAN LEISURE LTD. (Commercial)

Qty		Date	Odds	Sets
L25	Open Champions (Golf)	1995	–	£8.50

GARDEN NEWS

Qty		Date	Odds	Sets
T6	Flowers	1988	–	£6.00
T6	Vegetables	1988	–	£6.00

GATEAUX (IRELAND)

Qty		Date	Odds	Sets
22	Irish World Cup Squad (Soccer)	1990	£4.50	£100.00

GAUMONT CHOCOLATE BAR

Qty		Date	Odds	Sets
KF50	Film Stars...	1936	£3.75	—

GAYCON PRODUCTS LTD. (Confectionery)

25	Adventures Of Pinky & Perky, 1st Series...........................	1961	£3.20	£80.00
25	Adventures Of Pinky & Perky, 2nd Series..........................	1961	£3.25	—
50	British Birds And Their Eggs..	1961	—	£15.00
25	British Butterflies..	1962	—	£20.00
25	Do You Know?, 1st Series...	1964	£1.60	£40.00
25	Do You Know?, 2nd Series..	1964	£1.60	£40.00
50	Flags Of All Nations	1963	£2.75	—
25	History Of The Blue Lamp, 1st Series...............................	1962	—	£15.00
25	History Of The Blue Lamp, 2nd Series	1962	—	£15.00
30	Kings And Queens	1961	—	£3.00
25	Modern Motor Cars	1959	£5.00	—
25	Modern Motor Cars Of The World, 1st Series	1962	£5.00	£125.00
25	Modern Motor Cars Of The World, 2nd Series	1962	£5.50	—
25	Red Indians, 1st Series..	1960	£0.60	£15.00
25	Red Indians, 2nd Series...	1960	—	£12.50
25	Top Secret, 1st Series	1963	£3.50	—
25	Top Secret, 2nd Series	1963	£3.50	—

GDS CARDS (Commercial)

L25	American Civil War Battles	2006	—	£9.50
L25	Birds By C R Bree..	2007	—	£9.50
L25	Birds By Cassell (1860)..	2007	—	£9.50
L20	Birds Of North America By John Cassin	2007	—	£8.50
L20	Birds Of The United States..	2007	—	£8.50
L20	British Birds Of Prey	2006	—	£8.50
L20	British Birds Of Prey , Series 2	2008	—	£8.50
L20	British Fresh-Water Fish	2006	—	£8.50
P4	Cattle Breeds...	2007	—	£4.50
L20	Champion Hurdle...	1997	—	£12.00
L20	Cheltenham Gold Cup	1997	—	£12.00
L20	Clippers And Yachts	2007	—	£8.50
L16	Derby Winners 1953-1968	1994	—	£10.00
L20	Dogs	2006	—	£8.50
L20	Earl Of Derby Collection Of Racehorse Paintings	2004	—	£13.00
L20	European Birds	2007	—	£9.50
L20	Famous Jockeys Of Yesterday - Series 1	2003	—	£12.00
L20	Famous Jockeys - Series 1	2001	—	£9.50
L20	Famous Titled Owners And Their Racing Colours................	2003	—	£12.00
L20	Famous Trainers - Series 1..	2001	—	£9.50
L20	Grand National..	1997	—	£9.50
L20	Great Racehorses	2003	—	£12.00
L16	Great Racehorses Of Our Time	2000	—	£14.00
L25	Hawks And Owls Of The Americas....................................	2007	—	£9.50
L20	Heads Of Famous Winners...	2001	—	£9.50
L25	Indian Chiefs Of North America	2006	—	£9.50
L25	Indian Chiefs Of North America, Series 2	2007	—	£9.50
L20	Indian Tribes Of North America	2007	—	£8.50
L16	Lester Piggott's Classic Winners.......................................	1994	—	£10.00
L25	Monkeys By J.G. Keulemans..	2007	—	£9.50
L25	1950's Racehorse Winners...	2008	—	£10.50
L20	1960's Racehorse Winners...	2007	—	£10.50

GDS CARDS (COMMERCIAL) – cont.

Qty		Date	Odds	Sets
L25	1970's Racehorse Winners	2007	—	£10.50
L20	One Thousand Guineas Winners 1981-2000	2005	—	£10.50
L25	Parrots	2007	—	£9.50
L25	Pigeons	2006	—	£9.50
L25	Poultry	2006	—	£9.50
L25	Poultry By Harrison Weir 1904	2008	—	£9.50
L20	St Leger 1776-1815 Winning Owners Colours	2005	—	£10.50
L20	Tropical Birds	2007	—	£8.50
L20	Trotters	2006	—	£8.50
L20	Two Thousand Guineas Winners 1981-2000	2005	—	£10.50

GEES FOOD PRODUCTS

30	Kings And Queens	1961	—	£12.50
16	See Britain By Coach	1959	—	£3.50

GEM LIBRARY (Periodical)

MF4	Footballers - Autographed Action Series	1923	£5.50	£22.00
MF6	Footballers - Autographed Real Action Photo Series	1922	£5.00	£30.00
MF15	Footballers - Special Action Photo	1922	£5.00	£75.00
L16	Marvels Of The Future	1929	£3.25	£54.00

GENERAL FOODS(S.A.)(PTY)LTD. (S Africa)

X50	Animals And Birds	1973	£0.35	£17.50

ALFRED GERBER (Cheese)

M143	Glorious Switzerland	1952	£1.50	—

GIRLS CINEMA (Periodical)

F6	Film Stars (Autographed)	1929	£6.00	—

GIRLS FRIEND (Periodical)

M6	Actresses (Silk)	1913	£10.00	£60.00

GIRLS MIRROR (Periodical)

MF10	Actors & Actresses	1922	£4.25	£42.50

GIRLS WEEKLY

12	Flower Fortune Cards	1912	£12.50	—

GLENGETTIE TEA

25	Animals Of The World	1964	—	£3.00
25	Birds And Their Eggs	1970	£0.40	—
25	British Locomotives	1959	—	£3.00
25	Do You Know?	1970	—	£2.50
25	Historical Scenes	1968	—	£3.00
25	History Of The Railways, 1st Series	1974	—	£3.00
25	History Of The Railways, 2nd Series	1974	—	£3.00
25	International Air-Liners	1963	£0.40	—
25	Medals Of The World (Black Back)	1959	—	£3.00
25	(Blue Back)	1959	£0.60	—
25	Modern Transport (Black Back)	1963	—	£12.50
25	(Blue Back)	1963	—	£15.00

GLENGETTIE TEA – cont.

Qty		Date	Odds	Sets
25	Naval Battles	1971	–	£2.50
25	Rare British Birds	1967	–	£6.00
25	Sovereigns, Consorts & Rulers Of GB, 1st	1970	£1.00	£25.00
25	Sovereigns, Consorts & Rulers Of GB, 2nd	1970	£1.00	£75.00
25	The British Army 1815 (Black Back)	1976	–	£3.50
25	(Blue Back)	1976	–	£3.00
25	Trains Of The World	1966	–	£4.00
25	Veteran And Vintage Cars	1966	–	£15.00
25	Wild Flowers	1961	–	£10.00

GLENTONS LTD. (Shop)

Qty		Date	Odds	Sets
24	World's Most Beautiful Butterflies	1910	£7.00	–

J. GODDARD & SONS LTD. (Metal Polish)

Qty		Date	Odds	Sets
L4	Cleaning A Silver Teapot	1928	£3.50	–
L3	Four Generations	1923	£2.50	£7.50
L12	London Views	1925	£2.25	£27.00
L12	Old Silver	1924	£1.50	£18.00
L9	Old Silver At The Victoria & Albert Museum	1933	£2.00	£18.00
L12	Ports Of The World	1928	£2.50	£30.00
L12	Present Day Silverware	1937	£2.00	£24.00
L4	Silverware With Flowers I	1928	£2.00	£8.00
L8	Silverware With Flowers II	1933	£2.00	£16.00
L2	Use & Cleaning Of Silverware I	1926	£0.75	£1.50
L6	Use & Cleaning Of Silverware II	1937	£3.50	£21.00
L8	Views Of Leicester	1934	£5.00	£40.00
L12	Views Of Old Leicester	1928	£5.00	£60.00

GOLD ENTERTAINMENT INC. (U.S.A.)

Qty		Date	Odds	Sets
X5	Babe Ruth Series (Holograms)	1992	–	£11.50

GOLDEN ERA (Commercial)

Qty		Date	Odds	Sets
T25	Aircraft Of The First World War	1993	–	£7.50
L7	A.J.S.	1995	–	£3.00
L7	Alfa Romeo	1998	–	£3.00
X10	American Automobiles Of The 1950s	2003	–	£4.50
X7	Anglia, Prefect, Popular: Small Fords 1953-1967	2005	–	£3.75
L7	Antique Dolls	1996	–	£3.00
L7	Ariel	1995	–	£3.00
L7	Aston Martin	1993	–	£3.00
L7	Aston Martin - The Post-War Competition Cards	2001	–	£3.00
L10	Austin	1996	–	£3.75
L7	Austin Healey: The Big Healeys 1953-68	1995	–	£3.00
L10	British Buses Of The 1950s	1999	–	£3.75
L10	British Buses Of The 1960s	1999	–	£3.75
L10	British Lorries 1950s & 1960s	1999	–	£3.75
L10	British Military Vehicles Of WWII	2000	–	£3.75
T25	British Motor Cycles Of The Fifties	1993	–	£7.50
L7	British Tanks Of WWII	2000	–	£3.00
L10	British Trucks	2010	–	£3.75
L7	British Vans Of The 1950s	2002	–	£3.00
L7	British Vans Of The 1960s	2002	–	£3.00
L7	BSA Motor Cycles	1993	–	£3.00
L7	BSA Motor Cycles, 2nd Series	1999	–	£3.00

Qty		Date	Odds	Sets
X10	Buses In Britain 1950s	2005	–	£4.50
X10	Buses In Britain 1960s	2005	–	£4.50
L10	Bygone Buses	2010	–	£3.75
X7	Camaro 1967-69	2004	–	£3.75
L7	Capri Mk 1 1969-1974	2007	–	£3.00
L7	Capri Mk 3 1978-86	2007	–	£3.00
X7	Capri Mk I Performance Models	2004	–	£3.75
X7	Capri Mk II Performance Models	2004	–	£3.75
X7	Capri Mk III Performance Models	2004	–	£3.75
L26	Cat Portraits	1995	–	£7.50
L25	Cats	1993	–	£7.50
L7	Citroen 2CV Models	2001	–	£3.00
L10	Classic American Motor Cycles	1998	–	£3.75
L9	Classic BMW	1999	–	£3.75
L26	Classic British Motor Cars	1992	–	£7.50
T25	Classic British Motor Cycles Of 50s/60s	1993	–	£7.50
L7	Classic Citroen Models	2001	–	£3.00
L7	Classic Honda	1999	–	£3.00
L7	Classic Ducati	1999	–	£3.00
L7	Classic Ferrari F1 1961-2000	2002	–	£3.00
L7	Classic Fiat Models	2002	–	£3.00
L10	Classic 'Jeep'	2002	–	£3.75
L7	Classic Kawasaki	1999	–	£3.00
L10	Classic Lorries	2010	–	£3.75
L10	Classic Lorries Of The 1950s	2000	–	£3.75
L10	Classic Lorries Of The 1960s	2000	–	£3.75
L7	Classic Lotus	1995	–	£3.00
L7	Classic Lotus-2nd Series	1997	–	£3.00
L10	Classic Mercedes	2000	–	£3.75
L7	Classic MG	1992	–	£3.00
L7	Classic MG-2nd Series	1993	–	£3.00
L7	Classic MG Sports Cars	1996	–	£3.00
X10	Classic Mini	2005	–	£4.50
L7	Classic Morgan Sports Cars	1997	–	£3.00
L13	Classic Porsche	1996	–	£4.50
L7	Classic Rally Cars Of The 70s	2001	–	£3.00
L7	Classic Rally Cars Of The 80s	2001	–	£3.00
L7	Classic Rolls Royce Models	1997	–	£3.00
L7	Classic Rover	1995	–	£3.00
L10	Classic Scooters	2000	–	£3.75
L7	Classic Suzuki	1999	–	£3.00
L10	Classic Tractors	1998	–	£3.75
L7	Classic TVR	1997	–	£3.00
L13	Classic VW	1993	–	£4.50
L7	Classic Volkswagen Golf GTI 1975-1992	2002	–	£3.00
L7	Classic Volkswagen Karmann Ghia 1955-1974	2002	–	£3.00
L7	Classic Volvo	2003	–	£3.00
L7	Classic Yamaha	1999	–	£3.00
L7	Cobra	1996	–	£3.00
X7	Consul, Zephyr, Zodiac: Big Fords 1951-1971	2005	–	£3.75
L7	Cortina Mk1 1962-1966	2007	–	£3.00
X10	Corvette	1994	–	£4.50
L7	Daimler Classics	2004	–	£3.00
L7	Dolls	1996	–	£3.00
L10	Eight Wheelers - Classic British Lorries	2007	–	£3.75

GOLDEN ERA (Commercial) – cont.

Qty		Date	Odds	Sets
L7	Escort Mk1 RS Models	2007	–	£3.00
X7	Escort Mk I - The Performers	2004	–	£3.75
L7	Escort Mk2 1975-80	2007	–	£3.00
X7	Escort Mk II - The Performers	2004	–	£3.75
L7	Escort (Twin-Cam, RS And Mexico)	1999	–	£3.00
L7	Escort (Works Rally Cards)	1999	–	£3.00
L10	F1 Champions 1991-2000	2001	–	£3.75
X10	Famous Bombers	1997	–	£4.50
X10	Famous Fighters	1997	–	£4.50
L10	Famous TT Riders	1998	–	£3.75
L7	Ferrari 1950s And 1960s	2003	–	£3.00
L7	Ferrari 1970s And 1980s	2003	–	£3.00
L7	Ford & Fordson (Tractors)	2010	–	£3.00
L6	Ford Executive	1994	–	£3.00
L10	Ford In The Sixties	1996	–	£3.75
L7	Ford RS Performance Models 1983-92	2001	–	£3.00
X7	Ford Sierra - The Performers	2005	–	£3.75
L7	Ford XR Models 1980-89	2001	–	£3.00
L10	Formula 1	1996	–	£3.75
L7	German Military Vehicles Of WWII	2001	–	£3.00
L7	Graham & Damon Hill	2000	–	£3.00
X7	Granada: Consul And Granada Mkl & MkII	2005	–	£3.75
L10	Grand Prix Greats	1996	–	£3.75
L26	Grand Prix: The Early Years	1992	–	£7.50
L10	Heavy Haulage	2000	–	£3.75
L7	Jaguar Classics	1992	–	£3.00
L7	Jaguar Classics, 2nd Series	1993	–	£3.00
L7	Jaguar Classics, 3rd Series	1997	–	£3.00
L7	Jaguar Classics, 4th Series	2003	–	£3.00
L7	Jaguar Modern Classics, 5th Series	2003	–	£3.00
L7	Jim Clark	2000	–	£3.00
L7	Lambretta	2000	–	£3.00
L10	Lambretta The World's Finest Scooter	2007	–	£3.75
L7	Lancia	1998	–	£3.00
L7	Land Rover Discovery 1989-98	2001	–	£3.00
L7	Land Rover Legends Series I	2000	–	£3.00
L7	Land Rover Legends Series II	2000	–	£3.00
L7	Land Rover Legends Series III	2000	–	£3.00
L7	Land Rover Ninety, One Ten And Defender	2000	–	£3.00
L7	Land Rover Series I	1996	–	£3.00
L7	Land Rover Series II	1996	–	£3.00
L7	Land Rover Series III	1996	–	£3.00
L10	London's Buses Of The Post-War Years	1997	–	£3.75
L10	London's Buses Of The Pre-War Years	1997	–	£3.75
L10	London's Country Buses Of The Post-War Years	2000	–	£3.75
L7	Matchless	1995	–	£3.00
L7	Mercedes SL	1994	–	£3.00
L10	Micro & Bubble Cars	2000	–	£3.75
P4	Mini Cooper	1994	–	£2.25
L10	Mini - Special Editions	1999	–	£3.75
L10	Mini Cooper - The 1960s	2007	–	£3.75
L7	Mini Moke 1961-69	2007	–	£3.00
P4	Monte Carlo Minis	1994	–	£2.25
L9	Morris Minor	1993	–	£3.75
L9	Morris Minor - Fifty Years	1998	–	£3.75

GOLDEN ERA (Commercial) – cont.

Qty		Date	Odds	Sets
P4	Morris Minor Van	1994	–	£2.25
L10	Motorcycling Greats	1997	–	£3.75
L10	Municipal Buses Of The 1950s And 1960s	2007	–	£3.75
X10	Mustang	1994	–	£4.50
L7	Norton Motor Cycles	1993	–	£3.00
L7	Norton Motor Cycles, 2nd Series	1998	–	£3.00
L7	Old Teddy Bears	1995	–	£3.00
L10	On The Move - Classic Trucks In Britain	2004	–	£3.75
P4	Police Vehicles	1994	–	£2.25
X7	Pontiac - GTO 1964-74	2004	–	£3.75
L7	Porsche 356 1950-65	2003	–	£3.00
L7	Porsche 911 1963-77	2003	–	£3.00
L7	Porsche 911 1978-98	2003	–	£3.00
L7	Racing & Rallying Coopers Of The 60s	2000	–	£3.00
X7	Racing Legends (Formula 1)	2004	–	£3.75
L7	Range Rover	1996	–	£3.00
L10	Road Haulage - Classic British Lorries	2004	–	£3.75
X10	Rootes Sixties Classics	2005	–	£4.50
L7	Senna - The Legend Lives On	2000	–	£3.00
L7	Spitfire (Triumph)	1994	–	£3.00
L7	Sporting Ford	1992	–	£3.00
L7	Spridget - Austin-Healey Sprite & MG Midget 58-79	2002	–	£3.00
L13	Superbikes Of The 70s	2000	–	£4.50
L7	Tanks Of WWII	2000	–	£3.00
L7	Teddies	1997	–	£3.00
L7	Teddy Bears (Antique)	1994	–	£3.00
L7	The Classic Bentley	1997	–	£3.00
L7	The E - Type Collection	1993	–	£3.00
L10	The Ford Capri	1995	–	£3.75
L7	The Ford Cortina Story 1962-1982	2002	–	£3.00
L7	The London Taxi	2001	–	£3.00
L10	The Mini Legend	1995	–	£3.75
L7	The Ringmaster (Michael Schumacher)	2002	–	£3.00
L7	The World Famous Mini Cooper	1994	–	£3.00
L10	Thirty Five Years Of The Mini	1993	–	£3.75
X7	Thunderbirds - American Classics	2003	–	£4.00
L10	Traction Engines	1999	–	£3.75
L7	Tractors Of The Fifties	1999	–	£3.00
L7	Tractors Of The Sixties	1999	–	£3.00
L7	TR Collection	1992	–	£3.00
L10	Triumph Herald 1959-71	2007	–	£3.75
L7	Triumph Motor Cycles	1993	–	£3.00
L7	Triumph Motor Cycles, 2nd Series	1998	–	£3.00
L7	Triumph Saloon Cars - Sixties And Seventies	2002	–	£3.00
L7	Triumph Spitfire 1962-80	2007	–	£3.00
L7	Triumph Stag 1970-1977	1995	–	£3.00
L7	Triumph TR2 & TR3 1953-61	2007	–	£3.00
L7	Triumph TR4/TR5/TR6 1961-76	2007	–	£3.00
L7	Triumph Vitesse 1962-71	2007	–	£3.00
L7	U.S. Military Vehicles Of WWII	2001	–	£3.00
L7	Vauxhall - Classic Vauxhalls Of The 1950s & 1960s	2002	–	£3.00
L7	Velocette Motor Cycles	1993	–	£3.00
L7	Vespa	2000	–	£3.00
L7	Vincent	1995	–	£3.00
L7	Vintage Vespa	2005	–	£3.00

GOLDEN ERA (Commercial) – cont.

Qty		Date	Odds	Sets
L7	VW Beetle 1949-66	1999	–	£3.00
L7	VW Beetle 1967-80	1999	–	£3.00
L7	VW Transporter Classic Split-Screen	2005	–	£3.00
L7	VW Transporter 1950-79	1999	–	£3.00
L7	VW Transporter 1968-80 Bay Window Models	2007	–	£3.00
X7	World Champions (Formula 1)	2004	–	£3.75

SPORTS SERIES

Qty		Date	Odds	Sets
M20	Famous Footballers By Stubbs - Arsenal	2001	–	£5.00
M21	Famous Footballers By Stubbs - Aston Villa	2002	–	£5.00
M21	Famous Footballers By Stubbs - Chelsea	2001	–	£5.00
M21	Famous Footballers By Stubbs - Leeds United	2001	–	£5.00
M20	Famous Footballers By Stubbs - Liverpool	2001	–	£5.00
M20	Famous Footballers By Stubbs - Manchester United	2001	–	£5.00
M21	Famous Footballers By Stubbs - Newcastle United	2002	–	£5.00
M21	Famous Footballers By Stubbs - Spurs	2001	–	£5.00
M21	Famous Footballers By Stubbs - West Ham United	2002	–	£5.00

GOLDEN FLEECE (Australia)

Qty		Date	Odds	Sets
X36	Pedigree Dogs	1972	–	£35.00

GOLDEN GRAIN TEA

Qty		Date	Odds	Sets
25	Birds	1970	£1.20	£30.00
25	British Cavalry Uniforms Of The 19th Century	1964	–	£6.50
25	Garden Flowers	1971	–	£2.50
25	Passenger Liners	1970	£0.40	£10.00

GOLDEN WONDER (Potato Crisps)

Qty		Date	Odds	Sets
24	Soccer All Stars	1978	£1.00	£24.00
14	Space Cards (Round Corners)	1979	–	£2.00
14	(Square Corners)	1979	–	£3.00
24	Sporting All Stars	1979	–	£5.00
24	TV All Stars	1979	–	£3.00
36	World Cup Soccer All Stars	1978	£1.00	£36.00

GOLF GIFTS LTD. (Commercial)

Qty		Date	Odds	Sets
M24	Ryder Cup '89	1991	–	£12.50

GOODIES LTD. (Confectionery)

Qty		Date	Odds	Sets
50	Doctor Who And The Daleks	1965	£10.00	–
25	Flags And Emblems	1961	–	£4.00
25	Indian Tribes	1975	£5.50	–
25	Mini Monsters	1975	£1.60	£40.00
24	Olympics	1972	£2.75	£66.00
25	Pirates	1976	£3.20	£80.00
25	Prehistoric Animals	1969	£3.00	–
25	Robbers & Thieves	1976	£2.00	£50.00
25	The Monkees, First Series	1967	£1.40	£35.00
25	The Monkees, Second Series	1968	£5.00	–
25	Vanishing Animals	1977	£1.80	£45.00
25	Weapons Through The Ages	1974	£1.60	£40.00
25	Wicked Monarchs	1973	£1.60	£40.00
25	Wide World/People Of Other Lands	1968	£1.50	£37.50

GOODIES LTD. (Confectionery) – cont.

Qty		Date	Odds	Sets
25	Wild Life	1977	£1.50	£37.50
25	World Cup	1974	£3.20	£80.00

D. W. GOODWIN & CO. (Flour)

Qty		Date	Odds	Sets
36	Careers For Boys & Girls	1930	£8.50	—
24	Extra Rhymes, Second Series	1930	£12.50	—
36	Flags Of All Nations	1930	£6.00	£215.00
36	Jokes Series	1930	£10.00	—
36	Optical Illusions	1930	£12.50	—
X60	Recipe Cards (Vertical Back, 1-60)	1930	£2.00	—
X60	Recipe Cards (Horizontal Back, 301-360)	1930	£2.00	—
36	Ships Series	1930	£11.00	—
25	Wireless	1930	£13.00	—
36	World Interest Series	1930	£7.00	—
24	World's Most Beautiful Birds	1930	£9.00	—
24	World's Most Beautiful Fishes	1930	£9.00	—

WILLIAM GOSSAGE & SONS LTD. (Soap)

Qty		Date	Odds	Sets
48	British Birds & Their Eggs	1924	£3.00	£144.00
48	Butterflies & Moths	1924	£2.00	£96.00

GOWERS & BURGONS (Tea)

Qty		Date	Odds	Sets
25	British Birds And Their Nests	1970	—	£8.00
25	Family Pets	1964	—	£3.00
25	People & Places	1970	—	£2.50
25	Prehistoric Animals	1969	£1.20	£30.00
25	Sailing Ships Through The Ages	1971	£1.00	—
25	The Circus	1964	£2.50	—
25	Veteran And Vintage Cars	1965	£1.20	£30.00
25	Veteran Racing Cars	1964	£1.30	£32.50

GRAFFITI INC. (U.S.A.)

Qty		Date	Odds	Sets
X90	Goldeneye	1995	—	£25.00

GRAIN PRODUCTS (New Zealand)

Qty		Date	Odds	Sets
L20	Fire Engines	1988	—	£20.00
P10	Vintage & Veteran Cars	1985	—	£12.50

GRANGERS

Qty		Date	Odds	Sets
12	Dr Mabuse Series	1926	£11.00	£132.00

GRANOSE FOODS LTD.

Qty		Date	Odds	Sets
M48	Adventures Of Billy The Buck	1956	—	£5.00
L16	Air Transport	1957	—	£3.00
L16	Animal Life	1957	—	£2.50
25	Animals In The Service Of Man	1965	£3.00	—
L16	Aquatic & Reptile Life	1957	—	£2.50
M48	King Of The Air	1956	£0.50	—
M48	Life Story Of Blower The Whale	1956	£0.60	£30.00
M48	Lone Leo The Cougar	1955	£0.50	£25.00
L20	150 Years Of British Locomotives	1981	—	£17.50
L16	Our Winged Friends	1957	£0.35	—

GRANOSE FOODS LTD. – cont.

Qty		Date	Odds	Sets
L16	Plant Life	1957	£0.75	–
M48	Silver Mane The Timber Wolf	1955	–	£5.00
L16	Space Travel	1957	–	£7.00
M48	Tippytail The Grizzly Bear	1956	–	£5.00
L16	Water Transport	1957	–	£2.50
L16	World Wide Visits	1957	–	£2.50

WILLIAM GRANT & SONS LTD. (Distillers)

25	Clan Tartans	1993	–	£12.50

GREGG (Jelly, New Zealand)

M48	Aquatic Birds	1974	£0.40	–
M40	Introduced And Other Birds	1967	£0.60	£24.00
M40	Land Birds Of New Zealand	1974	£0.50	£20.00
M40	Native Birds Of New Zealand	1971	£0.50	–
M35	Rare And Endangered Birds	1974	–	£17.50
M40	Remarkable Birds Of The World	1974	£0.60	–
M35	Unusual Birds Of The World	1974	£0.60	£21.00

ARTHUR GUINNESS, SON & CO. (Great Britain) Ltd. (Brewers)

P18	The Pint Size Guinness Book Of Records (Booklets)	1984	£1.20	£22.00

H. B. ICE CREAM LTD. (Ireland)

24	Do You Know	1968	£5.00	–

H. P. REPRINT (Commercial)

L11	Famous Golfers Of The 1920s (The Liverpool & London & Globe Ins. Co.)	1996	–	£6.00
M18	Golf Girl Series (Dah Tung Nan Tob. Co. China)	1996	–	£6.00

NICHOLAS HALL & SONS (Tea)

25	War Series	1917	£20.00	–

HALPINS (Tea)

25	Aircraft Of The World	1958	–	£3.00
L20	Aircraft Of The World (Double Cards)	1958	£1.20	£25.00
25	Nature Studies	1958	–	£4.00

HAMPSHIRE CRICKET CLUB

24	Sunday League Era	1987	–	£6.00

HAPPY HOME (Periodical)

M32	Child Studies (Silk)	1912	£16.00	–
M9	Flags (Silk)	1914	£8.00	£72.00
M9	Our Lucky Flowers (Silk)	1912	£14.00	–
K14	The Happy Home Silk Button (Silk)	1914	£8.00	£112.00
M12	Women On War Work (Silk)	1914	£10.00	£120.00

HARBOUR REPROGRAPHICS

30	Cricket, Surrey v Yorkshire	1988	–	£9.00

HARDEN BROS. & LINDSAY LTD. (Tea)

Qty		Date	Odds	Sets
50	Animals Of The World	1960	£0.50	£25.00
50	British Birds And Their Eggs	1960	£1.00	—
50	National Pets	1961	—	£5.00

HARRISON (Pomade)

Qty		Date	Odds	Sets
25	Beauties	1902	£26.00	£650.00

JOHN HAWKINS & SONS LTD. (Cotton)

Qty		Date	Odds	Sets
LF30	The Story Of Cotton	1925	£5.50	£165.00

HEINEKEN (Beer)

Qty		Date	Odds	Sets
P12	The Heineken Story (Beer Mats)	1976	—	£6.00

S HENDERSON & SONS LTD (Biscuits)

Qty		Date	Odds	Sets
T132	General Interest Series	1908	£10.00	£1,300.00

HERALD ALARMS

Qty		Date	Odds	Sets
10	Feudal Lords	1986	—	£20.00
X10	Feudal Lords	1986	—	£10.00

HERON PETROL

Qty		Date	Odds	Sets
K16	Holidays	1960	£1.50	—

HERTFORDSHIRE POLICE FORCE

Qty		Date	Odds	Sets
X12	Postage Stamps	1985	—	£6.00

HIGSONS (Brewery)

Qty		Date	Odds	Sets
X26	Famous Old Higsonians	1987	£1.50	—

JOHN HINDHAUGH & CO. (Bread)

Qty		Date	Odds	Sets
25	Railway Engines	1913	£32.50	—

HITCHMAN'S DAIRIES LTD.

Qty		Date	Odds	Sets
25	Aircraft Of World War II (Black Back)	1966	—	£10.00
25	(Blue Back)	1966	£1.00	£25.00
25	Animals Of The World	1964	—	£12.50
25	British Birds And Their Nests	1970	£1.00	£25.00
25	British Railways	1971	—	£4.00
25	Buses And Trams	1966	—	£6.00
25	Merchant Ships Of The World	1970	—	£12.50
25	Modern Wonders	1962	—	£7.50
25	Naval Battles	1971	—	£6.00
25	People & Places	1971	—	£5.00
25	Regimental Uniforms Of The Past	1973	—	£3.00
25	Science In The 20th Century	1966	—	£7.50
25	The Story Of Milk	1965	£0.50	£12.50
25	Trains Of The World	1970	—	£25.00

HOADLEY'S CHOCOLATES (Australia)

Qty		Date	Odds	Sets
50	British Empire Kings & Queens	1940	£1.70	£85.00
?33	Cricketers (Black Front)	1928	£15.00	—

HOADLEY'S CHOCOLATES (Australia) – cont.

Qty		Date	Odds	Sets
36	Cricketers (Brown Front)	1933	£11.50	£420.00
50	Early Australian Series	1938	£1.90	£105.00
50	Empire Games And Test Teams	1932	£9.50	£475.00
40	Test Cricketers	1936	£12.50	£500.00
M36	Test Cricketers (Different)	1938	£14.00	£500.00
50	The Birth Of A Nation	1938	£2.20	£110.00
50	Victorian Footballers (Heads, 1-50)	1938	£7.50	£375.00
50	Victorian Footballers (51-100)	1938	£7.50	£375.00
50	Victorian Footballers (Action)	1938	£7.50	–
50	Wild West Series	1938	£2.50	£125.00

HOBBYPRESS GUIDES (Books)

Qty		Date	Odds	Sets
20	Preserved Railway Locomotives	1983	–	£3.00
20	Preserved Steam Railways, 1st Series	1983	–	£3.00
20	Preserved Steam Railways, 2nd Series	1984	–	£3.00
20	The World's Great Cricketers	1984	£0.50	£10.00

THOMAS HOLLOWAY LTD. (Pharmaceutics)

Qty		Date	Odds	Sets
X39	Natural History Series (Animals Heads)	1900	£7.50	£292.50
X39	Natural History Series (Birds)	1900	£7.50	£292.50
X60	Natural History Series (Full Length)	1900	£11.00	–
X50	Pictorial History Of The Sports And Pastimes Of All Nations	1900	£11.00	£550.00

HOME & COLONIAL STORES LTD.

Qty		Date	Odds	Sets
26	Advertising Alphabet	1914	£7.00	£180.00
M100	Flag Pictures	1916	£4.00	–
M40	War Heroes	1916	£7.50	£300.00
M40	War Pictures	1916	£7.00	–
100	War Pictures (Different)	1916	£4.25	£425.00

HOME COUNTIES DAIRIES TEA

Qty		Date	Odds	Sets
25	Country Life	1964	–	£4.00
25	International Air-Liners	1965	–	£3.00
25	The Story Of Milk	1965	–	£5.00

HOME MIRROR (Periodical)

Qty		Date	Odds	Sets
M4	Cinema Star Pictures (Silk)	1919	£15.00	£60.00

HOME WEEKLY (Periodical)

Qty		Date	Odds	Sets
12	Little Charlie Cards	1920	£17.50	–

GEORGE W. HORNER & CO. (Confectionery)

Qty		Date	Odds	Sets
P24	Wireless Cards	1926	£14.00	

HORNIMAN (Tea)

Qty		Date	Odds	Sets
P10	Boating Ways	1910	£22.50	–
P12	British Birds & Eggs	1910	£20.00	–
48	Dogs	1961	–	£6.00
P10	Naval Heroes	1910	£22.50	£225.00
48	Pets	1960	–	£6.00
48	Wild Animals	1958	–	£6.00

HORSLEY'S STORES

Qty		Date	Odds	Sets
25	British Uniforms Of The 19th Century	1968	—	£10.00
25	Castles Of Britain	1968	£1.75	—
25	Family Pets	1968	—	£8.00

VAN HOUTEN (Chocolate)

P12	How Nature Protects The Weak	1908	£12.00	£144.00

HUGHES BISCUITS

20	War Series	1915	£16.50	—

HULL CITY FOOTBALL CLUB

X20	Footballers	1950	£12.50	£250.00

HUNT CROPP & SONS (Vedast)

15	Characters From Dickens	1912	£12.00	£180.00

DAVID J. HUNTER (Commercial)

L7	Coldstream Guards, 1st Series	2009	—	£3.00
L7	Grenadier Guards, 1st Series	2009	—	£3.00
L7	Grenadier Guards, 2nd Series	2009	—	£3.00
L7	Irish Guards, 1st Series	2009	—	£3.00

INFANTRY REGIMENTAL COLOURS

L7	King's Regiment (Liverpool)	2005	—	£3.00
L7	Scots Guards, 1st Series	2009	—	£3.00
L7	Seaforth Highlanders	2006	—	£3.00
L7	The Argyll And Sutherland Highlanders	2008	—	£3.00
L7	The Bedfordshire And Hertfordshire Regiment	2009	—	£3.00
L7	The Black Watch (Royal Highland Regiment)	2006	—	£3.00
L7	The Border Regiment	2005	—	£3.00
L7	The Buffs (Royal East Kent Regiment)	2005	—	£3.00
L7	The Cameronians (Scottish Rifles)	2009	—	£3.00
L7	The Cheshire Regiment	2006	—	£3.00
L7	The Devonshire Regiment	2006	—	£3.00
L7	The Duke Of Cornwall's Light Infantry	2007	—	£3.00
L7	The Duke Of Wellington's Regiment	2006	—	£3.00
L7	The Durham Light Infantry	2009	—	£3.00
L7	The East Lancashire Regiment	2007	—	£3.00
L7	The East Surrey Regiment	2004	—	£3.00
L7	The Essex Regiment	2007	—	£3.00
L7	The Gloucestershire Regiment	2006	—	£3.00
L7	The Gordon Highlanders	2004	—	£3.00
L7	The Highland Light Infantry	2007	—	£3.00
L7	The King's Own Royal Regiment (Lancaster)	2005	—	£3.00
L7	The King's Own Scottish Borderers	2004	—	£3.00
L7	The King's Own Yorkshire Light Infantry	2009	—	£3.00
L7	The King's Shropshire Light Infantry	2004	—	£3.00
L7	The King's Shropshire Light Infantry, 2nd Series	2008	—	£3.00
L7	The London Regiment, 1st Series	2008	—	£3.00
L7	The London Regiment, 2nd Series	2008	—	£3.00
L7	The Loyal Regiment (North Lancashire)	2009	—	£3.00
L7	The Manchester Regiment	2005	—	£3.00
L7	The Middlesex Regiment	2007	—	£3.00

DAVID J. HUNTER (Commercial) – cont.

Qty		Date	Odds	Sets
L7	The North Staffordshire Regiment	2004	–	£3.00
L7	The North Staffordshire Regiment, 2nd Series	2008	–	£3.00
L7	The Northamptonshire Regiment	2007	–	£3.00
L7	The Oxfordshire And Buckinghamshire Light Infantry	2007	–	£3.00
L7	The Queen's Own Cameron Highlanders	2006	–	£3.00
L7	The Queen's Own Royal West Kent Regiment	2005	–	£3.00
L7	The Queen's Royal Regiment (West Surrey)	2004	–	£3.00
L7	The Royal Fusiliers (City Of London Regiment)	2005	–	£3.00
L7	The Royal Hampshire Regiment	2008	–	£3.00
L7	The Royal Inniskilling Fusiliers	2005	–	£3.00
L7	The Royal Irish Fusiliers	2008	–	£3.00
L7	The Royal Irish Regiment (18th Foot)	2006	–	£3.00
L7	The Royal Lancashire Fusiliers	2005	–	£3.00
L7	The Royal Leicestershire Regiment	2006	–	£3.00
L7	The Royal Lincolnshire Regiment	2006	–	£3.00
L7	The Royal Marines, 1st Series	2008	–	£3.00
L7	The Royal Marines, 2nd Series	2008	–	£3.00
L7	The Royal Norfolk Regiment	2004	–	£3.00
L7	The Royal Northumberland Fusiliers	2005	–	£3.00
L7	The Royal Scots	2004	–	£3.00
L7	The Royal Scots, 2nd Series	2007	–	£3.00
L7	The Royal Scots Fusiliers	2006	–	£3.00
L7	The Royal Sussex Regiment	2007	–	£3.00
L7	The Royal Warwickshire Fusiliers	2005	–	£3.00
L7	The Royal Welch Fusiliers	2008	–	£3.00
L7	The Sherwood Foresters	2004	–	£3.00
L7	The Sherwood Foresters, 2nd Series	2007	–	£3.00
L7	The South Lancashire Regiment	2007	–	£3.00
L7	The South Staffordshire Regiment	2004	–	£3.00
L7	The South Staffordshire Regiment, 2nd Series	2008	–	£3.00
L7	The South Wales Borderers	2006	–	£3.00
L7	The Suffolk Regiment	2004	–	£3.00
L7	The Suffolk Regiment, 2nd Series	2008	–	£3.00
L7	The Welch Regiment	2005	–	£3.00
L7	The Worcestershire Regiment	2004	–	£3.00
L7	The Worcestershire Regiment, 2nd Series	2007	–	£3.00
L7	The York And Lancaster Regiment	2009	–	£3.00
L7	Welsh Guards	2009	–	£3.00

HUNTLEY & PALMERS (Biscuits)

Qty		Date	Odds	Sets
P12	Animals	1900	£7.50	£90.00
P12	Aviation	1908	£50.00	£600.00
P12	Biscuits In Various Countries	1900	£6.50	£78.00
P6	Biscuits With Travellers	1900	£7.50	£45.00
P12	Children Of Nations I (Gold Border)	1900	£7.50	£90.00
P12	Children Of Nations II (White Border)	1900	£6.50	£78.00
P12	Children At Leisure & Play	1900	£7.50	£90.00
P12	Harvests Of The World	1900	£16.50	–
P12	Hunting	1900	£8.50	£100.00
P8	Inventors	1900	£20.00	–
X11	Rondes Enfantines	1900	£20.00	–
P12	Scenes With Biscuits	1900	£6.00	£72.00
X8	Shakespearian Series	1900	£7.50	£60.00
P12	Soldiers Of Various Countries	1900	£12.50	£150.00

OKAPI - CONGO

37

Silks is the name given to all items woven in, or printed on, fabrics of all sorts, including satin, canvas, blanket and leather.

Many tobacco and a few other trade firms issued silks in the early part of this century. The best known of these are Godfrey Phillips in Britain, mainly with their B.D.V. brand, the American Tobacco Co. in the U.S.A. and the British American Tobacco Co. in the Commonwealth, usually under the names of their subsidiaries such as the I.T.C. (Canada) or United Tobacco Co. (South Africa). Among trade issues the majority were given away with magazines such as Happy Home and My Weekly. Noteworthy however are the series of cabinet size silks given with each Christmas number of 'The Gentlewoman' between 1890 and 1915.

In some cases the subjects on silks are Dogs of their Breed', but the majority are new subjects, and cover a very wide range of interests. These include Flags, Regimental Badges and Colours, County Cricket Badges, Famous Queens, Paintings, Red Indians, Great War Leaders, Dogs, Flower and even Automobile Pennants. Manufacturers encouraged the smokers to use the satin issues to make cushion covers and the like – I.T.C. of Canada issued large centrepieces for this purpose, and Godfrey Phillips even issued a set of CARDS entitled 'Prizes for Needlework'.

Silks are often thought of as a specialised subject, but the general collector should consider some of these as an attractive addition to his album.

We can supply a superb illustrated 342 page book listing all known Worldwide Tobacco and Trade silk issues for £50.50 (post paid in U.K.)

BENEVOLENT PROTECTIVE ORDER OF ELKS

OLD MILL CIGARETTES

JAPAN

MARGUERITE

In view of the enormous number of cards that have been produced, most of which have detailed descriptions, it is hardly surprising that mistakes occur occasionally. In some cases these were brought to light at an early stage, and a corrected card was also issued, but sometimes the error remained undetected until many years after the set appeared.

Some of the mistakes can best be described as 'Howlers', and among the best known are Carreras Figures of Fiction showing Uncle Tom with white feet, Pattreiouex Coastwise giving the date of the Battle of Trafalgar as 1812 and Player Sea Fishes with three versions of the Monk (or Angle) Fish, one of which states that it is inedible, while another describes its flesh as 'quite wholesome'. Gallaher, in its Great War Series, showed a Tommy with his rifle sloped on the wrong shoulder, and Carreras Britains Defence No. 47 can be found with the picture upside down. Most of these have been illustrated elsewhere, so we have shown here a different selection, with no comments other than – find the mistake for yourself.

Varieties occur as the result of deliberate changes by the issuer. Common examples of this are the updating of army ranks and decorations, new sports statistics, and changes of rank or title caused by a death. The most fruitful series for a study of varieties are probably in the series of Guinea Gold cards and also Wills Transvaal series, where over 250 different cards can be collected within the 66 numbers of the series.

SWAN RIVER DAISIES

SWAN RIVER DAISIES

12 NORWICH CROPPER.
OGDEN'S CIGARETTES.

12 POUTER.
OGDEN'S CIGARETTE

MORGAN PLUS 4

MORGAN PLUS

HEAD-DRESSES OF THE WORLD

A SERIES OF 25

No. 18
DUTCH GIRL
Some of the old Dutch towns still retain their traditional costumes. They can show where a woman comes from, whether she is married or single, Catholic or Protestant. This girl is wearing Sunday dress, the cap being made of white lace. The men in some parts still wear black baggy breeches.

Issued by
RATT & COLT
IN ENGLAND

HEAD-DRESSES OF THE WORLD

A SERIES OF 25

No. 8
DUTCH GIRL
Some of the old Dutch towns still retain their traditional costumes. They can show where a woman comes from, whether she is married or single, Catholic or Protestant. This girl is wearing Sunday dress, the cap being made of white lace. The men in some parts still wear black baggy breeches.

Issued by
BARRATT & CO LTD
LONDON ENGLAND

HUNTLEY & PALMERS (Biscuits) – cont.

Qty		Date	Odds	Sets
P12	Sports (Semi-Circular Background)	1900	£15.00	£180.00
P12	Sports (Plain Background)	1900	£15.00	£180.00
P12	The Seasons	1900	£12.50	£150.00
P12	Travelling During The 19th Century	1900	£22.50	–
P12	Views Of Italy & The French Riviera	1900	£11.00	–
P12	Warships Of Nations	1900	£12.50	£150.00
P8	Watteau	1900	£8.00	£64.00
P8	Wonders Of The World	1900	£22.50	£180.00

HUSTLER SOAP

Qty		Date	Odds	Sets
20	Animals, First Series	1925	£1.20	£24.00
20	Animals, Second Series	1925	£1.20	£24.00
20	Animals, Third Series	1925	£1.20	£24.00
30	Regimental Nicknames	1924	£2.75	£82.50

R. HYDE & CO. LTD. (Bird Seed)

Qty		Date	Odds	Sets
80	British Birds	1928	£2.25	£180.00
80	Cage Birds	1930	£1.60	£130.00
80	Canary Culture	1930	£1.00	£120.00
M10	Cartoons	1924	£13.50	–
M24	Modern Wonders	1924	£15.00	£360.00

I.P.C. MAGAZINES LTD.

Qty		Date	Odds	Sets
M25	Lindy's Cards Of Fortune	1975	–	£5.00
M160	My Favourite Soccer Stars (Blue Back)	1970	£0.90	£144.00
M160	My Favourite Soccer Stars (Red Back)	1971	£0.90	£144.00

IDEAL ALBUMS LTD

Qty		Date	Odds	Sets
L25	Boxing Greats	1991	–	£8.50
L2	Promotional Cards	1991	–	£0.65

IMPERIAL PUBLISHING LTD (Commercial)

Qty		Date	Odds	Sets
50	A.F.C. Nicknames (Ogdens)	1996	–	£8.50
50	Aircraft Of The R.A.F. (Player)	1990	–	£8.50
25	Angling (Mitchell)	1993	–	£6.00
25	Aviation (Lambert & Butler)	1997	–	£6.00
15	Billiard Terms (Salmon & Gluckstein)	1997	–	£5.00
25	Boxing (Franklyn Davey)	2002	–	£6.00
L7	Cathedrals (Wills)	2000	–	£2.50
L24	Cats (Player)	1997	–	£8.50
25	Characters From Dickens, 2nd (Player)	1990	–	£6.00
L25	Country Sports (Player)	2000	–	£8.50
50	Cricket Caricatures By 'Rip' (Player)	1993	–	£8.50
50	Cricketers 1930 (Player)	2000	–	£8.50
50	Cricketers, 1934 (Player)	1993	–	£8.50
25	Dance Band Leaders (Lambert & Butler)	1992	–	£6.00
50	Dog's Heads (Player, Eire)	1994	–	£8.50
50	Fire Fighting Appliances (Player)	1991	–	£8.50
50	Flags & Funnels Of Leading Steamship Lines (Ogdens)	1997	–	£8.50
54	Frisky (With 2 Instructions) (Churchman)	1994	–	£8.50
50	Gilbert & Sullivan, 2nd Series(Player)	1990	–	£8.50
25	Highland Clans (Player)	1997	–	£6.00
25	Hints & Tips For Motorists (Lambert & Butler)	1994	–	£6.00

IMPERIAL PUBLISHING LTD (Commercial) – cont.

Qty		Date	Odds	Sets
50	Horsemanship (Lambert & Butler)	1994	–	£8.50
50	Kings & Queens Of England (Player)	1990	–	£8.50
50	Landmarks In Railway Progress (Churchman)	1994	–	£8.50
25	London Characters (Lambert & Butler)	1992	–	£6.00
50	Military Aircraft (Wills)	1991	–	£8.50
50	Military Motors (Wills)	1994	–	£8.50
50	Motor Cars, A Series (Player)	1990	–	£8.50
50	Motor Cycles (Lambert & Butler)	1990	–	£8.50
50	Naval Dress & Badges (Wills)	1997	–	£8.50
50	Old English Garden Flowers 2nd (Wills)	1994	–	£8.50
L25	Old Hunting Prints (Player)	1997	–	£8.50
L6	Old Inns (Wills)	1990	–	£2.50
L25	Old Naval Prints (Player)	1997	–	£8.50
L25	Picturesque London (Player)	1997	–	£8.50
50	Pioneers (Churchman)	2000	–	£9.50
25	Poultry (1-25, With Ogdens On Front)	1998	–	£6.00
25	Poultry, 2nd Series (26-50) (Ogdens)	2000	–	£6.00
50	Poultry (Player)	2002	–	£8.50
50	Prominent Golfers (Churchman)	1993	–	£8.50
25	Prominent Racehorses (Faulkner)	1993	–	£6.00
25	Prominent Rugby Players (Smith)	1992	–	£8.00
L40	Puppies (Wills)	1990	–	£12.50
50	Railway Engines, 1924 (Wills)	1996	–	£8.50
50	Railway Engines, 1936 (Wills)	1993	–	£8.50
50	Railway Equipment (Wills)	1993	–	£8.50
50	Railway Locomotives (Wills)	1993	–	£8.50
50	Regimental Standards & Cap Badges (Player)	1993	–	£8.50
50	Regimental Uniforms-2nd Series (Player)	1995	–	£8.50
50	Roses, A Series (Wills)	1994	–	£8.50
50	Rugby Internationals (Wills)	1996	–	£8.50
50	Soldiers Of The King (Ogdens)	1993	–	£8.50
M48	The R.A.F. At Work (Churchman)	1995	–	£14.00
25	The World's Dreadnoughts (Wills)	1994	–	£6.00
L24	Treasures Of Britain (Player)	1995	–	£8.50
L25	Types Of Horses (Player)	1998	–	£8.50
50	Uniforms Of The T.A. (Player)	1990	–	£8.50
50	War Incidents, 2nd Series (Wills)	1995	–	£8.50
50	Waterloo (Wills)	1990	–	£15.00
L25	Wild Birds (Player)	1997	–	£8.50
25	Winter Sports (Lambert & Butler)	1998	–	£6.00
50	World's Locomotives (Lambert & Butler)	1989	–	£8.50
	ORIGINAL ISSUES			
L20	American Golfers	1990	–	£8.50
L24	Birds Of Britain	1994	–	£8.50
L6	Breeds Of Cats	2000	–	£3.00
	IMPERIAL DOG COLLECTION			
L6	Airedale Terriers	1999	–	£3.00
L6	Border Collies	1999	–	£3.00
L6	Boxers	1999	–	£3.00
L6	Bulldogs	1999	–	£3.00
L6	Cocker Spaniels	1999	–	£3.00
L6	Dachshunds	1999	–	£3.00
L6	Dalmatians	1999	–	£3.00
L6	Dobermann	1999	–	£3.00
L6	German Shepherds	1999	–	£3.00

IMPERIAL PUBLISHING LTD (Commercial) – cont.

Qty		Date	Odds	Sets
L6	Golden Retrievers	1999	–	£3.00
L6	Greyhounds	2000	–	£3.00
L6	Jack Russell Terriers	1999	–	£3.00
L6	Labrador Retrievers	1999	–	£3.00
L6	Pekingese	1999	–	£3.00
L6	Poodles	1999	–	£3.00
L6	Scottish Terriers	1999	–	£3.00
L6	Staffordshire Bull Terriers	2000	–	£3.00
L6	West Highland Terriers	2000	–	£3.00
L6	Yorkshire Terriers	1999	–	£3.00
L20	Native North Americans	1995	–	£8.50
L48	Olympic Champions	1996	–	£12.00
L18	Snooker Celebrities	1993	–	£12.00
L24	The History Of The Olympic Games	1996	–	£8.50

INDIA & CEYLON TEA CO. LTD.

Qty		Date	Odds	Sets
24	The Island Of Ceylon	1955	£5.00	–

IN LINE (COMMERCIAL, U.S.A.)

Qty		Date	Odds	Sets
X6	Classic Motorcycles (Prototype Set)	1992	–	£3.00
X57	Classic Motorcycles Series 1 (Inc Hologram)	1993	–	£10.00

INKWORKS (Commercial, U.S.A.)

Qty		Date	Odds	Sets
X90	The Adventures Of Pinocchio	1996	–	£12.00
X90	The Phantom	1996	–	£14.00

INTREPID T.C. INTERNATIONAL (Australia)

Qty		Date	Odds	Sets
X100	Atp Tennis Tour	1996	–	£12.00

JOHN IRWIN SONS & CO. LTD. (Tea)

Qty		Date	Odds	Sets
12	Characters From Dickens Works	1912	£17.50	–
6	Characters From Shakespeare	1912	£16.50	£100.00
8	The European War Series	1916	£17.50	£132.00

JF SPORTING COLLECTIBLES (Commercial)

Qty		Date	Odds	Sets
X24	"Ali" His Fights His Opponents	2004	–	£15.00
X15	Australian Cricketers - 1930	1999	–	£10.00
X36	Battle Of The Roses: Pre-War Personalities	2003	–	£25.00
L25	Boxers - World Champions	2000	–	£15.00
L24	British Yeomanry Uniforms	2004	–	£15.00
L40	Famous Footballers 1896-97	2000	–	£25.00
M36	Football Favourites 1940/50s, 1st Series	1999	–	£15.00
M36	Football Favourites 1940/50s, 2nd Series	1999	–	£15.00
M36	Football Favourites 1940/50s, 3rd Series	1999	–	£15.00
M36	Football Favourites 1940/50s, 4th Series	2000	–	£15.00
M36	Football Favourites 1940/50s, 5th Series	2000	–	£15.00
L24	Footballers In Action 1940/50s, 1st Series	2002	–	£16.00
L24	Footballers In Action 1940/50s, 2nd Series	2002	–	£16.00
L24	Footballers In Action 1940/50s, 3rd Series	2002	–	£16.00
L24	Footballers In Action 1940/50s, 4th Series	2002	–	£16.00
X24	Gentlemen v Players: Pre-War Personalities, Ist Series	2003	–	£15.00
X24	Gentleman v Players: Pre-War Personalities, 2nd Series	2004	–	£15.00
X24	Popular Footballers 1919-1939, 1st Series	2000	–	£16.00

JF SPORTING COLLECTIBLES (Commercial) – cont.

Qty		Date	Odds	Sets
X24	Popular Footballers 1919-1939, 2nd Series	2000	–	£16.00
X24	Popular Footballers 1919-1939, 3rd Series	2002	–	£16.00
X24	Rugby League Stars 1940/50s	2002	–	£16.00
L24	Scottish Clan Tartans, 1st Series	2002	–	£15.00
L24	Soldiers Of Queen Victoria's Army	2004	–	£15.00
X24	Speedway All-Time Greats, A Series	1999	–	£15.00
X24	Speedway All-Time Greats, 2nd Series	1999	–	£15.00
X24	Speedway All-Time Greats, 3rd Series	2000	–	£15.00
X24	Speedway Personalities In Action, 1st Series	2000	–	£15.00
X24	Speedway Personalities In Action, 2nd Series	2000	–	£15.00
L30	Stars Of Football 1940s	2002	–	£21.00
L24	Uniforms Of The Royal Regiment Of Artillery	2003	–	£15.00
X28	Victorian Cricket Personalities	2000	–	£20.00
X15	Wembley Speedway Stars, A Series	1999	–	£8.00
X21	Wembley Speedway Stars, 2nd Series	2000	–	£15.00
L24	World Heavyweight Boxing Champions	1999	–	£15.00
L20	World Heavyweight Championship Contenders	2000	–	£12.00

JACOB & CO. (Biscuits)

Qty		Date	Odds	Sets
D24	Banknotes That Made History (With Album)	1975	–	£4.50
D32	Famous Picture Cards From History (With Album)	1978	–	£3.00
E16	Jacob's Club Circus	1970	£3.50	£56.00
M16	Nursery Rhyme Competition	1969	£1.50	£24.00
M30	School Of Dinosaurs	1994	£0.30	£9.00
25	Vehicles Of All Ages	1924	£2.60	£65.00
25	Zoo Series (Brown Back)	1924	£1.80	£45.00
25	(Green Back)	1924	£1.20	£30.00

M V JASINSKI (Commercial, U.S.A.)

Qty		Date	Odds	Sets
X36	Flash Gordon	1990	–	£15.00
X36	Flash Gordon Conquers The Universe	1992	–	£12.50
X36	Flash Gordon's Trip To Mars	1991	–	£12.50

JESK (Confectionery)

Qty		Date	Odds	Sets
25	Buses And Trams	1959	£1.20	£30.00

JIBCO (Tea)

Qty		Date	Odds	Sets
28	Dominoes (2 Printings)	1956	£3.25	–
K52	Miniature Playing Cards	1956	£3.25	–
K50	Puzzle Cards	1955	£5.00	–
K25	Screen Stars (2 Printings)	1955	£4.50	–
K25	Screen Stars, 2nd Edition	1956	£1.20	£30.00

JIFFI (Condoms)

Qty		Date	Odds	Sets
M64	Kama Sutra	1989	–	£50.00

R. L. JONES & CO. LTD. (Drink)

Qty		Date	Odds	Sets
24	Jet Aircraft Of The World	1956	–	£4.00

JUBBLY (Drink)

Qty		Date	Odds	Sets
50	Adventurous Lives	1967	–	£5.00

JUNIOR PASTIMES (Commercial)

Qty		Date	Odds	Sets
51/52	Popular English Players	1951	£3.75	£190.00
52	Popular Players (Footballers)	1951	£7.50	–
51/52	Popular Railway Engines	1951	£2.50	£125.00
L77/80	Star Pix	1951	£1.70	£130.00

JUST SEVENTEEN (Magazine)

T17	Posters	1986	–	£2.50

K. P. NUTS & CRISPS

12	Sports Adventure Series	1978	–	£13.50
20	Wonderful World Of Nature	1983	£0.60	£12.00

KANE PRODUCTS LTD. (Confectionery)

36	ATV Stars (Packets)	1957	£5.00	–
50	British Birds And Their Eggs	1960	£0.55	£27.50
25	Cricket Clubs & Badges	1957	£0.20	£3.50
L50	Disc Stars	1960	£3.00	£150.00
X50	Disc Stars	1960	£1.80	£90.00
50	Dogs	1955	£2.75	–
X72	Film Stars (Plain Back)	1958	£1.75	£126.00
50	Flags Of All Nations	1959	–	£12.50
25	Football Clubs & Colours	1956	–	£4.00
50	Historical Characters	1957	–	£6.00
25	International Football Stars	1957	£2.00	£50.00
30	Kings And Queens	1959	–	£10.00
X30	Kings & Queens	1959	£0.30	£9.00
25	Modern Motor Cars	1959	£0.80	£20.00
50	Modern Racing Cars	1954	£0.50	£25.00
25	National Pets Club, Part I	1958	–	£10.00
25	National Pets Club, Part II	1958	£2.40	£60.00
25	1956 Cricketers, 1st Series	1956	£1.60	£40.00
25	1956 Cricketers, 2nd Series	1956	£1.50	£37.50
25	Red Indians 1st, Series	1957	£1.20	£30.00
25	Red Indians 2nd, Series	1957	£1.20	£30.00
25	Roy Rogers Colour Series	1958	£2.60	£65.00
25	Roy Rogers Series	1957	£4.00	£100.00
50	Space Adventure	1955	–	£30.00
50	20th Century Events	1955	£1.50	£75.00
K50	Wild Animals	1954	–	£5.00

KARDOMAH (Tea)

K?500	General Interest (Various Series)	1900	£3.50	–

KAYO CARDS LTD (U.S.A.)

X10	Heavyweight Holograms	1992	–	£15.00

M.& S.KEECH

15	Australian Cricket Team 1905	1986	–	£3.00
15	English Cricketers 1902	1987	–	£3.00

KEEPSAKE COLLECTIBLES (Commercial, USA)

X72	The Blue And The Gray	1997	–	£20.00
X72	Wild West	1996	–	£12.50

KEILLER (Confectionery)

Qty		Date	Odds	Sets
KF?146	Actresses & Views	1905	£11.00	—
F?146	Actresses & Views	1905	£9.00	—
XF18	Film Favourites	1926	£10.00	—
25	Scottish Heritage	1976	—	£6.50

KELLOGG LTD. (Cereals)

Qty		Date	Odds	Sets
16	A History Of British Military Aircraft	1963	£1.25	£20.00
16	Animals (3D)	1971	£3.50	—
12	Famous Firsts	1963	£0.25	£3.00
L20	Gardens To Visit	1988	£0.50	£10.00
12	International Soccer Stars	1963	£3.00	£36.00
M8	International Soccer Tips	1972	£5.00	—
40	Motor Cars (Black And White)	1949	£3.60	£144.00
40	(Coloured)	1949	£6.00	£240.00
X56	Playing Cards	1986	—	£4.00
8	Prehistoric Monsters And The Present	1985	£1.35	£11.00
16	Ships Of The British Navy	1962	£0.85	£13.50
M6	Space (Surprise Gifts)	1989	—	£3.00
12	The Story Of The Bicycle	1964	£3.50	£42.00
	The Story Of The Locomotive, A Series			
16	(English Issue)	1963	£1.25	£20.00
12	(Irish Issue)	1963	£4.00	£48.00
16	The Story Of The Locomotive, Series 2	1963	£0.75	£12.00
16	(Without Series 2)	1963	£2.75	£44.00
K8	Tony Racing Stickers	1988	—	£2.00
16	Veteran Motor Cars	1962	£0.85	£13.50

CANADIAN ISSUES

Qty		Date	Odds	Sets
M150	General Interest, 1st Set	1940	£1.75	£262.50
M150	General Interest, 2nd Set	1940	£1.75	—
M150	General Interest, 3rd Set	1940	£1.75	—

KENT COUNTY CONSTABULARY

Qty		Date	Odds	Sets
X24	England World Cup Squad 1982	1982	£3.00	—
X30	England World Cup Squad 1986	1986	£2.50	£75.00
X30	Olympic Athletes	1988	£1.40	£42.00

KENT COUNTY CRICKET CLUB

Qty		Date	Odds	Sets
51	Cricketers Of Kent	1986	—	£9.00

KENTUCKY FRIED CHICKEN

Qty		Date	Odds	Sets
L20	Star Wars Episode 1	1999	—	£6.50

KIDDY'S FAVOURITES LTD. (Commercial)

Qty		Date	Odds	Sets
52	New Popular Film Stars	1950	£4.00	—
50	Popular Boxers	1950	£3.00	£150.00
51/52	Popular Cricketers	1948	£3.40	£175.00
65	Popular Film Stars	1950	£5.00	—
51/52	Popular Footballers	1948	£3.50	£180.00
51/52	Popular Olympics	1948	£3.00	£150.00
52	Popular Players (Hearts On Front)	1950	£7.50	—
51/52	Popular Players (Shamrocks On Front)	1950	£3.50	£180.00
52	Popular Speedway Riders	1950	£3.50	—

KINGS OF YORK (Laundry)

Qty		Date	Odds	Sets
25	Flags Of All Nations (Silk)	1954	£2.50	£62.50
30	Kings & Queens Of England	1954	–	£2.75

KINGS LAUNDRIES LTD. (E. London)

Qty		Date	Odds	Sets
25	Famous Railway Engines	1953	£5.00	–
25	Modern British Warplanes	1953	£4.00	–
25	Modern Motor Cycles	1953	£4.00	–
25	Radio & Television Stars	1953	£4.00	–

KING'S SPECIALITIES (Food Products)

Qty		Date	Odds	Sets
26	Alphabet Rhymes	1915	£12.50	–
25	'Don'ts' Or Lessons In Etiquette	1915	£11.50	–
25	Heroes Of Famous Books	1914	£11.00	–
25	King's 'Discoveries'	1915	£11.00	–
25	King's 'Servants'	1915	£11.00	–
25	Proverbs	1915	£11.00	–
37	Unrecorded History	1915	£11.00	–
100	War Pictures	1915	£11.50	–
25	War Series	1915	£12.00	–
25	Where King's Supplies Grow	1914	£11.00	–

KITCHEN SINK PRESS (Commercial, U.S.A.)

Qty		Date	Odds	Sets
X90	The Crow	1996	–	£15.00

KLENE (Confectionery)

Qty		Date	Odds	Sets
L144	Animals Of The World	1954	£1.25	£180.00
L144	Birds Of The World	1954	£1.20	£175.00
L292	Film Stars	1954	£2.00	–
L50	Footballers	1936	£32.50	–
L48	Natural History Sketches	1954	£4.00	£200.00
L72	Popeye	1954	£5.00	–
L50	Shirley Temple Cards (1-50)	1935	£6.00	–
L20	Shirley Temple Cards (81-100, Coloured)	1935	£6.50	–
L60	Shirley Temple Cards (101-160)			
	(Black Title)	1935	£6.00	–
	(Blue Title, Different)	1935	£6.00	–
L50	Shirley Temple Cards (161-210)	1935	£6.50	–

KNOCKOUT (Periodical)

Qty		Date	Odds	Sets
20	Super Planes Of Today	1956	–	£5.00

KNORR (Cheese)

Qty		Date	Odds	Sets
T6	Great Trains Of Europe	1983	£5.00	–

KRAFT CHEESE

Qty		Date	Odds	Sets
12	Historic Military Uniforms	1971	–	£2.50

KYDD'S JAMS

Qty		Date	Odds	Sets
20	Fruits And Recipes	1912	£10.00	–

LACEY'S CHEWING GUM

Qty		Date	Odds	Sets
50	Footballers	1925	£32.50	–
?40	Uniforms	1923	£22.50	–

F. LAMBERT & SONS LTD. (Tea)

Qty		Date	Odds	Sets
25	Before Our Time	1961	—	£2.50
25	Birds And Their Eggs	1962	£1.00	£25.00
25	Butterflies And Moths	1960	—	£2.50
25	Cacti	1962	—	£2.50
25	Car Registration Numbers, A Series	1959	—	£6.00
25	Car Registration Numbers, Second Series	1960	£1.00	£25.00
25	Football Clubs And Badges	1958	—	£5.00
25	Game Birds And Wild Fowl	1964	£0.50	£12.50
25	Historic East Anglia	1961	—	£2.50
25	Interesting Hobbies	1965	—	£10.00
25	Passenger Liners	1965	—	£10.00
25	Past & Present	1964	—	£3.00
25	People & Places	1966	—	£5.00
25	Pond Life	1964	—	£7.50
25	Sports And Games	1964	—	£5.00

LANCASHIRE CONSTABULARY

Qty		Date	Odds	Sets
24	Cop-a-Cards	1987	—	£7.50
D11	Cop-a-Cards, Series 3	1989	—	£2.00
X12	Motor Cars	1987	—	£5.00

LANCASTER REPRINTS (Canada)

Qty		Date	Odds	Sets
X9	The Seven Ages Of Golf	1995	—	£4.50

HERBERT LAND (Cycles)

Qty		Date	Odds	Sets
30	Army Pictures, Cartoons, Etc.	1915	£45.00	—

LEAF BRANDS INC. (Confectionery)

Qty		Date	Odds	Sets
X50	Cliff Richard	1960	£3.75	—
X50	Do You Know?	1961	£0.30	£15.00
X90	Famous Artistes	1960	£1.90	£170.00
X50	Famous Discoveries And Adventures	1962	£2.50	£125.00
X50	Footballers	1961	£2.75	£135.00
X40	The Flag Game	1960	£0.40	£20.00
X50	Totem Pole Talking Signs	1962	£0.75	£37.00

LEGENDS WALL OF FAME (London)

Qty		Date	Odds	Sets
L20	British Rock Legends	1992	—	£9.00
X18	Illustrated Songs	1915	£4.00	—

LEVER BROS. (Soap)

Qty		Date	Odds	Sets
20	British Birds And Their Nests	1961	—	£2.00
F150	Celebrities	1900	£4.00	—
L39	Celebrities	1901	£7.00	£275.00
P24	The Life Of Queen Victoria (Series 3)	1902	£12.50	—

LEWIS'S LTD (Store)

Qty		Date	Odds	Sets
FX25	Real Photos Of Wild Animals	1930	£9.00	—

LIFEGUARD PRODUCTS (Soap)

Qty		Date	Odds	Sets
25	British Butterflies	1955	—	£3.00

LIME ROCK CO. INC. (Commercial USA)

Qty		Date	Odds	Sets
X110	Dream Machines (Cars)	1991	—	£15.00

LIMITED APPEAL (Commercial)

L10	Formula One 91	1992	—	£5.00

JOSEPH LINGFORD & SON (Baking Powder)

36	British War Leaders	1950	£1.75	£63.00

LIPTON LTD. (Tea)

48	Animals And Their Young (Canadian)	1991	£0.60	£30.00
60	Flags Of The World	1967	£0.30	—
50	The Conquest Of Space	1962	£0.80	£40.00

LITTLE CHEF (Restaurants)

M8	Disney Characters	1990	—	£16.00

LOCAL AUTHORITIES (School Meals)

5	British Sports Personalities	1997	—	£2.50

LONGLEAT HOUSE

25	Longleat House	1967	—	£2.50

LOS ANGELES FIRE DEPARTMENT (U.S.A.)

X4	Los Angeles Raiders	1985	—	£8.00

LOT-O-FUN (Periodical)

MF4	Sports Champions	1922	£6.00	£24.00

G.F. LOVELL & CO. (Confectionery)

36	British Royalty Series	1910	£35.00	—
36	Football Series	1910	£65.00	—
25	Photos Of Football Stars	1928	£22.50	—

BRIAN LUND POSTCARDS

6	Rugby Union Six Nations 2001	2001	—	£1.00
8	Rugby Union World Cup 1999	1999	—	£1.20

THE LYCHGATE PRESS

10	Eloise	2001	—	£4.00
10	Kings Of Comedy	2005	—	£4.00
10	Rock 'N' Roll Greats	2005	—	£4.50
L25	Soccer Gallery	2000	—	£7.50
10	The Beatles	2002	—	£4.00
18	Tottenham 2000	2000	—	£6.50

J. LYONS & CO. LTD. (Ice Cream & Tea)

40	All Systems Go	1968	£2.00	£80.00
48	Australia	1959	£0.40	£20.00
M20	Banknotes	1974	—	£6.50
M12	Beautiful Butterflies	1974	—	£3.00
25	Birds And Their Eggs	1962	£1.00	£25.00

J. LYONS & CO. LTD. (Ice Cream & Tea) – cont.

Qty		Date	Odds	Sets
40	British Wildlife	1970	£1.25	£50.00
L16	Catweazle Magic Cards	1971	–	£9.00
M20	County Badge Collection	1974	–	£2.50
X12	Did You Know?	1983	£0.50	£6.00
40	European Adventure	1969	£1.60	–
40	Famous Aircraft	1965	£0.60	£24.00
40	Famous Cars	1966	£2.00	£80.00
40	Famous Locomotives	1964	£2.50	£100.00
48	Famous People	1966	£0.90	£50.00
D12	Farmyard Stencils	1977	–	£6.50
M14	Flowers (Cut-Out)	1976	–	£28.00
32	HMS 1902-1962 (Descriptive)	1962	£0.25	£8.00
32	(Non-Descriptive)	1962	–	£8.00
X12	Horses In The Service Of Man	1984	–	£3.00
L35	Illustrated Map Of The British Isles	1959	£0.80	£28.00
40	International Footballers	1972	£5.00	–
40	Into The Unknown	1969	£1.50	£60.00
15	Jubilee	1977	£1.75	–
X10	Junior Champs	1983	–	£2.40
M24	Kings Of The Road	1977	£1.25	–
P6	150th Anniversary Of Postage Stamps	1990	–	£2.00
50	100 Years Of Motoring	1964	£1.20	£60.00
40	On Safari	1970	£1.20	£50.00
40	Pop Scene	1971	£2.50	£100.00
40	Pop Stars	1970	£2.50	£100.00
L10	Pop Stars (Shaped)	1975	–	£3.50
K48	Quick Puzzle Cards	1955	£1.60	–
40	Soccer Stars	1971	£4.50	–
40	Space Age Britain	1968	£1.60	–
40	Space Exploration	1963	£2.00	–
25	Space 1999	1976	£5.00	–
25	Star Trek	1979	£6.00	–
50	Train Spotters	1962	£0.60	£30.00
K100	Tricks & Puzzles	1926	£3.25	–
40	Views Of London	1967	£0.85	£34.00
48	What Do You Know?	1957	£0.20	£5.00
24	Wings Across The World (Descriptive)	1962	£0.20	£4.00
24	(Non-Descriptive)	1961	–	£8.00
24	Wings Of Speed (Descriptive Back)	1961	£0.20	£4.00
24	(Non-Descriptive)	1961	£0.50	£12.00

M.P. CARDS (Commercial)

Qty		Date	Odds	Sets
L14	Nishikigoi (Koi Carp)	1997	–	£15.00
L12	Samurai Warriors	1996	–	£10.00
L12	The Geisha Collection	1997	–	£10.00

M.P.L. LTD. (Records)

Qty		Date	Odds	Sets
M5	Wings - Back To The Egg	1981	–	£12.50

MAC FISHERIES (Shops)

Qty		Date	Odds	Sets
L12	Gallery Pictures	1924	£1.40	£17.00
L14	Japanese Colour Prints	1924	£1.40	£20.00
L12	Poster Pointers	1925	£1.20	£15.00
L12	Sporting Prints	1923	£4.50	£54.00

MACGIRR & CO. (Tea)

Qty		Date	Odds	Sets
24	Birds & Their Eggs	1912	£12.00	—

JOHN MACKINTOSH & SONS (Confectionery)

Qty		Date	Odds	Sets
16	Camping & Hiking Hints	1932	£17.50	—

MACROBERTSON (Confectionery, Australia)

Qty		Date	Odds	Sets
24	Flags Of All Nations	1916	£6.50	£156.00
24	Naval & Military Decorations	1916	£8.50	—
24	Sons/Allies Of The Empire	1916	£8.50	—
50	Sports Of The World	1916	£4.00	£200.00

WM. MCEWAN & CO LTD (Brewers)

Qty		Date	Odds	Sets
25	Old Glasgow	1929	£12.50	—

MCVITIE & PRICE (Food)

Qty		Date	Odds	Sets
8	The European War Series	1914	£17.50	£140.00

MCVITIE'S (Biscuits)

Qty		Date	Odds	Sets
M10	Superstars	1976	—	£20.00

MADISON CONFECTIONERY PRODUCTIONS LTD

Qty		Date	Odds	Sets
X16/32	Christmas Greeting Cards	1957	£1.25	£20.00
X48	Disc Jockey, 1st Series	1957	£2.50	£120.00
X48	Disc Jockey, 2nd Series	1958	£2.00	£100.00
X50	Recording Stars	1958	£1.75	£87.50

THE MAGNET LIBRARY (Periodical)

Qty		Date	Odds	Sets
MF15	Footballers	1922	£4.50	£67.50
MF6	Football Teams	1922	£5.00	£30.00
MF4	Football Teams	1923	£5.00	£20.00

MAINSTREAM PUBLISHING (Commercial)

Qty		Date	Odds	Sets
13	Shirt Of Legends - The Story Of Newcastle United's No.9 Heroes	2005	—	£6.00

MANCHESTER EVENING NEWS (Newspaper)

Qty		Date	Odds	Sets
L30	Footballers	1976	£3.50	—

MANCHESTER UNITED FOOTBALL CLUB

Qty		Date	Odds	Sets
X26	Manchester United Footballers	1991	—	£15.00

MAPLE LEAF GUM

Qty		Date	Odds	Sets
K75	Flag Tie Pins (Metal)	1960	£0.65	—
K90	Motor Car & Motor Cycle Badges (Metal)	1960	£1.25	—

R. MARCANTONIO LTD. (Ice Lollies)

Qty		Date	Odds	Sets
50	Interesting Animals	1953	—	£4.50

A. T. MARKS (Commercial)

Qty		Date	Odds	Sets
11	1892 Gloucestershire (Cricketers)	1990	—	£1.75
11	1892 Middlesex	1990	—	£1.75
11	1892 Surrey	1990	—	£2.75

A. T. MARKS (Commercial) – cont.

Qty		Date	Odds	Sets
11	1892 Sussex	1990	–	£2.75
12	1903 Middlesex	1990	–	£1.75
12	1903 Yorkshire	1990	–	£1.75
11	1912 Northamptonshire	1990	–	£2.75

MARLOW CIVIL ENGINEERING LTD

25	Famous Clowns	1990	–	£30.00

MARS CONFECTIONS LTD.

25	Ceremonies Of The Coronation			
	(Black Back, Blue Caption)	1937	£1.20	£30.00
	(Black Back, Brown Caption)	1937	£2.00	£50.00
	(Blue Back)	1937	£4.50	–
50	Famous Aeroplanes, Pilots & Airports	1938	£1.75	£87.50
50	Famous Escapes	1937	£1.40	£70.00
50	Famous Film Stars	1939	£1.75	£87.50
25	Wonders Of The Queen Mary	1936	£1.60	£40.00

JAMES MARSHALL (Glasgow) Ltd. (Food)

30	Colonial Troops	1900	£37.50	–
1	Marshall's Products Illustrated	1926	–	£5.00
40	Recipes	1926	£4.00	–

MASTER VENDING CO. LTD. (Gum)

X25	A Bombshell For The Sheriff	1959	£0.80	£20.00
X50	Cardmaster Football Tips	1958	£1.50	£75.00
X16	Cricketer Series-New Zealand 1958	1958	£1.25	£20.00
X50	Did You Know? (Football)	1959	£1.30	£65.00
X100	Jet Aircraft Of The World	1958	£1.75	£175.00
X100	(German Text)	1958	£2.00	–
X25	Taxing The Sheriff	1959	£0.70	£17.50
X36	Tommy Steele	1958	£3.50	£126.00

J. JOHN MASTERS & CO. (Matches)

X12	Food From Britain	1987	–	£1.50

MATCH (Periodical)

X31	F. A. Cup Fact File	1986	–	£7.50

MATCHBOX INT'L LTD. (Toys)

75	Matchbox Model Vehicles	1985	£0.70	£52.50

MAXILIN MARKETING CO.

25	Motor Cars	1951	–	£5.00

MAYNARDS LTD. (Confectionery)

12	Billy Bunter Series	1926	£22.50	–
?17	Football Clubs	1933	£35.00	–
18	Girl Guide Series	1921	£17.50	–
50	Girls Of All Nations	1921	£5.00	£250.00
12	Strange Insects	1935	£4.00	£50.00
8	The European War Series	1916	£17.50	£140.00

MAYNARDS LTD. (Confectionery) – cont.

Qty		Date	Odds	Sets
12	Wonders Of The Deep	1935	£5.75	£70.00
12	World's Wonder Series (Numbered)	1930	£4.50	£54.00
10	World's Wonder Series (Unnumbered)	1930	£5.50	£55.00

MAYPOLE (Grocers)

Qty		Date	Odds	Sets
25	War Series	1915	£10.00	£250.00

MAZAWATTEE (Tea)

Qty		Date	Odds	Sets
X39	Kings And Queens	1902	£4.50	£180.00

MEADOW DAIRY CO.

Qty		Date	Odds	Sets
50	War Series	1915	£9.00	£450.00

J. F. MEARBECK (Printer)

Qty		Date	Odds	Sets
30	Army Pictures, Cartoons, Etc.	1915	£45.00	–

MELLIN'S FOOD

Qty		Date	Odds	Sets
K2	Diamond Jubilee Coins	1897	£10.00	£20.00

MELOX (Dog Food)

Qty		Date	Odds	Sets
L50	Famous Breeds Of Dogs	1937	£7.00	£350.00
M32	Happy Families (Dogs)	1929	£8.00	£256.00

MERLIN TRADING CARDS (Commercial)

Qty		Date	Odds	Sets
X156	Premier Gold 98	1997	–	£30.00
X105	Premier Gold 2000	1999	–	£15.00
X20	Premier Gold 2000 - Club Badges	1999	–	£10.00
X20	Premier Gold 2000 - Top Scorer	1999	–	£10.00
X120	Premier League	1994	–	£15.00
X88	Premier League	1996	–	£12.50

MERRYSWEETS LTD.

Qty		Date	Odds	Sets
X48	Telegum TV Stars	1958	£1.60	£80.00
X48	Tracepiks	1960	£7.00	–
X48	World Racing Cars	1959	£3.00	£150.00

GEOFFREY MICHAEL PUBLISHERS LTD

Qty		Date	Odds	Sets
40	Modern Motor Cars	1949	£1.60	£64.00
F48	Mystery Cards - Modern Motor Cars	1953	£6.50	–

MIDLAND CARTOPHILIC BRANCH

Qty		Date	Odds	Sets
L24	Silhouettes Of Veteran & Vintage Cars	1991	–	£6.00

MIDLAND COUNTIES (Ice Cream)

Qty		Date	Odds	Sets
12	Action Soldiers (With Cadbury)	1976	–	£3.50
M20	Banknotes	1974	–	£12.50
D12	Farmyard Stencils	1977	–	£2.50
M24	Kings Of The Road	1977	–	£6.50
X10	Steam Power	1978	–	£4.00

MILK MARKETING BOARD

Qty		Date	Odds	Sets
P10	Milk Recipe Cards	1979	–	£2.50
25	Prehistoric Animals	1963	–	£7.50

MILLERS (Tea)

Qty		Date	Odds	Sets
25	Animals & Reptiles	1962	—	£3.00

ROBERT R. MIRANDA (Confectionery)

Qty		Date	Odds	Sets
50	150 Years Of Locomotives	1956	—	£6.00
50	100 Years Of Motoring	1955	—	£6.00
25	Ships Through The Ages	1957	—	£7.50
50	Strange Creatures	1961	—	£6.00

MISTER SOFTEE LTD. (Ice Cream)

Qty		Date	Odds	Sets
12	Action Soldiers (With Cadbury)	1976	—	£6.00
M12	Beautiful Butterflies	1977	£0.75	—
M20	County Badge Collection	1976	£0.20	£3.00
L12	Did You Know?	1976	£0.35	£4.25
25	Do You Know?	1961	£3.00	—
D20	Famous Sports Trophies	1975	—	£10.00
D12	Farmyard Stencils	1977	—	£4.00
M24	1st Division Football League Badges	1972	—	£6.50
M24	Kings Of The Road	1977	£0.30	£7.50
E1	Map Of The British Isles	1976	—	£2.50
15	Moon Mission	1962	£2.40	—
M24	Pop Discs	1972	£1.00	£24.00
P24	Pop Parade	1969	£1.75	—
M10	Pop Stars (Shaped)	1975	£0.85	£8.50
X1	Secret Code Computer	1977	—	£0.75
20	Sports Cups (Shaped)	1975	—	£12.00
M20	Stamp In A Million	1976	£0.50	£10.00
P12	Star Cards (Numbered, With Address)	1966	£2.00	£24.00
P12	Star Cards (Numbered, No Address)	1967	£2.00	£24.00
P24	Star Cards (Unnumbered)	1968	£2.00	£48.00
P24	Star Cards (Numbered)	1969	£2.00	£48.00
X24	Star Discs	1970	£2.00	£48.00
X10	Steam Power	1978	—	£3.00
M4	Super Human Heroes	1979	—	£3.00
P12	Top 10	1964	—	£7.50
P12	Top Ten (Address N.7.)	1965	£2.50	£30.00
P12	(Address W.6.)	1966	£4.50	—
20	Top 20	1963	£0.85	£17.00
25	T. V. Personalities	1962	£3.00	—
P12	Your World	1963	—	£4.00

MITCHAM FOODS LTD.

Qty		Date	Odds	Sets
25	Aircraft Of Today	1955	—	£3.50
25	Aquarium Fish, 1st Series	1957	£2.00	£50.00
25	Aquarium Fish, 2nd Series	1957	—	£3.50
50	Butterflies And Moths	1959	£1.25	£62.50
25	Footballers	1956	£3.00	—
50	Mars Adventure	1958	£6.00	—
25	Motor Racing	1960	£2.50	£62.50

MOBIL OIL CO. LTD.

Qty		Date	Odds	Sets
M30	Football Club Badges (Silk)	1983	£2.40	£72.00
X36	The Story Of Grand Prix Motor Racing	1971	—	£16.00
25	Veteran And Vintage Cars	1962	£2.50	£62.50
24	Vintage Cars	1966	—	£6.00

MODERN WEEKLY (Periodical)

Qty		Date	Odds	Sets
P3	Film Couples (Silk)	1928	£30.00	£90.00

MOFFAT B.& G. LTD. (Confectionery)

D102	Money That Made History	1981	—	£10.00

MOFFAT BROS (Confectionery)

L100	Cinema Artistes	1914	£12.50	—

THE MOLASSINE CO. (Dog Food)

50	Dogs (Full Length)	1963	£1.50	£75.00
50	Dogs (Heads)	1964	£2.00	£100.00
25	Dogs At Work	1970	—	£6.00
12	Dogs Of All Countries	1925	£10.00	£120.00
50	Puppies	1967	£2.00	£100.00

MONTAGU MOTOR MUSEUM

M24	Veteran & Vintage Cars	1965	£3.50	£84.00

MONTY GUM

M98	Bruce Lee	1980	—	£33.00
L72	Daily Fables, 1st Series	1968	—	£27.00
X50	Elvis	1978	£3.00	—
M72	Flag Parade	1972	—	£11.00
M100	Flags Of All Nations	1980	—	£8.50
X56	Footballers (P/C Inset)	1961	£3.30	—
M72	Kojak	1975	£0.55	£40.00
M54	Kojak (P/C Inset, Black Back)	1976	—	£27.50
M56	Kojak (P/C Inset, Red Back)	1976	£0.75	—
X56	Motor Cars (P/C Inset)	1956	£1.70	£95.00
M72	Starsky And Hutch	1978	£1.10	—
M100	The Cops 1st Series	1976	£0.55	£55.00
M124	The High Chaparral	1970	£0.85	—

MOORE'S TOFFEE

T50	The Post In Many Lands	1900	£22.50	—

MORNING FOODS LTD.

1	Advertisement Card	1953	—	£7.50
F25	British Planes (Numbered)	1953	£7.00	—
F25	(Unnumbered)	1953	£1.00	£25.00
F50	British Trains	1952	£7.00	—
25	British Uniforms	1954	—	£7.50
50	Modern Cars	1954	£0.70	£35.00
50	Our England	1955	—	£6.00
25	Test Cricketers	1953	£2.40	£60.00
12	The Cunard Line (Black Back)	1957	—	£3.00
12	(Blue Back)	1957	—	£5.00
25	World Locomotives (Black Back)	1954	—	£3.50
25	(Blue Back)	1954	£1.00	£25.00

E.D.L. MOSELEY (Confectionery)

M25	Historical Buildings	1954	—	£3.00

MOTOR CYCLE NEWS

Qty		Date	Odds	Sets
24	'Best Of British' Collection (With Folder)	1988	—	£3.00
L6	Motorcycle Classics	1995	—	£2.50

MOTOR MAGAZINE

24	The Great British Sports Car (Including Album)	1988	—	£6.00

MOTORSPORT CHARITY MEMORABILIA

50	Formula 1 World Championship	2000	—	£9.50

V. MUHLENEN & CO. (Cheese)

M6	Swiss Views, Series III	1955	—	£9.00
M6	Swiss Views, Series IV	1955	—	£9.00

MURCO PETROLEUM

P28	English Counties	1986	—	£5.00
D20	Nations Of Europe	1986	—	£6.00
M50	World's Airlines	1978	—	£5.00

C R S MURRAY & CO LTD (Chocolates)

1	The Caramel Chief	1930	—	£20.00

MUSEUM OF BRITISH MILITARY UNIFORMS

25	British Cavalry Uniforms	1987	—	£5.00
25	Military Maids	1987	—	£7.50
25	Warriors Through The Ages	1987	—	£5.00

MUSICAL COLLECTABLES (Commercial)

26	The G & S Collection, 1st Series (Player Reprint)	1994	—	£6.00
26	The G & S Collection, 2nd Series (Player Reprint)	1994	—	£6.00

MUSGRAVE BROS. LTD. (Tea)

25	Birds	1961	£1.20	£30.00
20	British Birds	1960	£10.00	£200.00
50	British Wild Life	1962	£7.50	£375.00
50	Butterflies Of The World	1964	£7.50	£375.00
25	Into Space	1961	—	£5.00
25	Modern Motor Cars	1962	£0.70	£17.50
25	Pond Life	1963	£0.50	£12.50
25	Products Of The World	1961	—	£3.00
50	Transport Through The Ages	1966	£5.00	£250.00
25	Tropical Birds	1964	—	£4.00
25	Wild Flowers	1961	£0.50	£12.50

MYERS & METREVELI (Gum)

KF48	Film Stars	1953	£3.25	—
X48	Film Stars & Biographies	1953	£6.50	—
X60	Hollywood Peep Show	1953	£4.50	—
L50	Spot The Planes	1953	£5.50	—

MY WEEKLY (Periodical)

M9	Battle Series (Silk)	1916	£8.00	£72.00
M12	Floral Beauties (Silk)	1914	£8.00	—

Nowadays one is accustomed to ading of multi-national corporations. urprisingly many of the larger cigarette rd issuers were such almost a century o. Duke issued cards in South Africa, oodwin in Australia, Allen & Ginter in ritain and the Canadian firm Ritchie in ermany, Australia, India and England. he American Tobacco Co. issued many rds in Britain with its Old Gold brand, d eventually through its purchase of gden, which precipitated the Tobacco ar. British firms flourished in their pected spheres of influence, the British npire, with many issues in Malta, India d Australia. In some cases a series as prepared specifically for one ntry, but often a set would be issued in several areas.

Sometimes the series had to be adapted to suit the requirements of the country in which it was to be issued. The text of the New Zealand version of Godfrey Phillips Annuals was amended to show different dates for "planting out", while Ardath changed just one card of the Mitchell Our Empire set to include the current New Zealand Prime Minister. In the case of the Player Hints on Association Football the fronts were re-drawn to show Oriental features for the B.A.T. Chinese set.

The criterion in this catalogue for determining whether series should be shown in Part 1 or Part 2 is generally based on the main location of the issuer rather than the area of issue. So all American based Companies will be found in Part 2. Ritchie, which issued cards in Britain, is essentially a Canadian firm, so is also in Part 2. Firms such as International Tobacco Co. and A. & M. Wix, which were based in England, but most of whose issues were abroad, are nevertheless shown in Part 1. One major exception is British American Tobacco Co., which was incorporated in Britain, but all of whose cigarettes were sold abroad, and is therefore shown in Part 2. The decision has in several cases been marginal, and entirely subjective, so when in doubt consult BOTH sections!

In 1902 at the conclusion of the "Tobacco War", the British American Tobacco Co. was incorporated in Britain for the purpose of marketing all I.T.C. and A.T.C. tobacco products in countries other than the U.S.A., Cuba, Great Britain and Ireland.

In many British Empire countries B.A.T. began to market under the name of a subsidiary Company. In Canada it was the Imperial Tobacco Co. of Canada, while in India the Imperial Tobacco Co. of India shared the stage with the Peninsular Tobacco Co. In South Africa the dominant name was United Tobacco Co. and in South America Cia Chilena and Cia Nobleza. In Australia the majority of issues bore the Wills name, either with Capstan or Vice-Regal, except that some also appeared as Havelock Cigarettes, with no issuer's name. Brands in New Zealand appeared under the names of Lambert & Butler, Player and Wills, as well as the local Dominion Tobacco Co; local arrangements were made with companies such as Ardath, as may be deduced from their issue in New Zealand of their versions of sets such as Churchman Eastern Proverbs, Player Tennis and Ogden Swimming Diving & Life Saving.

Card issues appeared with all the above firms' names, as well as some, particularly earlier issues such as the tobacco war Beauties, which have the B.A.T. name. There were also many in foreign languages such as Motor Cigarettes (Portugal), Albert (Belgium) and Gold Dollar (Germany), as well as a number in Chinese and Siamese characters. A large section of B.A.T.'s card output however appears with no clues as to the issuer, both with printed backs (often mentioning cigarettes) and with plain backs.

When the B.A.T. issue utilises the name of a British firm, such as Ogden or Wills, then in the Catalogue the cards will be found listed under that firm, often in a separate group. Anonymous series that were issued exclusively in Canada or South Africa are included in Part 2 under Imperial Tobacco Co. of Canada or United Tobacco Co. respectively. All other Anonymous sets known to have been produced by B.A.T. are listed under that firm in Part 2.

A more detailed explanation of the foundation and ramifications of B.A.T. may be found in the B.A.T. Book which is combined with the Cigarette Card Issues of Wills and is priced at £20.50.

MY WEEKLY (Periodical) – cont.

Qty		Date	Odds	Sets
M15	Language Of Flowers (Silk)	1914	£8.00	£120.00
M54	Lucky Emblems (Silk)	1912	£9.00	–
M6	Lucky Flowers (Silk)	1913	£12.50	–
M12	Our Soldier Boys (Silk)	1915	£8.00	£96.00
M14	Soldiers Of The King (Silk)	1914	£7.50	£105.00
M6	Sweet Kiss Series (Silk)	1913	£8.50	–
M6	War Heroes (Silk)	1916	£8.50	£51.00

NABISCO FOODS LTD.

M5	Aces In Action (Aviation)	1980	£4.00	£20.00
L24	Action Shots Of Olympic Sports	1980	£2.00	£48.00
X4	Adventure Books	1970	£6.00	–
12	British Soldiers	1971	–	£1.50
P20	Champions Of Sport	1961	£3.25	£65.00
P6	Eagle Eye Games	1979	–	£3.50
P8	England's Soccer Stars Tactic Cards	1980	£3.75	£30.00
12	E.T.	1983	–	£6.00
L24	Footballers (2 Printings)	1970	£3.25	£78.00
G12	Freshwater Fishes Of Britain	1974	£1.25	£15.00
L10	History Of Aviation	1970	£2.50	£25.00
D4	Johan Cruyff Demonstrates	1980	£5.00	£20.00
P10	Kevin Keegans Keep Fit With The Stars	1978	–	£17.50
P10	Motor Show	1960	£3.00	£30.00
P6	Play 'N Score	1989	–	£7.50
L6	World Super Stars & Sporting Trophies	1980	£4.50	–

AUSTRALIAN ISSUES

32	Leading Cricketers (Crispies Etc.)	1948	£4.00	£128.00
M66	Popular Pets	1962	£0.40	£26.00
L24	United Nations In Action	1968	–	£12.00

EDWARD NASSAR & CO. (Coffee, Gold Coast)

25	Transport, Present & Future	1955	–	£3.00

NATIONAL SPASTICS SOCIETY

24	Famous County Cricketers (Booklet)	1958	£2.50	£60.00
24	Famous Footballers	1959	£3.00	£72.00

NEEDLER'S (Confectionery)

12	Military Series	1916	£25.00	–

PHILIP NEILL COLLECTABLES (Commercial)

15	Arsenal - Double Legends Of 1970/71	2002	–	£5.50
10	Bizarre Club Shirts	2001	–	£4.00
12	Brazil 70	2005	–	£4.75
10	Brazilliant! (Pele)	2001	–	£4.00
20	British Internationals 1950-1952 (Soccer)	1999	–	£6.99
L7	Celtic '67	1999	–	£4.15
10	Classic Kits (Soccer)	2001	–	£4.00
15	Classic Soccer Strips	2006	–	£5.50
15	Derby County Champions Of 1971/72	2007	–	£5.50
L10	Elvis In Pictures	2003	–	£5.75
10	England's Top Goal Scorers	2002	–	£4.00

PHILIP NEILL COLLECTABLES (Commercial) – cont.

Qty		Date	Odds	Sets
25	Fergie's Heroes 2003/04	2003	—	£7.50
10	Football Heroes	2001	—	£4.00
10	Football In The Fifties	2001	—	£4.00
15	Football Stars Of The Seventies	2002	—	£5.50
15	Football Stars Of The Seventies, 2nd Series	2003	—	£5.50
15	Footballer Of The Year	1999	—	£5.50
12	Forest: Kings Of Europe '79	2005	—	£4.50
10	International Stars Of Yesteryear	2000	—	£4.00
10	International Stars Of Yesteryear 2	2001	—	£4.00
15	Kings Of Europe (Manchester United)	1999	—	£5.50
15	Leeds United - The Revie Era	2002	—	£5.50
15	Liverpool - Champions League 2005	2005	—	£5.50
15	Liverpool: Kings Of Europe 1977	2005	—	£5.50
15	Liverpool Legends	2000	—	£5.50
15	Maine Road Heroes	2003	—	£5.50
15	Manchester United's Classic Kits	2003	—	£5.50
15	Moscow Magic (Manchester United 2008)	2008	—	£5.50
15	Newcastle Heroes (Soccer)	2004	—	£5.50
15	Rangers Euro Kings Of '72	2006	—	£5.50
10	Scottish Footballers	2000	—	£4.00
10	Scottish Internationals	2002	—	£4.00
15	70s Soccer Stars	2003	—	£5.50
10	Soccer 70 - The Year In Football	2002	—	£4.00
10	Soccer In The 60s Volume 1	1999	—	£4.00
10	Soccer In The 60s Volume 2	2000	—	£4.00
10	Soccer Selection	2004	—	£4.50
10	Soccer Stars Of The 50s	2001	—	£4.00
10	Soccer Stars Of The 60s	2001	—	£4.00
L18	Super Reds	1998	—	£7.50
10	Ten Of The Best - George Best	2000	—	£4.00
15	The Busby Babes	2002	—	£5.50
15	The Busby Babes, A Second Series	2005	—	£5.50
15	Tottenham Double Winners	2004	—	£5.50
25	United Legends	2000	—	£7.50
15	United '68 (Manchester United European Cup Winners)	2006	—	£5.50
12	Villa Cup Winners 1957	2005	—	£4.50
10	Vintage Footballers Of The 1900s	2005	—	£4.00
L7	Visions Of Marilyn Monroe	2003	—	£4.15
15	West Ham United Cup Winning Sides Of 1964 & 65	2007	—	£5.50

NEILSON'S (Confectionery)

50	Interesting Animals	1954	—	£5.00

NELSON LEE LIBRARY (Periodical)

MF15	Footballers	1922	£4.50	£67.50
MF6	Modern British Locomotives	1922	£7.00	£42.00

NESTLE LTD. (Chocolate)

L12	Animal Bars (Wrappers)	1970	—	£2.50
24	Animals Of The World	1962	—	£12.50
P12	British Birds (Reward Cards)	1900	£13.00	£156.00
49	Happy Families	1935	£1.10	£65.00
144	Pictorial World Atlas	1934	£2.50	—
100	Stars Of The Silver Screen	1936	£1.50	£150.00

NESTLE LTD. (Chocolate) - cont.

Qty		Date	Odds	Sets
50	Stars Of The Silver Screen, Volume II	1937	£2.20	£110.00
136	This England	1936	£0.85	£115.00
T24	Wild Animals, Serie II	1910	£7.00	−
156	Wonders Of The World, Volume I	1932	£0.70	−
144	Wonders Of The World, Volume II	1933	£0.75	−

NEW ENGLAND CONFECTIONERY CO. (U.S.A.)

M12	Real Airplane Pictures	1929	£4.50	£54.00

NEW HOLLAND MACHINE CO.

P12	Traction Engines	1960	£4.50	£54.00

NEWMARKET HARDWARE

L24	Some Of Britain's Finest Bikes	1993	−	£6.00

NEWTON, CHAMBERS & CO. (Toilet Rolls)

P18	More Rhyme Time (19-36)	1934	£3.75	£67.50
P18	Nursery Rhyme Pictures (1-18)	1934	£3.75	£67.50

NEW ZEALAND MEAT PRODUCERS BOARD

X25	Scenes Of New Zealand Lamb	1930	£4.00	£100.00

90 MINUTES (Magazine)

X56	Footballers (Playing Card Inset)	1993	−	£25.00

NORTHERN CO-OPERATIVE SOCIETY (Tea)

25	Birds	1963	£1.20	£30.00
25	History Of The Railways, 1st Series	1964	£0.50	£12.50
25	History Of The Railways, 2nd Series	1964	£0.60	£15.00
25	Passenger Liners	1963	−	£3.00
25	Then And Now	1963	−	£30.00
25	Tropical Birds	1962	−	£12.50
25	Weapons Of World War II	1962	−	£15.00
25	Wonders Of The Deep	1965	−	£2.50

NORTH WEST TOURIST BOARD

T40	Attractions In The North East	2008	−	£5.00
T40	Stockport	1995	−	£5.00
T40	Wigan	1992	−	£5.00

THE NOSTALGIA CLASSIC COLLECTION (Reprints)

P4	Adkin - Games By Tom Browne	2001	−	£4.00
9	Allen & Ginter (U.S.A.) - Women Baseball Players	2001	−	£3.00
X50	Allen & Ginter (U.S.A.) - The World's Champions, Second Series	2001	−	£17.50
35	Ardath - Hand Shadows	2001	−	£7.50
25	A. Baker - Star Girls	2001	−	£6.00
20	Bradford - Boer War Cartoons	2001	−	£5.00
L16	Brigham - Down The Thames From Henley To Windsor	2001	−	£6.50
25	B.A.T. - Beauties, Blossom Girls	2001	−	£6.00
T6	Cadbury - Sports Series	2001	−	£3.00
10	Chappel - British Celebrities	2001	−	£3.00

THE NOSTALGIA CLASSIC COLLECTION – cont.

Qty		Date	Odds	Sets
30	Clarke - Cricketer Series..	2001	–	£7.50
P7	Cope - The Seven Ages Of Man...	2001	–	£6.00
6	Empire Tobacco - Franco British Exhibition........................	2001	–	£2.00
25	Faulkner - Beauties (Coloured)...	2001	–	£6.00
25	Globe Cigarette Co. - Actresses - French..........................	2001	–	£6.00
17	Goode (Australia) - Prominent Cricketer Series..................	2001	–	£5.00
8	Hall (U.S.A.) - Presidential Candidates & Actresses...........	2001	–	£2.00
P12	Huntley & Palmers - Aviation...	2001	–	£7.50
M20	James & Co. - Arms Of Countries......................................	2001	–	£7.50
50	Kimball - Champions Of Games And Sports........................	2001	–	£10.00
15	Kinnear - Australian Cricket Team.....................................	2001	–	£4.00
50	Kriegsfeld - Phrases & Advertisements..............................	2001	–	£10.00
25	Kuit - Principal British Streets...	2001	–	£6.00
50	Lacey's - Footballers...	2001	–	£10.00
20	Lambert & Butler - International Yachts.............................	2001	–	£5.00
20	J. Lees - Northampton Town Football Club.........................	2001	–	£5.00
X6	Liebig (France) - Famous Explorers (S.1094).....................	2001	–	£5.00
25	Lusby - Scenes From Circus Life......................................	2001	–	£6.00
15	Marburg (U.S.A.) - Beauties, "PAC"..................................	2001	–	£4.00
35	Mayo (U.S.A.) - Prizefighters..	2001	–	£7.50
13	National (Australia) - English Cricket Team 1897-8.............	2001	–	£4.00
50	Ogden - Cricketers & Sportsmen......................................	2001	–	£10.00
X16	Old Calabar - Sports And Games......................................	2001	–	£7.50
40	Orlando Cigarette Co. - Home & Colonial Regiments..........	2001	–	£8.50
30	Godfrey Phillips - Beauties, Nymphs.................................	2001	–	£7.50
20	Godfrey Phillips - Russo Japanese War Series..................	2001	–	£5.00
20	Richmond Cavendish - Yachts (White Back).......................	2001	–	£5.00
6	E. Robinson & Sons - Medals & Decorations			
	Of Great Britain...	2001	–	£2.00
25	E. Robinson & Sons - Regimental Mascots........................	2001	–	£6.00
16	S.D.V. Tobacco - British Royal Family...............................	2001	–	£4.00
30	Salmon & Gluckstein - Music Hall Stage Characters...........	2001	–	£7.50
50	Singleton & Cole - Footballers..	2001	–	£10.00
25	F. & J. Smith - Advertisement Cards.................................	2001	–	£6.00
50	F. & J. Smith - Champions Of Sport (Unnumbered).............	2001	–	£10.00
10	Spiro Valleri - Footballers...	2001	–	£3.00
12	Spratt - Prize Dogs...	2001	–	£3.50
5	Taddy - English Royalty...	2001	–	£2.00
20	Taddy - Royalty, Actresses & Soldiers.............................	2001	–	£5.00
10	United Tobacconists - Actresses, "MUTA".........................	2001	–	£3.00
22	Henry Welfare - Prominent Politicians...............................	2001	–	£6.00

NOSTALGIA REPRINTS

Qty		Date	Odds	Sets
28	Baseball Greats Of 1890 ((U.S.A. Tobacco).......................	1991	–	£6.00
2	Baseball Stars (Ruth, Sisler)...	1992	–	£0.50
50	Celebrated American Indian Chiefs (Allen & Ginter)............	1989	–	£8.50
20	Clowns And Circus Artistes (Taddy)..................................	1991	–	£6.00
50	Cope's Golfers..	1984	–	£10.00
238	County Cricketers (Taddy)...	1987	–	£32.00
15	Derbyshire..	1987	–	£2.50
15	Essex...	1987	–	£2.50
16	Gloucestershire...	1987	–	£2.50
15	Hampshire..	1987	–	£2.50
15	Kent...	1987	–	£2.50

NOSTALGIA REPRINTS – cont.

Qty		Date	Odds	Sets
15	Lancashire	1987	–	£2.50
14	Leicestershire	1987	–	£2.50
15	Middlesex	1987	–	£2.50
15	Northamptonshire	1987	–	£2.50
14	Nottinghamshire	1987	–	£2.50
15	Somersetshire	1987	–	£2.50
15	Surrey	1987	–	£2.50
15	Sussex	1987	–	£2.50
15	Warwickshire	1987	–	£2.50
14	Worcestershire	1987	–	£2.50
15	Yorkshire	1987	–	£2.50
50	Cricketers 1896 (Wills)	1983	–	£8.50
20	Cricketers Series 1902 (Gabriel)	1992	–	£3.50
12	Cricket Terms (Faulkner)	1999	–	£2.50
50	Dickens Gallery (Cope)	1989	–	£12.50
25	Fishers (Duke, U.S.A.)	2002	–	£6.00
12	Football Terms, 1st Series (Faulkner)	1999	–	£2.50
12	Football Terms, 2nd Series (Faulkner)	1999	–	£2.50
50	Fruits (Allen & Ginter, U.S.A.)	1989	–	£8.50
25	Generals Of The Late Civil War (Ellis, U.S.A.)	1991	–	£6.00
12	Golf Terms (Faulkner)	1999	–	£2.50
12	Grenadier Guards (Faulkner)	1999	–	£2.50
25	Humorous Golfing Series (Berlyn)	1989	–	£6.00
25	Leaders (Kinney, U.S.A.)	1990	–	£6.00
50	Military Series (Player)	1984	–	£8.50
12	Military Terms, 1st Series (Faulkner)	1999	–	£2.50
12	Military Terms, 2nd Series (Faulkner)	1999	–	£2.50
24	Motor Bike Cards (Thomson)	1993	–	£6.00
20	Motor Cycles (Thomson)	1993	–	£6.00
25	National Costumes (Wills)	1999	–	£6.00
25	Natives Of The World (Taddy)	1999	–	£6.00
12	Nautical Terms, 1st Series (Faulkner)	1999	–	£2.50
12	Nautical Terms, 2nd Series (Faulkner-Grenadier)	1999	–	£2.50
25	Parrot Series (C.W.S.)	2001	–	£6.00
12	Policemen Of The World (Faulkner-Grenadier)	1999	–	£2.50
12	Police Terms (Faulkner)	1999	–	£2.50
	Prominent Footballers (Taddy, 1907)			
15	Aston Villa	1992	–	£2.50
15	Chelsea	1998	–	£2.50
15	Everton	1998	–	£2.50
15	Leeds City	1992	–	£2.50
15	Liverpool	1992	–	£2.50
15	Manchester United	1992	–	£2.50
15	Middlesbrough	1998	–	£2.50
15	Newcastle United	1992	–	£2.50
15	Queen's Park Rangers	1992	–	£2.50
15	Sunderland	1998	–	£2.50
15	Tottenham Hotspur	1998	–	£2.50
15	West Ham United	1998	–	£2.50
15	Woolwich Arsenal	1992	–	£2.50
4	Promotional Cards	1992	–	£0.75
12	Puzzle Series (Faulkner-Grenadier)	1999	–	£2.50
12	Sporting Terms (Faulkner)	1999	–	£2.50
18	Spurs Footballers (Jones Bros.)	1987	–	£2.50
12	Street Cries (Faulkner)	1999	–	£2.50

NUGGET POLISH CO.

Qty		Date	Odds	Sets
X30	Allied Series	1910	£15.00	–
50	Flags Of All Nations	1925	£5.00	£250.00
X40	Mail Carriers And Stamps	1910	£13.50	£540.00

NUMBER ONE (Periodical)

P5	Get Fit And Have Fun	1991	–	£2.00

NUNBETTA (Grocer)

25	Motor Cars	1955	£10.00	£250.00

O.V.S. TEA COMPANY

K25	Modern Engineering	1955	–	£6.00

O'CARROLL KENT LTD (Confectionery)

50	Railway Engines	1955	£4.50	£225.00

NICK OLDHAM (Commercial)

13	Golf Legends Series 1	2005	–	£6.00

TONY L. OLIVER (Commercial)

25	Aircraft Of World War II	1964	£5.00	–
50	German Orders & Decorations	1963	£3.00	–
50	German Uniforms	1971	–	£15.00
M25	Vehicles Of The German Wehrmacht	1965	–	£30.00

ONLY FOOLS & HORSES APPRECIATION SOCIETY

L15	Only Fools & Horses	2002	–	£9.99

ORBIT ADVERTISING(Commercial)

28	Great Rugby Sides (NZ Tourists 1905)	1987	–	£4.00
16	New Zealand Cricketers 1958	1988	–	£6.00

OVALTINE BISCUITS

25	Do You Know?	1965	–	£8.00

OWBRIDGE'S (Pharmaceutics)

32	Happy Families	1914	£6.00	–

OXO LTD. (Liebig's Meat Extract)

K47	Advertisement Series	1926	£8.00	–
K20	British Cattle	1934	£4.50	£90.00
15	Bull Series	1937	£3.00	£45.00
K24	Feats Of Endurance	1934	£3.00	£72.00
K20	Furs And Their Story	1932	£3.00	£60.00
K36	Lifeboats And Their History	1935	£3.25	£117.00
K30	Mystery Painting Pictures	1928	£3.00	£90.00
P6	OXO Cattle Studies	1930	£32.50	–
25	OXO Recipes	1936	£3.00	£75.00

P. M. R. ASSOCIATES LTD. (Commercial)

25	England, The World Cup, Spain '82	1982	–	£3.00

PACIFIC TRADING CARDS (Commercial, U. S. A.)

Qty		Date	Odds	Sets
X110	I Love Lucy	1991	—	£12.50
X110	The Wizard Of Oz	1990	—	£12.50

H.J. PACKER & CO.LTD. (Confectionery)

K30	Footballers	1924	£50.00	—
50	Humorous Drawings	1936	£4.00	£200.00

PAGE WOODCOCK WIND PILLS

20	Humorous Sketches By Tom Browne	1902	£22.50	—

PALMER MANN & CO. LTD. (Salt)

24	Famous Cricketers	1950	£20.00	—
24	Famous Footballers	1950	£20.00	—
12	Famous Jets	1950	£12.50	—
12	Famous Lighthouses	1950	£10.00	—

PALS (Periodical)

MF27	Australian Sportsmen	1923	£12.00	£325.00
M8	Famous Footballers	1922	£8.50	£68.00
MF12	Football Series	1922	£5.00	£60.00

PANINI (Commercial, With Albums)

M240	A Team	1983	—	£20.00
M240	Auto 2000	1988	—	£20.00
X44	England Soccer Stars (No Album)	1996	—	£15.00

JAMES PASCALL LTD. (Confectionery)

48	Boy Scout Series	1912	£12.50	—
24	British Birds	1925	£3.50	£84.00
30	Devon Ferns	1927	£2.00	£60.00
30	Devon Flowers	1927	£2.00	£60.00
24	Devon Worthies	1927	£2.50	£60.00
18	Dogs	1924	£4.50	£80.00
10	Felix The Film Cat	1928	£26.00	—
30	Flags & Flags With Soldiers	1905	£16.00	—
30	Glorious Devon	1929	£2.00	£60.00
36	Glorious Devon 2nd Series (Black Back)	1929	£2.00	£72.00
36	(Green Back)	1929	£2.25	£81.00
36	(Non-Descriptive)	1929	£5.00	—
2	King George V & Queen Mary	1910	£30.00	—
44	Military Series	1912	£20.00	—
20	Pascall's Specialities	1926	£17.50	—
12	Royal Naval Cadet Series	1912	£20.00	—
?8	Rulers Of The World	1916	£32.50	—
65	Town And Other Arms	1914	£12.50	—
50	Tricks And Puzzles	1926	£11.00	—
?13	War Portraits	1915	£25.00	—

J. PATERSON AND SON LTD. (Biscuits)

M48	Balloons	1960	£2.00	£96.00

PATRICK (Garages)

T24	The Patrick Collection (Cars)	1986	—	£15.00
P24	The Patrick Collection (With Coupons)	1986	—	£20.00

GEORGE PAYNE (Tea)

Qty		Date	Odds	Sets
25	American Indian Tribes	1962	£1.20	£30.00
25	British Railways	1962	—	£3.00
12	Characters From Dickens Works (Numbered)	1912	£13.50	—
6	(Unnumbered)	1912	£15.00	—
25	Dogs Heads	1963	£0.60	£15.00
25	Science In The 20th Century	1963	—	£2.50

PEEK FREAN & CO. (Biscuits)

Qty		Date	Odds	Sets
X12	English Scenes	1884	£11.00	£132.00
X4	Shakespeare Scenes	1884	£15.00	£60.00
X4	Views Abroad	1883	£12.50	£50.00

PENGUIN BISCUITS

Qty		Date	Odds	Sets
E6	Farm Animal Series (Pairs)	1968	£2.50	—
E6	(Singles)	1968	£2.50	—
E10	Home Hints	1974	£2.25	—
E12	Lake Nakuru Wildlife	1973	£2.50	—
E10	Making The Most Of Your Countryside	1975	£2.25	£22.50
E10	Pastimes	1972	£2.25	£22.50
E12	Playday	1973	£2.00	£24.00
E5	Zoo Animal Series (Pairs)	1969	£2.50	£12.50

PENNY MAGAZINE

Qty		Date	Odds	Sets
MF12	Film Stars	1931	£4.00	£48.00

PEPSI COLA INC.

Qty		Date	Odds	Sets
L7	Star Wars Episode 1: Game cards	1999	—	£5.00

PERFETTI (Gum)

Qty		Date	Odds	Sets
40	Famous Trains	1983	£3.50	£140.00

PERIKIM CARDS (Commercial)

Qty		Date	Odds	Sets
L7	The Boxer	2001	—	£3.00
L7	The Bulldog	2005	—	£3.00
L7	The Bull Terrier	2005	—	£3.00
L7	The Cocker Spaniel	2001	—	£3.00
L7	The Dalmatian	2005	—	£3.00
L7	The Doberman	2001	—	£3.00
L7	The English Springer Spaniel	2001	—	£3.00
L7	The German Shepherd	2001	—	£3.00
L7	The Golden Retriever	2001	—	£3.00
L7	The Irish Setter	2005	—	£3.00
L7	The Jack Russell	2001	—	£3.00
L7	The King Charles Cavalier	2005	—	£3.00
L7	The Rottweiler	2005	—	£3.00
L7	The Rough Collie	2005	—	£3.00
L7	The Staffordshire Bull Terrier	2005	—	£3.00
L7	The West Highland	2005	—	£3.00
L7	The Yorkshire Terrier	2005	—	£3.00

PETERKIN (Foods)

Qty		Date	Odds	Sets
M8	English Sporting Dogs	1930	£13.50	£108.00

PETPRO LTD.

Qty		Date	Odds	Sets
35	Grand Prix Racing Cars	1962	—	£8.50

PHILADELPHIA CHEWING GUM CORP.

Qty		Date	Odds	Sets
X88	War Bulletin	1965	£2.00	£175.00

PHILLIPS (Tea)

25	Army Badges Past And Present	1964	–	£3.00
25	British Birds And Their Nests	1966	–	£40.00
25	British Rail	1965	–	£7.50

PHOTAL

P2	Duncan Edwards Collection	2001	–	£5.00
P4	Manchester United Collection Series 1	2001	–	£8.00
P20	Manchester United Collection Series 2	2001	–	£30.00
P6	Northern Footballing Knights Collection	2001	–	£12.00
P10	Sir Tom Finney Collection	2001	–	£16.00

PHOTO ANSWERS (Periodical)

X12	Holiday Fax	1990	–	£2.50

FERD, PIATNIK & SONS (Austria)

X55	Elvis Playing Cards	1997	–	£8.00
X55	Masters Of The Old Course-St. Andrews-Open Champions	1998	–	£8.00

STEVE PILKINGTON (Engineering)

X18	Central Lancashire Cricket League	1997	–	£7.00

PLANET LTD. (Gum)

X50	Racing Cars Of The World	1965	£3.00	£150.00

PLANTERS NUT & CHOCOLATE CO. (U.S.A.)

M25	Hunted Animals	1933	£3.60	£90.00

PLUCK (Periodical)

MF27	Famous Football Teams	1922	£4.00	£108.00

POLAR PRODUCTS LTD. (Ice Cream, Barbados)

25	International Air-Liners	1970	–	£12.50
25	Modern Motor Cars	1970	–	£20.00
25	Tropical Birds	1970	–	£12.50
25	Wonders Of The Deep	1970	–	£10.00

H. POPPLETON & SONS (Confectionery)

50	Cricketers Series	1926	£27.50	–
16	Film Stars	1928	£8.00	–
?15	War Series	1916	£27.50	–
12	Wembley Empire Exhibition Series	1924	£26.50	–

THE POPULAR (Periodical)

G26	Railway Locomotives	1922	£7.50	£195.00

POPULAR MOTORING (Periodical)

X4	P.M. Car Starter	1972	–	£2.00

POSTER STAMP ASSOCIATION

Qty		Date	Odds	Sets
25	Modern Transport	1957	–	£2.50

PRESCOTT (Confectionery)

L36	Speed Kings	1966	£1.25	£45.00

PRESCOTT-PICKUP & CO. (Commercial)

50	Railway Locomotives	1980	£0.70	£35.00

PRESTON DAIRIES (Tea)

25	Country Life	1966	–	£2.50

PRICE'S PATENT CANDLE CO. LTD.

P12	Famous Battles	1910	£12.50	£150.00

W. R. PRIDDY (Antiques)

80	Famous Boxers	1992	–	£25.00

PRIMROSE CONFECTIONERY CO. LTD.

24	Action Man	1976	£3.50	–
50	Amos Burke-Secret Agent	1970	–	£48.00
50	Andy Pandy	1960	£0.90	£45.00
50	Bugs Bunny	1964	£1.60	£80.00
50	Burke's Law	1967	£5.50	–
25	Captain Kid	1975	£5.75	–
50	Chitty Chitty Bang Bang	1971	£1.30	£65.00
50	Cowboy	1960	–	£15.00
25	Cup Tie Quiz	1973	–	£3.00
25	Dads Army	1973	–	£12.50
50	Famous Footballers F.B.S.I.	1961	–	£30.00
25	Football Funnies	1974	–	£10.00
25	Happy Howlers	1975	–	£3.00
50	Joe 90	1969	£2.20	£110.00
50	Krazy Kreatures From Outer Space	1970	–	£10.00
50	Laramie	1964	£2.40	£120.00
50	Laurel & Hardy	1968	£3.20	£160.00
M22	Mounties (Package Issue)	1960	£6.50	£142.00
50	Popeye	1960	£5.75	–
50	Popeye, 2nd Series	1961	£5.75	–
50	Popeye, 3rd Series	1962	–	£16.00
50	Popeye, 4th Series	1963	–	£16.00
50	Queen Elizabeth 2	1969	£1.40	£70.00
50	Quick Draw McGraw	1964	£4.20	–
50	Space Patrol	1970	–	£17.00
50	Space Race	1969	–	£6.50
12	Star Trek	1971	–	£5.00
50	Superman	1968	–	£22.00
50	The Flintstones	1963	£1.00	£50.00
50	Yellow Submarine	1968	£5.50	–
50	Z-Cars	1968	£0.70	£35.00

PRINCE EDWARD THEATRE

XF?4	Josephine Baker Cards	1930	£30.00	–

MICHAEL PRIOR (Commercial)

Qty		Date	Odds	Sets
25	Racing Colours	1987	—	£6.50

S. PRIOR (Bookshop)

25	Do You Know?	1964	—	£15.00

PRIORY TEA CO. LTD.

50	Aircraft	1961	£1.00	—
50	Birds	1962	£0.70	£35.00
24	Bridges	1960	—	£2.50
24	Cars	1958	£4.00	£96.00
50	Cars (Different)	1964	£1.25	£62.50
50	Cycles & Motorcycles	1963	£2.00	£100.00
24	Dogs	1957	—	£4.00
24	Flowering Trees	1959	—	£2.50
24	Men At Work	1959	—	£2.50
24	Out And About	1957	—	£4.00
24	People In Uniform	1956	£2.25	£54.00
24	Pets	1957	—	£3.50
50	Wild Flowers	1963	£0.65	£32.50

PRO SET INC. (U.S.A., Commercial)

X100	Bill & Ted's Movie Cards	1991	—	£6.00
X100	Footballers And Fixture Lists	1991	—	£6.00
X100	Guinness Book Of Records	1992	—	£6.00
X100	P.G.A. Tour Cards	1990	—	£13.50
X100	Thunderbirds	1992	£0.20	£10.00

PROPERT SHOE POLISH

25	British Uniforms	1955	—	£4.00

PUKKA TEA CO. LTD.

50	Aquarium Fish	1961	—	£50.00

PYREX LTD. (Glassware)

P16	Guide To Simple Cooking	1976	—	£2.50

QUAKER OATS

X12	Armour Through The Ages	1968	£1.60	£20.00
M4	Famous Puffers	1983	£5.00	£20.00
M54	Historic Arms Of Merrie England	1938	£1.25	—
X8	Historic Ships	1967	£4.00	£32.00
M6	Honey Monster's Circus Friends	1985	£2.50	—
15	Honey Monster's Crazy Games Cards	1985	£1.50	£22.50
M16	Jeremy's Animal Kingdom	1980	£1.25	£20.00
X4	Minibooks	1969	£3.50	£14.00
12	Monsters Of The Deep	1984	£2.00	—
M6	Nature Trek	1976	£0.50	£3.00
X12	Prehistoric Animals	1967	£5.00	£60.00
L8	Return To Oz	1985	£2.00	—
X12	Space Cards	1968	£5.00	—
X12	Vintage Engines	1967	£4.50	£54.00

QUAKER OATS – cont.

Qty	PACKAGE ISSUES	Date	Odds	Sets
12	British Customs	1961	£0.75	£9.00
L36	British Landmarks	1961	£0.85	—
12	Characters In Literature	1961	£1.50	—
12	Exploration & Adventure	1974	£1.25	£15.00
12	Famous Explorers	1961	£1.25	£15.00
12	Famous Inventors	1961	£1.50	£18.00
12	Famous Ships	1961	£1.50	—
12	Famous Women	1961	£1.00	—
12	Fascinating Costumes	1961	£0.75	£9.00
12	Great Feats Of Building	1961	£0.75	£9.00
L36	Great Moments Of Sport	1961	£2.50	—
12	History Of Flight	1961	£1.25	£15.00
12	Homes And Houses	1961	£0.85	£10.00
L36	Household Hints	1961	£0.70	—
12	National Maritime Museum	1974	£1.25	—
12	National Motor Museum	1974	£1.65	£20.00
12	On The Seashore	1961	£0.65	£8.00
L36	Phiz - Quiz	1961	£1.25	—
L36	Railways Of The World	1961	£2.25	—
12	Royal Air Force Museum	1974	£1.65	—
12	Science & Invention	1974	£1.25	£15.00
L36	The Story Of Fashion	1961	£0.75	—
12	The Wild West	1961	£1.40	£17.00
12	Weapons & Armour	1961	£1.65	£20.00

QUEEN ELIZABETH LAUNDRY

Qty		Date	Odds	Sets
45	Beauties	1912	£16.50	—

QUEENS OF YORK (Laundry)

Qty		Date	Odds	Sets
30	Kings & Queens Of England	1955	—	£35.00

QUORN SPECIALITIES LTD. (Foods)

Qty		Date	Odds	Sets
25	Fish And Game	1963	£6.50	—

R. K. CONFECTIONERY CO LTD

Qty		Date	Odds	Sets
32	Felix Pictures	1930	£37.50	—

RADIO FUN (Periodical)

Qty		Date	Odds	Sets
20	British Sports Stars	1956	—	£5.00

RADIO REVIEW (Periodical)

Qty		Date	Odds	Sets
L36	Broadcasting Stars	1936	£4.50	£162.00
E20	Broadcasting Stars	1936	£5.00	£100.00

RALEIGH BICYCLES

Qty		Date	Odds	Sets
L48	Raleigh The All-Steel Bicycle	1957	£1.60	£75.00

REDDINGS TEA CO.

Qty		Date	Odds	Sets
25	Castles Of Great Britain	1965	£2.40	£60.00
25	Cathedrals Of Great Britain	1964	£2.40	£60.00
25	Heraldry Of Famous Places	1966	£1.60	£40.00

REDDINGS TEA CO. – cont.

Qty		Date	Odds	Sets
48	Ships Of The World	1964	–	£8.50
25	Strange Customs Of The World	1970	–	£3.00
48	Warriors Of The World	1962	£2.00	£96.00

REDDISH MAID CONFECTIONERY

50	Famous International Aircraft	1963	£3.20	£160.00
25	Famous International Athletes	1964	£7.00	–
25	International Footballers Of Today	1965	£8.50	–

RED HEART (Pet Food)

P6	Cats	1954	–	£35.00
P6	Dogs First Series	1953	–	£40.00
P6	Dogs Second Series	1953	–	£40.00
P6	Dogs Third Series	1954	–	£45.00

RED LETTER (Periodical)

P29	Charlie Chaplin Cards	1915	£12.50	£365.00
P?100	Fortune Cards (Playing Card Backs)	1932	£3.50	–
M4	Luck-Bringers (Silk)	1924	£15.00	£80.00
X72	Midget Message Cards	1916	£2.50	£180.00
X12	Red Letter Message Cards	1916	£3.25	£40.00
M100	The Handy Cooking Cards	1926	£1.25	–

REEVES LTD. (Confectionery)

25	Cricketers	1912	£32.00	£800.00

REFLECTIONS OF A BYGONE AGE (Card Fairs)

12	Nottingham Heritage Cards	1996	–	£2.00
6	Nottinghamshire Towns	2000	–	£1.00
6	Railways Around Nottingham	1996	–	£1.00
M4	Rugby Union World Cup 2003	2003	–	£1.00
6	Steam Around Britain	2000	–	£1.00
12	Visitors To Nottingham Card Fair	1993	–	£2.00

REGENT OIL

T25	Do You Know?	1965	–	£3.00

RICHARDS COLLECTION (Commercial)

25	Soccer Stars Of Yesteryear, 2nd Series	1997	–	£8.75
25	Soccer Stars Of Yesteryear, 3rd Series	1997	–	£8.75
25	Soccer Stars Of Yesteryear, 4th Series	1998	–	£5.00
20	Sporting Stars By Jos. Walker (Cricket)	1997	–	£5.00

RIDGWAY'S TEA

X20	Journey To The Moon (Package Issue)	1958	£8.00	–

ESTEVE RIERA S.A. (Chocolate, Spain)

X24	Costumes Through The Ages	1923	–	£30.00

RINGTONS LTD. (Tea)

25	Aircraft Of World War II	1962	£2.40	–
25	British Cavalry Uniforms Of The 19th Century	1971	£1.60	£40.00

RINGTONS LTD. (Tea) – cont.

Qty		Date	Odds	Sets
25	Do You Know?	1964	—	£2.50
25	Fruits Of Trees And Shrubs	1964	—	£2.50
25	Head-Dresses Of The World	1973	—	£3.00
25	Historical Scenes	1964	—	£4.00
25	Old England	1964	—	£3.00
25	People & Places	1964	—	£2.50
25	Regimental Uniforms Of The Past	1966	—	£6.00
25	Sailing Ships Through The Ages	1967	—	£3.50
25	Ships Of The Royal Navy	1961	£0.60	£15.00
25	Sovereigns Consorts & Rulers, First Series	1961	—	£8.00
25	Sovereigns Consorts & Rulers, Second Series	1961	—	£8.00
25	The West	1968	—	£6.00
25	Then & Now	1970	£1.20	£30.00
25	Trains Of The World	1970	—	£3.50

RISCA TRAVEL AGENCY

25	Holiday Resorts	1957	—	£25.00

RIVER WYE PRODUCTIONS (Commercial)

X90	Laurel & Hardy	1997	—	£16.00
X72	Laurel & Hardy Millennium 2000 Celebrations	2000	—	£14.00
X72	Sherlock Holmes - Premiere Collection	2002	—	£20.00

D.ROBBINS & CO. (Bread, U.S.A.)

P24	Frontiers Of Freedom	1942	—	£60.00
P24	Good Neighbors Of The Americas	1942	—	£60.00
P24	Modern Wonders Of The World	1942	—	£60.00
P23/24	Story Of Transportation	1942	—	£50.00

ROBERTSON LTD. (Preserves)

1	Advertisement Gollywog	1962	—	£3.00
6	British Medals	1914	£20.00	—
L6	British Medals (Circular)	1914	£35.00	—
10	Musical Gollywogs (Shaped)	1956	£4.00	—
10	Sporting Gollywogs (Shaped)	1955	£4.00	£40.00

ROBERTSON & WOODCOCK (Confectionery)

50	British Aircraft Series	1933	£2.80	£140.00

C ROBINSON ARTWORKSHOP (Commercial)

X16	The Pilgrims F.A. Cup Squad 1983-84	1984	—	£8.00

ROBINSON'S BARLEY WATER

X30	Sporting Records (With Folder)	1983	—	£5.00

ROBINSON BROS. & MASTERS LTD. (Tea)

25	Tea From The Garden To The Home	1930	£11.00	£275.00

ROB ROY CARDS (Commercial)

L20	Manchester United, Series 1	1995	—	£15.00

ROCHE & CO. LTD. (Matches)

K49/50	Famous Footballers	1927	£12.00	—

THE ROCKET (Periodical)

Qty		Date	Odds	Sets
MF11	Famous Knock-Outs..	1923	£9.00	£100.00

ROCKWELL PUBLISHING (Commercial)

Qty		Date	Odds	Sets
10	Airship - The Story Of The R101	2004	–	£4.50
L10	Airship - The Story Of The R101	2004	–	£7.00
10	Bodyline - The Fight For The Ashes 1932-3	2005	–	£4.50
L10	Bodyline - The Fight For The Ashes 1932-3	2005	–	£7.00
10	Britain's Lost Railway Stations	2005	–	£4.50
L10	Britain's Lost Railway Stations	2005	–	£7.00
10	British Armoured Vehicles Of World War II............................	2001	–	£4.50
L10	British Armoured Vehicles Of World War II............................	2001	–	£7.00
10	British Fighting Jets	2003	–	£4.50
L10	British Fighting Jets	2003	–	£7.00
10	British Warplanes Of The Second World War.......................	2000	–	£4.50
L10	British Warplanes Of The Second World War.......................	2000	–	£7.50
L7	Classic Chelsea	2005	–	£5.00
L7	Classic Everton...	2005	–	£4.50
10	Classic Football Teams Before The First World War (Coloured Borders)..	2000	–	£4.00
10	Classic Football Teams Before The First World War (Sepia Borders)	2000	–	£4.50
L10	Classic Football Teams Before The First World War ªColoured Borders)..	2000	–	£6.00
L10	Classic Football Teams Before The First World War.......... (Sepia Borders)	2000	–	£7.00
10	Classic Football Teams Of The 1960s (Coloured Borders) ..	2000	–	£4.00
10	Classic Football Teams Of The 1960s (Sepia Borders)	1999	–	£4.50
L10	Classic Football Teams Of The 1960s (Sepia Border)	1999	–	£7.00
L10	Classic Football Teams Of The 1960s (Coloured Borders) ..	1999	–	£6.00
L7	Classic Gunners (Soccer)	2001	–	£4.50
L7	Classic Hammers..	2004	–	£5.00
L7	Classic Liverpool..	2005	–	£4.50
L7	Classic Reds (Manchester United)...	2004	–	£5.00
10	Classic Sci-Fi 'B' Movies	2006	–	£4.50
L10	Classic Sci-Fi 'B' Movies	2006	–	£7.00
L7	Classic Spurs...	2002	–	£4.50
10	Cunard In The 1950's	2003	–	£4.50
L10	Cunard In The 1950's	2003	–	£7.00
10	Early Allied Warplanes	2000	–	£4.50
L10	Early Allied Warplanes	2000	–	£7.00
X10	Early Allied Warplanes	2000	–	£7.50
10	Early Balloon Flight	2001	–	£4.50
L10	Early Balloon Flight	2001	–	£7.00
10	Early Locomotives Series One..	2005	–	£4.50
L10	Early Locomotives Series One..	2005	–	£7.00
10	Early Locomotives Series Two..	2005	–	£4.50
L10	Early Locomotives Series Two..	2005	–	£7.00
10	Family Cars Of The 1950's	2000	–	£4.50
L10	Family Cars Of The 1950's	2000	–	£7.50
X10	Family Cars Of The 1950's	2000	–	£7.50
10	Flying So High West Ham United 1964-66..........................	2005	–	£4.50
L10	Flying So High West Ham United 1964-66..........................	2005	–	£7.00
10	German Armoured Vehicles Of World War II	2001	–	£4.50
L10	German Armoured Vehicles Of World War II	2001	–	£7.00
X10	German Armoured Vehicles Of World War II	2001	–	£7.50

ROCKWELL PUBLISHING (Commercial) – cont.

Qty		Date	Odds	Sets
10	German Warplanes Of The Second World War	2000	—	£4.50
L10	German Warplanes Of The Second World War	2000	—	£7.00
X10	German Warplanes Of The Second World War	2000	—	£7.50
L10	Heath Robinson - Sporting Eccentricities	2005	—	£7.00
L10	Heath Robinson - Urban Life	2005	—	£7.00
10	Hurricane Flying Colours	2002	—	£4.50
L10	Hurricane Flying Colours	2002	—	£7.00
10	Lost Warships Of WWII	2002	—	£4.50
L10	Lost Warships Of WWII	2002	—	£7.00
10	Mighty Atoms (Boxers)	2004	—	£4.50
L10	Mighty Atoms (Boxers)	2004	—	£7.00
25	Olympic - Titanic - Britannic	2001	—	£8.50
L25	Olympic - Titanic - Britannic	2001	—	£10.00
10	Postcard Images Of World War One	1999	—	£4.50
L10	Postcard Images Of World War One	1999	—	£7.50
X10	Postcard Images Of World War One	1999	—	£7.50
10	Post War Wimbledon Ladies' Champions	2004	—	£4.50
L10	Post War Wimbledon Ladies' Champions	2004	—	£7.00
10	Post War Wimbledon Ladies' Champions 2nd Series	2005	—	£4.50
L10	Post War Wimbledon Ladies' Champions 2nd Series	2005	—	£7.00
10	Post War Wimbledon Men's Champions	2004	—	£4.50
L10	Post War Wimbledon Men's Champions	2004	—	£7.00
10	Post War Wimbledon Men's Champions 2nd Series	2005	—	£4.50
L10	Post War Wimbledon Men's Champions 2nd Series	2005	—	£7.00
10	Relegated To History - England's Lost Football Grounds	2004	—	£4.50
L10	Relegated To History - England's Lost Football Grounds	2004	—	£7.00
10	Solar System	2001	—	£4.50
L10	Solar System	2001	—	£7.00
10	Spitfire Flying Colours	1999	—	£4.50
L10	Spitfire Flying Colours	1999	—	£7.50
X10	Spitfire Flying Colours	1999	—	£7.50
10	Spurs Great Postwar Goalscorers Series 1	2006	—	£4.50
L10	Spurs Great Postwar Goalscorers Series 1	2006	—	£7.00
10	Spurs Great Postwar Goalscorers Series 2	2006	—	£4.50
L10	Spurs Great Postwar Goalscorers Series 2	2006	—	£7.00
10	Spurs 1960-1963 The Glory Years	2005	—	£4.50
X10	Spurs 1960-1963 The Glory Years	2005	—	£7.50
10	Suffragettes	2005	—	£4.50
L10	Suffragettes	2005	—	£7.00
10	The Great Heavyweights	2002	—	£4.50
L10	The Great Heavyweights	2002	—	£7.00
10	The Great Middleweights	2002	—	£4.50
L10	The Great Middleweights	2002	—	£7.00
10	The Hornby Book Of Trains	2005	—	£4.50
L10	The Hornby Book Of Trains	2005	—	£7.00
10	The 1948 Australians	2006	—	£4.50
L10	The 1948 Australians	2006	—	£7.00
25	The Titanic Series	1999	—	£9.00
L25	The Titanic Series	2000	—	£12.00
L7	World Cup 1966 The Final	2005	—	£4.50
10	World War One Posters	2001	—	£4.50
L10	World War One Posters	2001	—	£7.00
L10	World War II Posters - Industry	2005	—	£7.00
L10	World War II Posters - Morale	2005	—	£7.00
10	World War II Posters - The Home Front	2001	—	£4.50

ROCKWELL PUBLISHING (Commercial) – cont.

Qty		Date	Odds	Sets
L10	World War II Posters - The Home Front	2001	–	£7.00
10	World War II Posters - The Services	2001	–	£4.50
L10	World War II Posters - The Services	2001	–	£7.00

RODEO BUBBLE GUM

M42	Western Stars	1953	£7.50	–

ROLLS ROYCE (Cars)

X25	Bentley Cars	1986	–	£65.00
X25	Bentley Cars, Second Edition	1987	–	£65.00
X25	Rolls Royce Cars	1986	–	£65.00
X25	Rolls Royce Cars, Second Edition	1987	–	£65.00

ROSSI'S (Ice Cream)

M48	Flag Cards	1975	£0.20	£6.00
25	The History Of Flight, 1st Series	1963	£1.50	£37.50
25	The History Of Flight, 2nd Series	1963	£1.50	£37.50
25	World's Fastest Aircraft	1964	–	£25.00

DAVID ROWLAND (Commercial)

25	Association Footballers (Series 1)	1999	–	£7.50
25	Association Footballers (Series 2)	1999	–	£7.50
25	Association Footballers (Series 3)	1999	–	£7.50
25	Association Footballers (Series 4)	1999	–	£7.50
25	Association Footballers (Series 5)	1999	–	£7.50
20	Boxers (Series 1)	1999	–	£7.00
20	Boxing Legends (Series 1)	1999	–	£7.00
25	Cricketers (Series 1)	1999	–	£7.50
25	Cricketers (Series 2)	1999	–	£7.50
20	Famous Footballers, Series 1	1999	–	£6.00
20	Famous Footballers, Series 2	1999	–	£6.00
20	Famous Footballers, Series 3	1999	–	£6.00
20	Famous Footballers, Series 4 (Managers)	1999	–	£6.00
20	Famous Footballers, Series 5	1999	–	£6.00

ROWNTREE & CO. (Confectionery)

K12	British Birds (Packet Issue)	1955	–	£24.00
25	Celebrities	1905	£27.50	–
X8	Circus Cut-Outs	1960	£6.50	£54.00
M20	Merry Monarchs	1978	–	£5.00
M18	Prehistoric Animals	1978	–	£8.00
L6	Punch & Judy Show	1976	£37.50	£22.50
L42	Railway Engines (Caramac)	1976	–	£20.00
L2	Smartie Models	1976	–	£5.00
M10	Texan Tall Tales Of The West	1977	£2.00	£20.00
48	The Old & The New	1934	£5.50	£264.00
120	Treasure Trove Pictures	1932	£2.00	–
24	York Views	1924	£14.00	–

ROYAL LEAMINGTON SPA CORPORATION

25	Royal Leamington Spa	1975	–	£2.50

ROYAL NATIONAL LIFEBOAT INSTITUTION

M16	Lifeboats	1979	–	£7.00

ROYAL SOCIETY FOR THE PREVENTION OF ACCIDENTS

Qty		Date	Odds	Sets
24	Modern British Cars	1954	£3.00	£72.00
22	Modern British Motor-Cycles	1953	£3.50	£77.00
25	New Traffic Signs	1958	–	£6.50
24	Veteran Cars, First Series	1955	£3.00	£72.00
24	Veteran Cars, Second Series	1957	£2.25	£54.00

RUBY (Periodical)

TF6	Famous Film Stars	1923	£10.00	£60.00

RUGBY FOOTBALL UNION

50	English Internationals 1980-1991	1991	–	£12.50

RUGLYS

K22	English World Cup Rugby Squad	1999	–	£7.25
K22	Rugby World Cup All Stars	1999	–	£7.25
K25	Welsh Rugby World Cup Squad	1999	–	£8.20

S & B PRODUCTS (Commercial)

64	Torry Gillick's Internationals	1948	£10.00	–

S.C.M.C.C.

15	Stoke's Finest Hour (Soccer)	2002	–	£5.50

SAGION STUFFING

28	Dominoes Without The Dot	1939	£0.35	£10.00

J. SAINSBURY LTD. (Groceries)

M12	British Birds	1924	£8.00	£96.00
M12	Foreign Birds	1924	£8.00	£96.00

SANDERS BROS. (Custard)

25	Birds, Fowls, Pigeons & Rabbits	1925	£7.00	–
20	Dogs	1926	£6.00	£120.00
25	Recipes	1924	£4.50	£112.50

SANITARIUM HEALTH FOOD CO. (Oceania)

X12	Alpine Sports	1986	–	£4.00
X12	Ball Sports	1989	–	£5.00
L20	Big Rigs	1983	–	£3.25
L20	Big Rigs At Work	1986	–	£3.00
L20	Big Rigs 3	1992	–	£3.00
L20	Cars Of The Seventies	1976	–	£6.50
X12	Curious Conveyances	1984	–	£3.00
L20	Discover Indonesia	1977	–	£3.00
L20	Discover Science With The DSIR	1989	–	£3.00
L20	Exotic Cars	1987	–	£6.00
L24	Famous New Zealanders	1971	–	£5.00
L20	Farewell To Steam	1981	–	£5.00
L30	Fascinating Orient	1974	–	£3.00
X12	Focus On New Zealand, Series 1	1979	–	£2.50
L20	History Of Road Transport-New Zealand	1979	–	£5.00
L20	Kiwis Going For Gold	1992	–	£3.50
L20	Looking At Canada	1978	–	£2.50
L20	Mammals Of The Sea	1985	–	£2.75

SANITARIUM HEALTH FOOD CO. (Oceania) – cont.

Qty		Date	Odds	Sets
X12	Man Made Wonders Of The World	1987	–	£2.50
X12	Mountaineering	1987	–	£3.25
X12	New Zealand Disasters	1991	–	£2.50
X12	New Zealand Inventions And Discoveries	1991	–	£4.00
L20	New Zealand Summer Sports	1984	–	£4.00
L30	New Zealand To-Day	1974	–	£4.00
L20	New Zealand's Booming Industries	1975	–	£2.00
L20	New Zealanders In Antarctica	1987	–	£5.00
L20	New Zealanders On Top Of The World	1991	–	£3.00
L20	'1990 - Look At How We've Grown'	1990	–	£2.50
L20	N.Z. Energy Resources	1976	–	£3.00
L20	N.Z. Rod And Custom Cars	1979	–	£5.00
X12	Ocean Racers	1986	–	£3.25
L20	100 Years Of New Zealand National Parks	1987	–	£2.50
X12	Our Fascinating Fungi	1980	–	£3.00
L20	Our Golden Fleece	1981	–	£2.75
L20	Our South Pacific Island Neighbours	1974	–	£4.00
L20	Our Weather	1980	–	£2.50
X12	Power Boats In New Zealand	1990	–	£4.00
X12	Spanning New Zealand (Bridges)	1992	–	£2.50
L20	Spectacular Sports	1974	–	£6.00
X12	Surf Life-Saving	1986	–	£3.00
X10	The Hunchback Of Notre Dame (Disney)	1996	–	£5.00
L20	The Many-Stranded Web Of Nature	1983	–	£2.75
L20	The 1990 Commonwealth Games	1989	–	£4.50
L20	The Story Of New Zealand Aviation	1977	–	£5.00
L20	The Story Of New Zealand In Stamps	1977	–	£5.00
L20	The Wild South	1986	–	£2.50
M20	This World Of Speed	1968	–	£4.00
L20	Timeless Japan	1975	–	£3.25
L20	Treasury Of Maori Life	1980	–	£2.75
L20	Vintage Cars	1973	–	£7.00
X12	Windsports	1989	–	£3.25
L20	Wonderful Ways Of Nature	1978	–	£2.50
X12	Wonderful Wool	1988	–	£2.50
L20	'World's Greatest Fun Parks'	1990	–	£4.50
L20	Your Journey Through Disneyland	1988	–	£7.00

SAVOY PRODUCTS LTD. (Foods)

Qty		Date	Odds	Sets
M56	Aerial Navigation	1926	£2.50	£140.00
M56	Aerial Navigation, Series B	1927	£2.40	£135.00
M56	Aerial Navigation, Series C	1928	£2.40	£135.00
M56	Famous British Boats	1928	£2.25	£110.00

SCANLEN'S (Gum, Australia)

Qty		Date	Odds	Sets
X84	Cricket World Series	1990	–	£15.00
X84	International Cricketers	1989	–	£20.00
X90	World Series Cricket	1982	–	£20.00

THE SCHOOL FRIEND (Periodical)

Qty		Date	Odds	Sets
L6	Famous Film Stars	1927	£10.00	£60.00
X10	Popular Girls Of Cliff House School	1922	£10.00	£100.00
XF6	Popular Pictures	1923	£4.00	£24.00

THE SCHOOLGIRL (Periodical)

Qty		Date	Odds	Sets
MF16	Zoological Studies	1923	£3.25	£52.00

SCHOOLGIRLS OWN (Periodical)

Qty		Date	Odds	Sets
12	Characters From Cliff House School	1932	£7.50	—
F7	Film Stars (Anon)	1929	£4.50	£31.50
12	Film Stars (Anon, Brown)	1932	£4.25	£50.00
12	The Royal Family (Anon, Brown)	1932	£4.00	£48.00

THE SCHOOLGIRLS' WEEKLY (Periodical)

Qty		Date	Odds	Sets
F12	Famous Film Stars (Anon)	1929	£5.50	—
XF1	HRH The Duke Of York	1922	—	£6.00
XF4	Popular Pictures	1922	£4.00	£16.00

SCOTTISH DAILY EXPRESS

Qty		Date	Odds	Sets
X24	Scotcards (Soccer)	1972	£7.00	—

THE SCOUT (Periodical)

Qty		Date	Odds	Sets
L9	Birds' Eggs	1925	£6.50	£60.00
M12	Railway Engines	1924	£7.00	£84.00

SCRAPBOOK MINICARDS

Qty		Date	Odds	Sets
27	Pendon Museum (Model Railway Etc.)	1978	—	£2.50

SCREEN STORIES (Periodical)

Qty		Date	Odds	Sets
F8	Film Stars (Anon)	1930	£6.00	—

SECRETS (Periodical)

Qty		Date	Odds	Sets
K52	Film Stars (Miniature Playing Cards)	1935	£1.65	—

SELF SERVICE LAUNDERETTES

Qty		Date	Odds	Sets
50	150 Years Of Locomotives	1955	£5.50	—

SELLOTAPE PRODUCTS LTD (Adhesive Tape)

Qty		Date	Odds	Sets
35	Great Homes And Castles	1974	£0.50	£20.00

A.J. SEWARD & CO LTD (Perfumes)

Qty		Date	Odds	Sets
40	Stars Of The Screen	1939	£11.00	—

SEYMOUR MEAD & CO. LTD. (Tea)

Qty		Date	Odds	Sets
24	The Island Of Ceylon	1955	—	£2.50

SHARMAN (Newspapers)

Qty		Date	Odds	Sets
T24	Golden Age Of Flying	1979	—	£17.50
T24	Golden Age Of Motoring	1979	—	£20.00
T24	Golden Age Of Steam	1979	—	£20.00

EDWARD SHARP & SONS (Confectionery)

Qty		Date	Odds	Sets
20	Captain Scarlet	1970	£7.50	—
25	Hey Presto!	1970	—	£3.00
K53	Miniature Playing Cards	1924	£2.25	—
100	Prize Dogs	1924	£6.00	—

TONY SHELDON COLLECTIBLES PROMOTIONS

Qty		Date	Odds	Sets
25	Famous Cricketers (Palmer Mann Reprint)............................	2001	—	£6.00
10	Famous Old Standians	2000	—	£3.95
20	Kenyan Cricketers...	1999	—	£7.25
20	Olden Goldies (Cricketers)..	1998	—	£8.00
X18	Out Of The Blue...Into The Red (Labour Cabinet)................	1997	—	£6.75
20	The Don - Birthday Memories..	2010	—	£10.00

SHELL (Oil)

M16	Animals (3-D)	1975	£1.25	£20.00
14	Bateman Series	1930	£8.00	£112.00
P20	Great Britons..	1972	£1.75	£35.00
K20	Historic Cars (Medals) Including Mount.............................	1970	—	£24.00
K16	Man In Flight (Medals) Including Mount.............................	1970	£1.50	£24.00
M12	Olympic Greats (With Album).......................................	1992	—	£6.50
M16	Wonders Of The World (3-D)	1976	£0.75	£12.00

AUSTRALIAN ISSUES

M60	Beetle Series (301-360)...	1962	£0.60	£36.00
M60	Birds (121-180)	1960	£0.60	£36.00
M60	Butterflies And Moths (181-240)....................................	1960	£0.75	—
M60	Citizenship Series	1965	£0.40	£24.00
M60	Discover Australia With Shell.......................................	1959	£0.50	£30.00
M60	Meteorology Series (361-420)......................................	1963	£0.40	£24.00
M60	Pets (481-540)	1964	—	£27.00
M60	Shells, Fish And Coral (61-120)	1959	£0.45	£27.00
M60	Transportation Series (241-300)	1961	£0.60	£36.00

NEW ZEALAND ISSUES

M48	Aircraft Of The World..	1970	—	£12.00
M60	Cars Of The World	1970	—	£22.50
M48	Racing Cars Of The World...	1970	£0.50	£24.00
40	Vintage Cars (Transfers)...	1970	£0.35	£14.00
L40	World Of Cricket	1992	—	£12.00
P20	World Of Cricket(Doubles)	1992	—	£15.00

SHELLEY'S ICE CREAM

25	Essex-County Champions...	1984	£0.25	£6.25

SHEPHERDS DAIRIES LTD.

100	War Series	1915	£9.00	—

SHERIDAN COLLECTIBLES (Commercial)

X12	Bobby Jones And St. Andrews..	1995	—	£6.50
X1	Bobby Jones And St. Andrews, Promo Card	1995	—	£0.50
L7	Railway Posters-Golf	1996	—	£2.50
X1	St. Andrews, Advertisement Card	1995	—	£0.50
X12	The Bobby Jones Story	1993	—	£6.50
L6	The Golf Adventures Of Par Bear	1994	—	£3.00
X25	The Players Of The Ryder Cup '93	1994	—	£10.00
X12	The Tom Morris Story	1994	—	£6.50
X2	The Tom Morris Story, Substitute Cards...........................	1995	—	£1.00
L7	'Underground Art' Football & Wembley..............................	1996	—	£2.50

SHERIDAN COLLECTIBLES (Commercial) – cont.

Qty		Date	Odds	Sets
L7	'Underground Art' Rugby	1996	–	£3.00
L7	'Underground Art' Wimbledon	1996	–	£2.50
L7	'Underground Art' Windsor	1996	–	£3.00
L12	Winners Of The Ryder Cup '95	1996	–	£6.50

SHERMAN'S POOLS LTD.

P8	Famous Film Stars	1940	£1.00	£8.00
P37	Famous Teams	1938	£5.00	£175.00
P2/37	(Aston Villa & Blackpool)	1938	–	£1.00
P38	Searchlight On Famous Players	1937	£5.50	£210.00

W. SHIPTON LTD (Commercial)

75	Trojan Gen-Cards	1959	£0.90	£82.50

SHUREY'S PUBLICATIONS LTD.

P?750	Views (Various Printings)	1906	£1.75	–

SIDELINES (Commercial)

L23	19th Century Cricket Teams	1988	–	£4.00

SILVER KING CO. (Theatrical)

1	Advertisement Card	1905	–	£15.00

SINGER SEWING MACHINE CO.

52	Beauties (Playing Card Inset)	1898	£17.50	£900.00
P36	Costumes Of All Nations	1892	£8.00	£288.00
P18	Costumes Of All Nations (Different)	1894	£13.00	£235.00

SKETCHLEY CLEANERS

25	A Nature Series	1960	–	£6.50
25	Communications	1960	–	£9.00
25	Tropical Birds	1960	–	£11.00

SKYBOX INTERNATIONAL (Commercial, U.S.A.)

X60	Babylon 5	1996	–	£17.50
X81	Babylon 5 : Season 5	1998	–	£20.00
P60	Star Trek: First Contact (Widevision)	1996	–	£20.00
X96	Star Trek: TNG: The Episodes-Season 2	1995	–	£25.00
X108	Star Trek: TNG: The Episodes-Season 3	1995	–	£18.00
X108	Star Trek: TNG: The Episodes-Season 4	1995	–	£18.00
X108	Star Trek: TNG: The Episodes-Season 5	1996	–	£12.50
X108	Star Trek TNG Season 6	1997	–	£12.50
X100	Star Trek: 30 Years Phase	1995	–	£12.00

SLADE & BULLOCK LTD. (Confectionery)

25	Cricket Series	1924	£60.00	–
25	Football Terms	1924	£30.00	–
25	Modern Inventions	1925	£12.00	–
20	Now & Then Series	1925	£15.00	–
25	Nursery Rhymes	1925	£15.00	–
25	Science & Skill Series	1925	£15.00	–
25	Simple Toys & How To Make Them	1925	£16.50	–

P. SLUIS (Bird Food)

Qty		Date	Odds	Sets
X30	Tropical Birds	1962	—	£17.50

SMART NOVELS (Periodical)

MF12	Stage Artistes & Entertainers	1924	£5.00	£60.00

JOHN SMITH (Brewers)

P5	Limericks (Beer Mats)	1976	—	£2.50

SNAP CARDS (Gum)

L50	ATV Stars Series No.1	1959	£2.70	£135.00
L48	ATV Stars Series No.2	1960	£2.20	£105.00
L50	Associated-Rediffusion Stars	1960	£3.00	—
L50	Dotto Celebrities	1959	£1.75	£87.50

H.A. SNOW (Films)

12	Hunting Big Game In Africa	1923	£6.50	—

SOCCER BUBBLE GUM

T48	Soccer Teams No.1 Series	1956	£2.50	£120.00
T48	Soccer Teams No.2 Series	1958	£3.50	£170.00

SODASTREAM (Confectionery)

25	Historical Buildings	1957	—	£2.50

SOLDIER MAGAZINE

M24	The British Army - 1993	1993	—	£4.50

SOMPORTEX LTD. (Gum Vending)

X72	Adventures Of Sexton Blake	1968	£4.50	—
L60	Famous T. V. Wrestlers	1966	£4.00	£240.00
L60	Film Scene Series James Bond 007	1966	£7.00	—
L72	John Drake Danger Man	1966	£6.50	£470.00
L50	The Exciting World Of James Bond 007	1965	£7.25	—
L72	The Saint	1967	£7.25	—
L71/72	Thunderball	1967	£4.30	£310.00
L72	Thunderball	1967	—	£350.00
X73	Thunderbirds (Coloured)	1967	£7.50	—
L72	Thunderbirds (Black & White)	1967	£6.40	£460.00
X72	Thunderbirds (Black & White)	1967	£3.50	£250.00
X36	Weirdies	1968	£1.25	£45.00
26	You Only Live Twice (Film Strips)	1969	£11.00	—

SONNY BOY (Confectionery)

50	Railway Engines	1960	—	£10.00

SOUTH AFRICAN EGGS

L6	Oeufs Travel Collection	1988	—	£4.00

SOUTH WALES CONSTABULARY

X36	British Stamps	1983	—	£10.00
L36	Castles And Historic Places In Wales	1988	—	£12.00
X36	Merthyr Tydfil Borough Council	1987	—	£10.00
X37	Payphones Past And Present	1987	—	£25.00
X36	Rhymney Valley District Council	1986	—	£9.00

SOUTH WALES CONSTABULARY – cont.

Qty		Date	Odds	Sets
M36	Sport-A-Card	1991	–	£20.00
X35	The '82 Squad (Rugby)	1982	£0.85	£45.00

SPAR GROCERS

X30	Disney On Parade	1972	£6.00	–

SPILLERS NEPHEWS (Biscuits)

25	Conundrum Series	1910	£22.50	–
40	Views Of South Wales & District	1910	£20.00	–

SPORT AND ADVENTURE (Periodical)

M46	Famous Footballers	1922	£4.50	£200.00

SPORTING PROFILES (Commercial)

L15	Action Comics	2006	–	£6.50
L16	AKA Cassius Clay	2002	–	£9.99
L8	Arsenal FA Cup Winners 1930	2006	–	£5.00
L9	Arsenal FA Cup Winners 1971	2006	–	£5.00
L10	Aston Villa European Cup Winners 1982	2006	–	£5.00
L15	Ayrton Senna 1960-1994	2005	–	£6.50
15	Boxing Greats	2003	–	£5.00
L15	Bruce Lee	2005	–	£6.50
L20	Carry On (Films)	2005	–	£7.50
L20	Charles Buchan's Football Monthly	2004	–	£7.50
L10	Chelsea European Cup Winners 1971	2006	–	£5.00
L10	Chelsea 1970	2006	–	£5.00
L8	Circus Posters	2005	–	£4.00
L15	Classic Le Mans Posters	2007	–	£6.50
L15	Classic Monaco Posters	2007	–	£6.50
L10	Dad's Army	2006	–	£5.00
L20	Diana - The People's Princess	2006	–	£7.50
L6	England - World Cup 1966	2006	–	£3.50
L12	England Players World Cup 1966	2007	–	£6.00
L17	FA Cup Final Programmes	2001	–	£7.50
L20	FA Cup Final Programmes Volume II	2004	–	£7.50
L20	FA Cup Final Programmes Volume III	2004	–	£7.50
L21	FA Cup Final Programmes Volume IV	2006	–	£7.50
L12	Fawlty Towers	2005	–	£6.50
L20	Frank Bruno	2005	–	£7.50
L15	Great British Cars Of The 1950s	2004	–	£6.50
L4	Heavyweight Champions Of The 'Naughty '90s'	2001	–	£1.50
L40	Henry Cooper: A Career History	1997	–	£10.95
L23	Heroes Of The Prize Ring	1993	–	£6.00
L14	Houdini	2007	–	£6.50
L8	Ipswich Town 1978 FA Cup Run	2007	–	£5.00
L30	'Iron' Mike Tyson	2004	–	£10.00
L5	Bonus Cards	2004	–	£2.00
L20	Jack Nicklaus	2005	–	£7.50
X25	Joe Louis	2000	–	£15.00
X11	John L. Sullivan Cradle To Grave	1997	–	£5.00
L36	Larry Holmes	2006	–	£10.00
L8	Leeds United 1972 FA Cup Run	2007	–	£5.00
L15	Liverpool - Champions League Winners 2005	2005	–	£7.50
L6	Liverpool - European Cup Finals	2006	–	£3.50
L9	Liverpool F.A. Cup Winners 1974	2008	–	£5.00

SPORTING PROFILES (Commercial) – cont.

Qty		Date	Odds	Sets
L10	Manchester United - 1968 European Cup	2004	–	£5.00
L15	Marilyn Monroe - Magazine Covers	2006	–	£6.50
L20	Marvin Hagler	2006	–	£7.50
L30	Movie Idols - Alfred Hitchcock	2005	–	£10.00
L15	Movie Idols - Basil Rathbone Is Sherlock Holmes	2004	–	£6.50
L30	Movie Idols - Errol Flynn	2004	–	£10.00
L10	Movie Idols - Fred Astaire & Ginger Rogers	2005	–	£5.50
L30	Movies Idols - Humphrey Bogart	2003	–	£10.00
L15	Movie Idols - James Cagney	2008	–	£6.50
L30	Movie Idols - John Wayne Vol. II	2006	–	£10.00
L30	Movie Idols - Marlon Brando	2004	–	£10.00
L15	Movie Idols - Modern Gangster Classics	2008	–	£6.50
L12	Movie Idols - The Marx Brothers	2006	–	£6.00
L30	Muhammad Ali - The Magazine Covers	2002	–	£9.00
L12	Newcastle United - Fairs Cup Winners 1968/9	2005	–	£6.00
L10	Nottingham Forest European Cup Winners 1980	2006	–	£5.00
L15	Only Fools & Horses	2003	–	£7.50
L20	Only Fools & Horses Volume II	2005	–	£7.50
L15	Pele	2005	–	£6.50
L12	Pink Floyd	2008	–	£6.00
L8	Rocky Marciano	2001	–	£3.00
L20	Smokin' Joe Frazier	2005	–	£7.50
L20	Steptoe & Son	2003	–	£9.99
L12	Stoke City: F.A. League Cup Winners 1972	2005	–	£6.00
L20	Team GB Olympic Gold Winners	2008	–	£6.00
L13	The Ashes 2005	2005	–	£6.50
L5	The Ashes 2005 Bonus 5 Card Set	2005	–	£3.50
L12	The Beatles Magazine Covers	2006	–	£6.00
L15	The Cliff Richard Collection	2004	–	£6.50
L9	The Golden Age Of Middleweights	2006	–	£5.00
L50	The Greatest (Muhammad Ali)	1993	–	£12.00
L13	The Rolling Stones - Concert Posters	2006	–	£6.50
L4	The Young Ones	2006	–	£1.50
L9	Tony Hancock - The Lad Himself	2002	–	£5.00
L8	Tottenham Hotspur - F.A. Cup Winners 1961	2008	–	£5.00
L9	Tottenham Hotspur - F.A. Cup Winners 1967	2008	–	£5.00
L9	Tottenham Hotspur - F.A. Cup Winners 1981	2008	–	£5.00
L6	Tottenham Hotspur League Cup 2008	2008	–	£4.50
L10	West Bromwich Albion F.A. Cup 1968	2007	–	£5.00
L7	West Ham United - FA Cup Winners 1964	2005	–	£5.00
L8	West Ham United F.A. Cup 1975	2007	–	£5.00
L8	West Ham United - FA Cup Winners 1980	2005	–	£5.00
L7	Wolverhampton Wanderers F.A. Cup 1960	2007	–	£5.00

SPORT IN PRINT (Commercial)

M64	Nottinghamshire Cricketers	1989	£0.50	£32.00

SPORT PHOTOS (Commercial)

96	'Smashers' (Soccer)	1950	£12.50	–

SPRATTS PATENT LTD. (Pet Food)

K100	British Bird Series (Numbered)	1935	£6.50	–
K50	(Unnumbered)	1935	£4.50	£225.00
42	British Birds	1926	£7.00	£290.00
36	Champion Dogs	1926	£14.00	–

SPRATTS PATENT LTD. (Pet Food) – cont.

Qty		Date	Odds	Sets
K20	Fish	1935	£13.00	£260.00
K100	Poultry Series	1935	£15.00	—
12	Prize Dogs	1910	£45.00	—
12	Prize Poultry	1910	£45.00	—
25	The Bonzo Series	1924	£6.00	£150.00

THE STAMP KING MANSFIELD

L7	Robin Hood	2002	—	£3.00

STAR JUNIOR CLUB

10	Animals	1960	£1.25	£12.50
10	Sports & Games (Numbered)	1960	£2.25	£22.50
5	Sports & Games (Unnumbered)	1960	£3.00	£15.00

STAVELEY'S (Shop)

24	World's Most Beautiful Birds	1924	£6.50	—

STOKES & DALTON (Cereals)

M20	The Crimson Cobra	1950	£3.25	£65.00

STOLL (Films)

25	Stars Of To-Day	1930	£8.50	—
25	The Mystery Of Dr. Fu-Manchu	1930	£12.50	—

STOLLWERCK (Chocolate)

T144	Animal World	1902	£1.35	£195.00
F?99	Views Of The World	1915	£6.00	—

THE SUN (Newspaper)

M134	Football Swap Cards	1970	£0.60	£80.00
M52	Gallery Of Football Action	1972	£3.25	£170.00
M54	Page 3 Playing Cards	1979	—	£15.00
P50	3D Gallery Of Football Stars	1972	£5.00	—

SUNBLEST (Bread, Australia)

M24	Sports Action Series	1975	—	£12.00
M25	Sunblest Explorer Cards	1975	—	£7.50

SUNBLEST TEA

25	Inventions & Discoveries, 1st Series	1960	—	£12.50
25	Inventions & Discoveries, 2nd Series	1960	—	£15.00
25	Prehistoric Animals, 1st Series	1960	—	£10.00
25	Prehistoric Animals, 2nd Series	1960	—	£9.00

SUNDAY EMPIRE NEWS

48	Famous Footballers Of Today (Durling)	1953	£5.00	£240.00

SUNDAY STORIES (Periodical)

M5	Flags (Silk)	1916	£13.50	£90.00
M6	The King & His Soldiers (Silk)	1916	£14.00	£84.00

THE SUNDAY TIMES (Newspaper)

Qty		Date	Odds	Sets
X100	Great Cars Of The World (With Album)...........................	1989	–	£8.50

SWEETACRE (Confectionery, Australia)

48	Aircraft Of The World..	1932	£3.25	£156.00
36	Cricketers (Minties)...	1926	£14.00	£500.00
24	Cricketers (Caricatures)...	1938	£27.50	–
48	Favourite Dogs..	1932	£5.00	£240.00
32	Prominent Cricketers (33-64)....................................	1932	£5.00	£160.00
48	Sports Champions..	1933	£4.00	£340.00
48	Steamships Of The World...	1932	£3.50	£188.00
32	Test Records (1-32)..	1932	£4.50	£144.00
48	This World Of Ours	1932	£5.00	–

SWEETULE PRODUCTS (Confectionery)

18	Aircraft (Packet)	1954	£6.00	£108.00
25	A Nature Series...	1960	–	£2.50
25	Animals Of The Countryside......................................	1959	–	£2.50
25	Archie Andrews Jokes..	1957	£8.50	–
25	Birds And Their Eggs...	1954	–	£3.00
25	Birds And Their Eggs (Black Back).............................	1959	–	£6.00
25	(Blue Back)............................	1959	–	£5.00
25	Birds & Their Haunts..	1958	£5.00	–
52	Birds, Fish & Flowers (P/C Inset)	1961	–	£27.50
25	Birds Of The British Commonwealth (Black Back)	1954	–	£3.00
25	Birds Of The British Commonwealth (Blue Back)................	1954	–	£2.50
M12	Coronation Series 1953 (Packet)................................	1953	£7.50	£90.00
25	Do You Know?...	1963	–	£3.50
25	Family Crests..	1961	–	£3.00
25	Famous Sports Records..	1957	£1.50	–
25	Football Club Nicknames...	1959	–	£12.50
K18	Historical Cars & Cycles	1957	–	£12.00
18	Home Pets (Packet)	1954	£7.50	–
25	International Footballers (Packet)...............................	1962	£9.00	–
25	Junior Service Quiz..	1959	–	£4.00
18	Landmarks Of Flying (Packet)....................................	1961	£6.50	£120.00
50	Modern Aircraft...	1954	–	£7.50
25	Modern Transport..	1955	–	£3.00
18	Motor Cars (Packet)...	1952	£10.00	–
50	Motorcycles Old And New..	1963	–	£80.00
30	National Flags & Costumes	1962	–	£20.00
25	Naval Battles..	1959	–	£3.50
25	Products Of The World	1958	–	£2.50
24	Racing Cars Of The World (Packet).............................	1960	£10.00	–
M18	Railway Engines (Package Issue)	1958	£7.00	£125.00
18	Railway Engines-Past & Present (Packet)......................	1953	£8.00	£144.00
25	Sports Quiz..	1958	–	£6.00
1	Stamp Card (Real Stamp Attached)	1962	–	£0.50
25	Stamp Cards...	1961	–	£5.00
25	The Wild West (Black Back).......................................	1960	–	£13.50
25	(Blue Back)	1960	–	£3.50
X30	Trains Of The World	1960	£1.60	£48.00
25	Treasure Island	1957	–	£8.00
25	Tropical Birds..	1954	–	£4.00
25	Vintage Cars	1964	–	£10.00

SWEETULE PRODUCTS (Confectionery) – cont.

Qty		Date	Odds	Sets
25	Weapons Of Defence	1959	–	£3.00
25	Wild Animals	1958	–	£2.50
25	Wild Flowers	1961	–	£2.50
25	Wonders Of The World	1956	–	£3.00

SWETTENHAM (Tea)

Qty		Date	Odds	Sets
25	Aircraft Of The World	1959	–	£15.00
25	Animals Of The Countryside	1959	–	£2.50
25	Birds And Their Eggs	1958	–	£2.50
25	British Coins And Costumes	1958	–	£6.00
25	Butterflies And Moths	1958	–	£2.50
25	Evolution Of The Royal Navy	1957	–	£3.00
25	Into Space	1959	–	£3.00
24	The Island Of Ceylon (Conqueror Tea)	1955	£4.50	–
25	Wild Animals	1958	–	£5.00

W. SWORD & CO. (Biscuits)

Qty		Date	Odds	Sets
25	British Empire At Work	1925	£15.00	–
20	Dogs	1926	£17.50	–
20	Inventors & Their Inventions	1926	£17.50	–
25	Safety First	1927	£12.50	–
25	Sports & Pastimes Series	1926	£17.50	–
25	Vehicles Of All Ages	1924	£15.00	–
25	Zoo Series (Brown)	1928	£10.00	£250.00
25	Zoo Series (Coloured, Different)	1928	£12.00	–

SYMONDS CIDER & ENGLISH WINE COMPANY LTD.

Qty		Date	Odds	Sets
M10	Sporting Greats (Early 1900s)	1998	–	£10.00

DES TAYLOR (Commercial)

Qty		Date	Odds	Sets
L20	My Favourite Fish	2000	–	£7.50

TEACHER'S WHISKY

Qty		Date	Odds	Sets
X12	Scottish Clans & Castles (Circular Advert)	1955	£5.00	–
X12	Scottish Clans & Tartans (Rectangular Advert)	1955	£3.50	£42.00

TEAMS LTD. (Commercial)

Qty		Date	Odds	Sets
40	40 Years Of Cards (Brooke Bond)	1994	–	£5.00

TEASDALE & CO. (Confectionery)

Qty		Date	Odds	Sets
50	Cinema Stars (Anon)	1935	£7.50	–
25	Great War Series	1916	£25.00	–

TESCO STORES

Qty		Date	Odds	Sets
P6	Nature Trail Stickers	1989	–	£1.50

TETLEY TEA

Qty		Date	Odds	Sets
48	British Birds	1970	£4.50	£216.00

TEXACO PETROL

Qty		Date	Odds	Sets
12	Texaco Trophy Cricket Cards	1984	£0.50	£6.00

Qty		Date	Odds	Sets
L30	Adventure Pictures	1922	£3.35	£100.00
M16	Badges Of The Fighting Flyers	1939	£4.70	£75.00
P26	Battles For The Flag	1939	£5.50	–
K80	Boys Of All Nations	1936	£1.25	–
20	British Birds And Eggs	1930	£3.20	£64.00
F11	British Team Of Footballers	1923	£3.35	£37.00
L20	Canvas Masterpieces (Silk)	1925	£10.00	–
16	Catch-My-Pal Cards	1939	£2.25	£35.00
X12	Coloured Photos Of Star Footballers	1927	£8.00	£96.00
64	County Cricketers	1957	£2.50	£160.00
16	Cricket Crests	1929	£9.50	£150.00
KF8	Cricketers	1923	£3.50	£28.00
X24	Cricketers	1924	£8.25	£198.00
P16	Cup-Tie Stars Of All Nations	1962	£4.25	£68.00
12	Dandy Dogs	1928	£5.20	£62.50
K28	Dominoes-School Caricatures	1936	£2.25	£63.00
20	Easy Scientific Experiments	1930	£3.00	£60.00
MF18	Famous British Footballers (English)	1921	£3.35	£60.00
K80	Famous Feats	1937	£1.40	–
24	Famous Fights	1934	£3.00	–
25	Famous Footballers	1955	£2.40	£60.00
24	Famous Footballers (Different)	1956	£2.50	£60.00
20	Famous Liners	1930	£4.00	£80.00
L32	Famous Ships	1931	£4.25	£150.00
P12	Famous Teams In Football History	1961	£6.00	£70.00
P16	Famous Teams In Football History, 2nd Series	1962	£5.25	£85.00
16	Flags Of All Nations	1929	£3.00	£48.00
K80	Flags Of The Sea	1937	£1.30	–
KF137	Footballers	1923	£1.40	–
F18	Footballers	1923	£3.25	£58.00
X8	Footballers	1933	£7.50	£60.00
K52	Footballers - Hunt The Cup Cards	1934	£3.00	–
24	Footballers - Motor Cars (Double-Sided)	1930	£8.25	£200.00
MF22	Footballers - Signed Real Photos	1923	£2.50	£55.00
F40	Football Photos	1925	£6.50	–
48	Football Stars	1957	£2.40	£120.00
44	Football Stars Of 1959	1959	£3.20	£140.00
K60/64	Football Team Cards	1935	£1.35	£80.00
64	Football Tips & Tricks	1959	£0.85	£54.00
L32	Football Towns And Their Crests	1931	£6.50	£210.00
T12	Great Captains	1972	£6.25	£75.00
12	Guns In Action	1938	£2.25	£27.00
M8	Hidden Treasure Clue Cards	1926	£13.00	–
P16	International Cup Teams	1964	£5.00	–
6	Ju-Jitsu Cards	1929	£6.00	£35.00
24	Motor Bike Cards	1929	£6.75	£162.00
20	Motor Cycles	1930	£7.00	£140.00
K100	Motor Cars	1934	£1.50	–
11	Mystic Menagerie	1926	£6.25	£70.00
36	1930 Speedway Stars	1930	£8.20	£295.00
K80	Punishment Cards	1936	£1.40	–
12	Queer Animals	1928	£3.35	–
16	Queer Birds	1929	£3.00	£48.00
K80	Secrets Of Cricket	1936	£2.35	–
36	Spadgers Monster Collection Of Spoofs	1935	£3.50	£125.00

D.C. THOMSON & CO. LTD. (Periodical) – cont.

Qty		Date	Odds	Sets
48	Speed	1932	£1.25	£60.00
12	Speedsters Of The Wilds	1928	£3.50	£42.00
48	Stars Of Sport And Entertainment	1958	£2.25	£108.00
8/14	Star Footballers (Metal)	1932	£13.00	—
P22	Star Teams Of 1961	1961	£4.15	£90.00
P16	The Great Stars Of Football	1968	£3.75	£60.00
20	The Wireless Telephone	1930	£3.00	£60.00
32	The World's Best Cricketers (Green Back)	1926	£3.00	£96.00
36	The World's Best Cricketers (Mauve Back)	1930	£6.25	£225.00
72	The World's Best Cricketers (Mauve back, different)	1956	£3.35	£240.00
X12	The World's Biggest	1936	£8.00	£95.00
30	This Seasons Latest Motor Cars (Metal)	1926	£22.00	—
K25	This Year's Motor Car Crests (Metal)	1925	£22.00	—
24	This Year's Top-Form Footballers	1927	£3.60	£86.00
P12	Top Cup Teams (Hornet)	1966	£6.25	£75.00
10	Vanguard Photo Gallery	1923	£14.00	—
96	VP Flips	1925	£1.60	—
24	Warrior Cards (Sectional Back)	1929	£2.75	£66.00
K28	Warrior Cards (Domino Back)	1935	£2.15	£60.00
K80	Warrior Cards	1937	£1.25	—
20	Why?	1930	£3.00	£60.00
K28	Wild West Dominoes	1936	£2.15	£60.00
20	Wonders Of The Rail	1930	£5.00	£100.00
20	Wonders Of The World	1930	£2.50	£50.00
64	World Cup Footballers	1958	£3.15	£200.00
M72	World Cup Stars	1970	£3.15	£225.00

THURMER & SYMES (Biscuits)

M96	Ocean Giants	1954	£3.00	—

TIMARU MILLING CO (Cereals, N. Zealand)

M36	Focus On Fame	1948	—	£17.50
M37	Peace & Progress	1947	—	£17.50

TIMES CONFECTIONERY CO. LTD.

MF24	Roy Rogers-In Old Amarillo (Plain Back)	1955	—	£8.50
M24	(Printed Back)	1955	—	£24.00
MF24	Roy Rogers-South Of Caliente (Plain Back)	1955	—	£8.50
M24	(Printed Back)	1955	—	£24.00

TIP TOP (Ice Cream, New Zealand)

M10	Galactic Bar	1977	—	£10.00

TIP TOP SALES COMPANY (Malta)

M25	European Football Action, Series A	1932	£30.00	£750.00

TIT-BITS (Periodical)

K54	Pin-Ups (P/C Inset)	1976	—	£8.00
MF17	Star Cover Girls	1953	£5.00	—
T12	Tit-Bits Clubs	1977	£2.00	£24.00

CHOCOLAT TOBLER LTD.

50	Famous Footballers	1939	£12.50	—
T186	General Interest Series	1900	£1.25	£232.50

TOBY (Periodical)

Qty		Date	Odds	Sets
24	Dogs (Anon)	1926	£4.50	–
24	Dogs, 2nd Series (25-48, Anon)	1926	£4.50	–
24	Sights Of London (Anon)	1926	£3.50	£84.00
24	Toby's Bird Series	1926	£4.00	–
24	Toby's Ship Series	1926	£4.00	£96.00
24	Toby's Travel Series	1926	£3.50	£84.00

TODAY (Newspaper)

Qty		Date	Odds	Sets
X14	Around Britain	1991	–	£2.50

TOMMY GUNN (Toys)

Qty		Date	Odds	Sets
50	Medals (Plain Back)	1971	–	£5.00

TOM THUMB (New Zealand)

Qty		Date	Odds	Sets
M24	Supercars	1980	–	£12.00

TONIBELL (Ice Cream)

Qty		Date	Odds	Sets
12	Action Soldiers (With Cadbury)	1976	–	£3.00
M20	Banknotes	1974	£0.20	£3.50
M12	Beautiful Butterflies	1974	£0.20	£2.00
M20	County Badge Collection	1974	£0.20	£3.00
25	Did You Know?	1963	–	£3.00
L12	Did You Know? (Different)	1975	£1.75	–
X12	England's Soccer Stars	1970	£4.00	£48.00
D19	Famous Sports Trophies	1976	–	£9.00
D12	Farmyard Stencils	1977	–	£4.00
M24	1st Division Football League Club Badges	1972	£2.75	£65.00
X12	Horses In The Service Of Man	1984	£0.80	£10.00
25	Inventions That Changed The World	1963	–	£3.00
X10	Junior Champs	1983	£0.60	£6.00
M24	Kings Of The Road	1977	£1.25	£30.00
L24	Pop Star Cameos	1975	–	£8.50
K36	Team Of All Time	1971	£2.25	£81.00
25	The World's Passenger Liners	1963	–	£3.00
25	This Changing World (With Line)	1963	–	£5.00
25	(Without Line)	1963	–	£7.50
25	Wonders Of The Heavens	1963	–	£10.00

TOP FLIGHT (Confectionery)

Qty		Date	Odds	Sets
25	Top Flight Stars (Sport)	1960	£3.50	£87.50

TOPICAL TIMES (Periodical)

Qty		Date	Odds	Sets
E8	Cricketers	1938	£16.00	£128.00
M6	Football Teams (Metal)	1924	£14.00	–
MF6	Football Teams	1928	£6.00	£36.00
MF10	Footballers (Pairs)	1930	£5.00	£50.00
E12	Footballers, Panel Portraits	1932	£5.50	£66.00
E24	Footballers, Panel Portraits	1933	£5.00	–
E14	Footballers, Panel Portraits	1934	£4.50	£63.00
E14	Footballers, Panel Portraits	1935	£4.50	£63.00
E16	Footballers, Panel Portraits(Coloured)	1936	£6.50	£104.00
E14	Footballers, Panel Portraits	1938	£4.50	£63.00
E16	Footballers, Panel Portraits	1939	£4.50	£72.00

TOPICAL TIMES (Periodical) – cont.

Qty		Date	Odds	Sets
E8	Footballers, Special Issue (Coloured)	1934	£6.50	£52.00
E8	Footballers, Triple Portraits	1937	£6.50	£52.00
L24	Great Players	1938	£3.50	£84.00
P24	Miniature Panel Portraits	1937	£3.50	£84.00
P24	Stars Of To-Day	1938	£3.50	£84.00

TOP NOTE SLIDES

P9	Pop Singers	1952	£7.00	–

TOP TRUMPS

X36	British Strikers	1980	–	£9.00
X36	International Greats	1980	–	£8.50

TOPPS CHEWING GUM INC.

L80	A. L. F.	1988	–	£12.50
L88	American Baseball Stars	1988	–	£30.00
L88	American Baseball Stars	1989	–	£35.00
X99	Autos Of 1977	1977	£1.75	£175.00
X98	Batman Returns (With Stickers)	1993	–	£5.00
X132	Battlestar Galactica	1979	£0.25	£32.50
X66	Bay City Rollers	1978	£0.30	£20.00
X49	Comic Book Heroes	1975	£2.50	£110.00
X99	Dick Tracy	1990	–	£12.50
X70	England 2002 (Soccer)	2002	–	£20.00
P18	England World Cup Supersquad	1990	–	£15.00
X330	Footballers (Blue Back)	1976	£1.20	£400.00
X220	Footballers (Red Back)	1975	£1.75	–
X88	Footballers (Scottish, Blue Back)	1975	£2.50	–
X132	Footballers (Scottish, Red Back)	1976	£2.25	–
X330	Footballers (Red Back)	1977	£1.35	–
X132	Footballers (Scottish, Yellow Back)	1977	£1.50	–
X396	Footballers (Orange Back)	1978	£0.35	£140.00
X132	Footballers (Scottish, Green Back)	1978	£1.50	–
X396	Footballers (Pale Blue Back)	1979	£1.60	£640.00
X132	Footballers (Scottish, Red Back)	1979	£2.00	–
X66	Footballers (Pink Back)	1980	£2.25	£150.00
X65	Footballers (Blue Back)	1981	£1.00	£65.00
X10/14	Footballers Stadium Promotion Cards	1992	–	£3.00
E18	Football Posters	1980	£1.00	£18.00
X77	Home Alone 2 (With Stickers)	1993	–	£6.50
X44	Home And Away	1987	–	£6.00
X110	Hook (With Stickers)	1991	–	£10.00
X99	Jurassic Park (With Stickers)	1993	–	£12.50
X49	Marvel Super Heroes	1980	£2.00	£100.00
X48	Monster In My Pocket	1991	–	£7.50
X66	Planet Of The Apes	1974	£2.40	£160.00
X125	Premier Gold 2002	2002	–	£20.00
X125	Premier Gold '04	2003	–	£20.00
X72	Railway Quiz (See A.& B.C.)	1959	–	–
L264	Saint & Greavsie	1988	–	£27.50
P18	Scotland World Cup Supersquad	1990	£2.50	£45.00
X50	Shocking Laffs	1977	£2.50	£125.00
X66	Spitting Image	1990	–	£16.50
X88	Star Trek, The Motion Picture	1980	£2.25	£200.00

TOPPS CHEWING GUM INC. – cont.

Qty		Date	Odds	Sets
X66	Star Wars (1-66)	1978	£2.00	£132.00
X66	Star Wars (1A-66A)	1978	£3.00	£200.00
X66	Superman The Movie, 1st Series (1-66)	1979	£0.30	£20.00
X66	Superman The Movie, 2nd Series (67-132)	1979	£0.30	£20.00
X77	Teenage Mutant Hero Turtles (TV)	1990	–	£8.00
X143	Teenage Mutant Ninja Turtles (Film)	1990	–	£8.00
M44	Terminator 2	1991	£0.35	£15.00
X88	The Black Hole	1980	£0.40	£35.00
X99	The Flintstones (With Stickers)	1994	–	£8.00
X66	Wacky Wrestling	1993	–	£6.50
X42	Wanted Posters	1978	£1.25	–

U.S.ISSUES

X154	Batman - The Movie (With Stickers)	1989	–	£20.00
X88	Buck Rogers In The 25th Century	1979	–	£18.00
X77	Close Encounters	1982	–	£30.00
X36	Donkey Kong	1982	–	£5.00
P72	Dragonheart (Widevision)	1996	–	£15.00
X99	Ghostbusters II (With Stickers)	1989	–	£17.50
X99	Greatest Olympians	1983	–	£12.00
X88	Gremlins 2	1990	–	£9.00
X59	Jaws 2	1978	–	£25.00
X99	Jurassic Park (With Stickers)	1993	–	£15.00
X33	Michael Jackson 1st Stickers	1984	–	£17.50
X55	Mysteries Of India	1967	–	£35.00
X66	Rambo	1985	–	£12.00
X22	Rambo (Stickers)	1985	–	£6.00
X99	Rocky II	1981	–	£10.00
X22	Rocky II (Stickers)	1981	–	£6.00
X66	Rocky IV	1986	–	£10.00
X11	Rocky IV (Stickers)	1986	–	£7.50
X50	Shocking Laffs	1976	£1.60	£80.00
G12	Smurf Tattoos	1983	–	£35.00
P80	Star Wars Episode I (Widevision)	1999	–	£20.00
P80	Star Wars Episode 1 Series Two (Widevision)	1999	–	£25.00
X88	Superman II	1981	–	£30.00
X99	Superman III	1983	–	£27.50
X143	Teenage Mutant Ninja Turtles (Film)	1990	–	£12.00
X99	Teenage Mutant Ninja Turtles (TV)	1989	–	£8.50
X66	The 'A' Team	1983	–	£16.50
X72	The X Files, Season One	1995	–	£15.00
X72	The X Files, Season Two	1996	–	£12.50
X72	The X Files, Season Three	1996	–	£12.50
P72	The X Files Showcase (Widevision)	1997	–	£15.00
X55	Weird Wheels	1980	–	£12.00

JOHN TORDOFF & SON LTD. (Tea)

25	Safety First	1926	£11.00	–
25	The Growth And Manufacture Of Tea	1926	£12.00	–

TOTAL PETROL

X25	Return To Oz	1985	–	£4.00

TOWER TEA

24	Illustrated Sayings	1910	£25.00	–

TREBOR BASSETT LTD. (Confectionery)

Qty		Date	Odds	Sets
48	Football 1991-2	1991	£0.85	£40.00
48	Football 1992-3	1992	–	£12.50
48	Football 1995-6	1995	–	£20.00
P20	Jurassic Park (Slides)	1993	–	£8.50
48	Premier Players	1995	–	£10.00
48	Sonic The Hedgehog	1991	–	£6.00
48	World Beaters (Soccer)	1994	–	£17.00

TREBOR/SHARP (Confectionery)

Qty		Date	Odds	Sets
25	Famous Pets	1972	–	£3.50
M48	Space Series	1964	£4.25	–
M48	V. C. Heroes	1964	£4.50	–

TRENOUTHS (Shop)

Qty		Date	Odds	Sets
24	World's Most Beautiful Butterflies	1924	£6.50	–

TRIO BARS (Confectionery)

Qty		Date	Odds	Sets
M6	Roland Rat Superstar	1990	–	£6.00

TRUCARDS (Commercial)

Qty		Date	Odds	Sets
M30	Animals	1972	–	£2.50
M30	Battle Of Britain	1972	–	£4.00
M30	Flowers	1972	–	£3.00
M30	History Of Aircraft	1972	–	£3.00
M30	Sport	1972	–	£3.00
M30	Veteran & Vintage Cars	1972	–	£3.50
M30	World War I	1972	–	£3.00
M30	World War II	1972	–	£3.00

TUCKETT'S (Confectionery)

Qty		Date	Odds	Sets
25	Photo's Of Cricketers	1925	£32.50	–
50	Photos Of Film Stars	1939	£6.50	–
25	Photos Of Football Stars	1928	£25.00	–

TUDOROSE STOCKINGS

Qty		Date	Odds	Sets
P20	Tudor Britain	1955	£3.25	£65.00

W. & E. TURNER (Shoes)

Qty		Date	Odds	Sets
20	War Pictures	1915	£17.50	£350.00

TWININGS TEA

Qty		Date	Odds	Sets
30	Rare Stamps	1960	£0.60	£18.00
30	Rare Stamps, 2nd Series	1960	–	£5.00
30	2nd Series (Red Overprint)	1961	–	£3.00

TYPHOO TEA LTD

Qty		Date	Odds	Sets
25	Aesop's Fables	1924	£3.20	£80.00
25	Ancient & Annual Customs	1922	£2.40	£60.00
T25	Animal Friends Of Man	1927	£5.00	£125.00
T25	Animal Offence & Defence	1928	£1.60	£40.00
T25	A Tale Of Two Cities	1931	£3.60	£90.00
24	British Birds & Their Eggs	1914	£12.50	£300.00

TYPHOO TEA LTD – cont.

Qty		Date	Odds	Sets
T25	British Birds And Their Eggs	1936	£1.60	£40.00
29/30	British Empire At Work	1925	£1.30	£39.00
30	British Empire At Work Continuation Card	1925	£7.00	–
1	British Empire At Work Last Chance Card	1926	–	£10.00
25	Calendar 1934 (Dogs)	1933	£30.00	–
25	Calendar 1936	1935	£16.00	–
T1	Calendar 1937	1936	–	£8.50
T25	Characters From Shakespeare	1937	£1.60	£40.00
25	Common Objects Highly Magnified	1925	£1.30	£32.00
25	Conundrums	1915	£18.00	–
24	Do You Know	1962	–	£3.50
T25	Famous Voyages	1934	£1.60	£40.00
M20	Flags & Arms Of Countries	1916	£15.00	£300.00
24	Great Achievements	1962	£1.35	£32.00
T25	Historical Buildings	1936	£2.00	£50.00
T25	Homes Of Famous Men	1934	£1.20	£30.00
T25	Horses	1935	£1.80	£45.00
T25	Important Industries Of British Empire	1939	£0.50	£12.50
T25	Interesting Events In British History	1938	£0.50	£12.50
T25	John Halifax, Gentleman	1932	£2.40	£60.00
T25	Lorna Doone	1930	£3.60	£90.00
10	Nursery Rhymes	1914	£23.00	–
24	Our Empire's Defenders	1916	£27.00	£650.00
48	Puzzle Pictures	1913	£32.00	–
T30	Robin Hood & His Merry Men	1928	£8.50	£255.00
M12	The Amazing World Of Doctor Who	1976	£2.00	£24.00
T30	The Story Of David Copperfield	1929	£3.00	£75.00
T25	The Swiss Family Robinson	1935	£2.00	£50.00
24	Travel Through The Ages	1962	–	£3.50
T25	Trees Of The Countryside	1938	£0.60	£15.00
T25	Whilst We Sleep	1928	£2.80	£70.00
24	Wild Flowers	1961	–	£3.00
T25	Wild Flowers In Their Families	1936	£1.00	£25.00
T25	Wild Flowers In Their Families, 2nd Series	1937	£1.00	£25.00
T25	Wonder Cities Of The World	1933	£1.50	£37.50
M24	Wonderful World Of Disney	1975	£3.75	£90.00
T25	Work On The Farm	1933	£4.00	£100.00
25	Zoo Series	1932	£0.90	£22.50

PACKAGE ISSUES

Qty		Date	Odds	Sets
20	By Pond & Stream	1955	£0.30	£6.00
20	Common British Birds	1955	£0.30	£6.00
20	Costumes Of The World	1955	£0.75	£15.00
24	Do You Know	1962	£0.30	£7.50
20	Famous Bridges	1955	£0.30	£6.00
20	Famous Buildings	1955	£0.25	£4.00
24	Famous Football Clubs	1962	£2.25	£54.00
24	Famous Football Clubs, 2nd Series	1963	£2.25	£54.00
35	Football Club Plaques	1973	£6.75	–
24	Football Stars, New Series	1973	£3.00	£72.00
24	Great Voyages Of Discovery	1962	£0.40	£10.00
24	International Football Stars	1967	£2.90	£70.00
24	International Football Stars, 2nd Series	1969	£2.85	–
24	100 Years Of Great British Achievements	1972	£0.75	£18.00
20	Pets	1955	£0.25	£5.00

TYPHOO TEA LTD – cont.

Qty		Date	Odds	Sets
20	Some Countryside Animals	1955	£0.25	£5.00
20	Some Popular Breeds Of Dogs	1955	£0.80	£16.00
20	Some World Wonders	1955	£0.30	£6.00
24	Travel Through The Ages	1962	£0.25	£6.00
20	Types Of Ships	1955	£0.35	£7.00
20	Wild Animals	1954	£0.20	£4.00
24	Wild Flowers	1961	£0.50	£12.00

PREMIUM ISSUES

Qty		Date	Odds	Sets
E24	Famous Football Clubs	1964	£13.00	–
E24	Famous Football Clubs, 2nd Series	1965	£10.00	£240.00
E24	Football Stars	1973	£9.50	£228.00
G24	Great Voyages Of Discovery	1967	£3.60	–
E24	International Football Stars, 1st Series	1967	£10.00	£240.00
E24	International Football Stars, 2nd Series	1969	£9.00	£216.00
G24	100 Years Of British Achievements	1972	–	£22.50

TYSON & CO. (Soap)

Qty		Date	Odds	Sets
28	Semaphore Signals	1912	£17.00	£475.00

UNION JACK (Periodical)

Qty		Date	Odds	Sets
MF6	Monarchs Of The Ring	1923	£10.00	£60.00
M8	Police Of All Nations	1922	£7.50	£60.00

UNITED AUTOMOBILE SERVICES

Qty		Date	Odds	Sets
25	Castles (Series No.1)	1925	£7.00	–
25	Churches (Series No.2)	1925	£6.50	–
25	Places Of Interest (Series No.4)	1925	£7.00	–
25	'United' (Series No.3)	1925	£7.00	–

UNITED CONFECTIONERY CO.

Qty		Date	Odds	Sets
50	Wild Animals Of The World	1905	£12.00	–

UNITED DAIRIES

Qty		Date	Odds	Sets
25	Aquarium Fish	1962	–	£8.00
25	Birds And Their Eggs	1961	–	£17.50
25	British Uniforms Of The 19th Century	1962	£1.00	£25.00
25	The Story Of Milk	1966	–	£7.50
25	The West	1963	–	£17.50

UNIVERSAL AUTOMATICS LTD.

Qty		Date	Odds	Sets
X30	Trains Of The World	1958	£1.00	£30.00

UNIVERSAL CIGARETTE CARD CO. LTD.

Qty		Date	Odds	Sets
15	Australian Cricket Team 1905	1986	–	£3.00
13	Car Registration Numbers (Irish)	1987	–	£4.00
15	English Cricketers 1902	1987	–	£3.00
25	Military Maids	1987	–	£4.50
25	People Of The World	1987	–	£3.50

UNUSUALLY FUNNY FACTORY LTD (Gum)

Qty		Date	Odds	Sets
M40	Prehistorigum	1990	–	£8.50
M40	Team - Spirits	1990	–	£6.50

VAUXHALL MOTORS LIMITED.

Qty		Date	Odds	Sets
L25	Vauxhall Motor Sport Series	1993	–	£11.00
L25	Vauxhall's 90th Anniversary Series	1993	–	£9.00

VENORLANDUS (Commercial)

M48	World Of Sport - Our Heroes	1980	–	£20.00

VERKADE'S FABRIEKEN (Biscuits, Holland)

T140	De Bloemen En Haar Vrienden	1933	–	£20.00
T140	De Boerderij	1935	–	£35.00
T138	Hans De Torenkraai	1936	–	£20.00
T132	Kamerplanten	1928	–	£30.00
T125/126	Mijn Aquarium	1925	–	£30.00
T126	Vetplanten	1926	–	£25.00

VICTORIA GALLERY (Commercial)
AUTHORISED REPRINTS OF IMPERIAL TOBACCO CO. ISSUES

P4	Advertisement Postcards (Wills)	1988	–	£5.00
50	Aeroplanes (Civil) (Player)	1990	–	£8.50
50	Aviary And Cage Birds (Player)	1989	–	£7.50
L25	Aviary & Cage Birds (Player)	1987	–	£8.50
50	Boxing Personalities (Churchman)	1990	–	£8.50
25	Characters From Dickens (Player)	1990	–	£6.00
50	Derby & Grand National Winners (Player)	1988	–	£8.50
L25	Dogs (Wills)	1987	–	£8.50
25	England's Naval Heroes (Player)	1988	–	£10.00
L25	Famous Golfers (Wills)	1987	–	£8.50
50	Film Stars, Third Series (Player)	1989	–	£8.50
50	Fish & Bait (Wills)	1990	–	£8.50
L25	Game Birds & Wild Fowl (Player)	1987	–	£8.50
L25	Golf (Player)	1986	–	£8.50
L25	Lawn Tennis, 1931 (Wills)	1988	–	£8.50
50	Motor Cycles (B.A.T.)	1991	–	£8.50
25	Motors (Lambert & Butler 1908)	1992	–	£6.00
58	Musical Celebrities 2nd (Wills)	1988	–	£10.00
25	Napoleon (Player)	1989	–	£6.00
L12	Prominent Golfers (Churchman)	1989	–	£6.00
50	Racing Greyhounds (Churchman)	1989	–	£8.50
L25	Racing Yachts (Player)	1987	–	£8.50
12	Recruiting Posters (Wills)	1988	–	£3.00
L25	Rigs Of Ships (Wills)	1987	–	£8.50

ORIGINAL ISSUES

L6	A Gathering Of Spirits	1994	–	£2.50
L20	American Civil War Leaders	1992	–	£7.50
L20	Boxing Champions	1991	–	£11.00
L21	Boxing Champions Second Series	1992	–	£7.50
L6	British Birds Of Prey	1994	–	£2.50
L6	British Birds Of Prey (Different)	1996	–	£2.50
L20	Caricatures Of The British Army	1994	–	£7.00
L20	Caricatures Of The British Army II	1994	–	£7.00
L1	Promotional Card	1994	–	£0.50
L6	Classic Motor Cycles (Harley Davidson)	1993	–	£2.50
L20	Endangered Wild Animals	1991	–	£7.00
L25	Hollywood Moviemen	1993	–	£9.00
L2	Promotional Cards	1993	–	£0.60

VICTORIA GALLERY (Commercial) – cont.

Qty		Date	Odds	Sets
L20	Legends Of Hollywood	1991	–	£7.50
L1	Promotional Card(John Wayne)	1991	–	£0.75
L25	Olympic Greats	1992	–	£9.00
L20	Partners (Cinema)	1992	–	£7.50
L20	Snooker Celebrities	1988	–	£7.00
L10	Spirit Of A Nation	1991	–	£5.00
L25	The Ryder Cup, 1991	1991	–	£15.00
L12	The Twelve Days Of Christmas	1992	–	£6.00
L20	Uniforms Of The American Civil War	1992	–	£7.50
L24	Uniforms Of The War Of Independence	1993	–	£9.00
L48	Wild West	1993	–	£14.00

CHOCOLAT DE VILLARS

Qty		Date	Odds	Sets
24	British Birds And Their Eggs	1926	£4.00	£96.00

VOMO AUTOMATICS

Qty		Date	Odds	Sets
X50	Flags Of The World	1965	£1.00	£50.00

JONATHAN WALES LTD.

Qty		Date	Odds	Sets
25	The History Of Flight, 1st Series	1963	£8.00	–
25	The History Of Flight, 2nd Series	1963	£8.00	–

WALES ON SUNDAY (Newspaper)

Qty		Date	Odds	Sets
T36	World Cup Heroes (Rugby)	1995	–	£17.50
T24	World Cup Rugby Greats (With Album)	1999	–	£17.50

WALKER, HARRISON AND GARTHWAITES LTD.

Qty		Date	Odds	Sets
M15	Dogs	1902	£24.00	–

WALKERS SNACK FOODS LTD.

Qty		Date	Odds	Sets
K50	Looney Tunes (Tazos)	1996	–	£7.50
K10	Wizard Monster (Tazos)	1996	–	£2.00
K20	World Tazos (51-70)	1996	–	£4.00

T. WALL & SONS (Ice Cream)

Qty		Date	Odds	Sets
24	Do You Know	1965	–	£4.00
36	Dr. Who Adventure	1966	£3.50	£126.00
20	Incredible Hulk Records	1979	£3.00	£60.00
48	Moon Fleet	1967	£0.60	–
M6	Prehistoric Animals (Magicards)	1971	–	£3.00
P6	Sea Creatures	1971	–	£2.50
20	Skateboard Surfer	1978	–	£6.50
20	Time Travel With Starship 4	1984	£4.00	–

WALTERS PALM TOFFEE

Qty		Date	Odds	Sets
50	Some Cap Badges Of Territorial Regiments	1938	£1.20	£60.00

WAND CONFECTIONERY LTD.

Qty		Date	Odds	Sets
X10	Chubby Checker-How To Do The Twist	1964	£8.00	–
25	Commemoration Stamp Series	1963	£3.00	£75.00
X35	Pop D.J.'S	1964	£3.70	£130.00

WAND CONFECTIONERY LTD. – cont.

Qty		Date	Odds	Sets
25	They Gave Their Names	1963	–	£10.00
23/25	They Gave Their Names	1963	–	£2.00

WARNOCK & CO (Tea)

24	The Island Of Ceylon	1955	£5.00	£125.00

WARUS CARDS (COMMERCIAL)

10	The Abbey Road Series...	1998	–	£5.00
10	The Beatles For Sale Series..	1998	–	£5.00
10	The Beatles For Sale No.2 EP Series	2005	–	£5.00
10	The Beatles' Hits EP Series	2005	–	£5.00
10	The Beatles' Million Sellers EP Series	2005	–	£5.00
10	The E.P. Series	2005	–	£5.00
10	The Hard Day's Night Series	1998	–	£5.00
10	The Help Series..	1998	–	£5.00
10	The Long Tall Sally EP Series	2005	–	£5.00
10	The Nowhere Man EP Series	2005	–	£5.00
10	The Please Please Me Series	1998	–	£5.00
10	The Revolver Series	1998	–	£5.00
10	The Rubber Soul Series	1998	–	£5.00
10	The Sgt. Pepper Series..	1998	–	£5.00
10	The Twist And Shout EP Series	2005	–	£5.00
10	The White Album	1998	–	£5.00
10	The Let It Be Series	1998	–	£5.00
10	The Magical Mystery Tour Series	1998	–	£5.00
10	The With The Beatles Series...	1998	–	£5.00
10	The Yellow Submarine Series..	1998	–	£5.00
10	The Yesterday EP Series	2005	–	£5.00
10	U.S.A. Albums - Beatles	2005	–	£5.00
10	U.S.A. Albums - Meet The Beatles	2005	–	£5.00
10	U.S.A. Albums - Something New...	2005	–	£5.00
10	U.S.A. Albums - The Beatles Second Album	2005	–	£5.00
10	U.S.A. Albums - Yesterday & Today.....................................	2005	–	£5.00

WARWICK DISTRICT COUNCIL

30	England's Historic Heartland...	1980	–	£3.00

WATFORD BISCUIT CO.

KF48	Cinema Stars	1954	£3.00	–

JOHN WATSON (Commercial)

X56	East Anglian Taverns	2004	–	£10.00

WEBCOSA & CO. (Gum)

X20	Trail Town	1963	£2.75	£55.00
M48	Victoria Cross Heroes..	1964	£3.75	–

WEEKLY WELCOME (Periodical)

12	Lest We Forget Cards..	1916	£10.00	£120.00

WEETABIX LTD. (Cereals)

XS25	Animal Cards	1960	£1.00	£25.00
T28	Asterix - His Friends & Foes	1976	£2.75	£77.00
T18	Batman And Wonder Woman...	1979	£3.50	£63.00
XS25	British Birds Cards...	1962	£2.40	£60.00

WEETABIX LTD. (Cereals) – cont.

Qty		Date	Odds	Sets
XS25	British Cars	1963	£3.50	£87.50
L25	Conquest Of Space, Series A	1959	£2.60	£65.00
L25	Conquest Of Space, Series B	1959	£2.60	£65.00
L4	Double Jigsaw	1991	–	£3.00
T24	Dr Who (Coloured Background)	1977	£6.50	£156.00
T24	Dr Who (White Background)	1975	£5.00	£120.00
T18	Flash Gordon	1981	£2.25	£40.00
T18	Huckleberry Hound	1977	£3.00	£54.00
T18	Mickey Mouse's Playmates	1978	£3.75	£67.50
XS25	Our Pets Cards	1961	£0.90	£22.50
T24	Robin Hood	1980	£2.25	£54.00
T18	Star Trek	1979	£4.50	£81.00
T18	Superman	1978	£2.75	£50.00
L25	The Western Story	1959	£1.80	£45.00
XS25	Thrill Cards	1960	£2.20	£55.00
P5	Weeta-Card	1989	–	£6.00
XS25	Working Dog Cards	1961	–	£12.00
T18	World Of Sport	1986	£5.00	£90.00

JAMES O. WELCH (Confectionery, U.S.A.)

50	Comics	1950	£5.00	£250.00

WELSH RUGBY UNION

50	Great Welsh Rugby Players	1981	–	£6.00

JOHN WEST FOODS LTD.

M8	Famous Sea Adventurers	1972	–	£2.50

WEST LONDON SYNAGOGUE

50	Jewish Life In Many Lands	1961	–	£65.00
50	Jewish Symbols And Ceremonies	1961	–	£60.00
25/50	-Ditto-	1961	–	£3.50

WESTCO (Confectionery)

F60	Westco Autocards	1954	£8.50	–

WEST MIDLANDS COLLECTORS CENTRE

24	Busby Babes	1990	–	£6.00
30	England Captains	1997	–	£5.00
24	Golden Wolves	1989	–	£5.00
24	Vintage Spurs	1993	–	£5.00

WEST MIDLANDS POLICE

X24	Cop Card-Toons	1989	–	£6.50
X36	Pictorial History - Walsall & District	1986	–	£22.50
X8	Play Safe - Stay Safe (With Album)	1992	–	£2.75
X24	The Old Bill Collection (With Album)	1990	–	£8.50

WESTON BISCUIT CO. LTD. (Australia)

L24	Veteran & Vintage Cars, 1st Series	1961	–	£50.00
L24	Veteran & Vintage Cars, 2nd Series	1962	–	£15.00

WEST RIDING COUNTY COUNCIL

Qty		Date	Odds	Sets
20	Health Cards	1924	£6.50	£130.00

WHAT CAMERA? (Magazine)

P12	Photocards	1989	–	£3.00

WHITBREAD & CO. LTD. (Brewers)

M1	Duke Without A Head	1958	–	£11.00
M50	Inn Signs, 1st Series (Metal)	1949	£3.70	£185.00
M50	Inn Signs, 2nd Series (Metal)	1950	£3.80	£190.00
M50	Inn Signs, 3rd Series (Metal)	1951	£4.80	£240.00
M50	(Card)	1952	£4.00	£200.00
M50	Inn Signs, 4th Series	1953	£3.80	£190.00
M50	Inn Signs, 5th Series	1955	£4.20	£210.00
M25	Inn Signs, Bournemouth	1973	£7.75	–
M25	Inn Signs, Devon & Somerset	1973	£2.20	£55.00
M25	Inn Signs, Isle Of Wight	1974	£7.50	–
M25	Inn Signs, Kent	1973	£8.00	–
M15	Inn Signs, London	1973	£3.25	£110.00
M10	Inn Signs, London (Different)	1974	£5.25	–
M25	Inn Signs, Marlow	1973	£7.50	£190.00
M25	Inn Signs, Portsmouth	1973	£9.50	–
M4	Inn Signs, Special Issue	1951	£7.00	£28.00
M25	Inn Signs, Stratford-Upon-Avon	1974	£6.50	–
M25	Inn Signs, West Pennine	1973	£7.50	£185.00
M25	Maritime Inn Signs	1974	£0.32	£8.00
M1	The Britannia Inn (Plain Back)	1958	–	£38.00
M1	(Printed Back)	1958	–	£55.00
M1	The Railway	1958	–	£13.00
M1	The Startled Saint	1958	–	£42.00

WHITE FISH AUTHORITY

25	The Fish We Eat	1954	–	£2.50

WHITEHAVEN LIBRARY

M6	The Port Of Whitehaven	1978	–	£6.00

WHITEHEAD (Lollies)

X25	Kings & Queens	1980	–	£3.25

WIGAN POLICE

X24	Riversiders	1991	–	£12.00

WIKO (Germany)

50	Soldaten Der Welt	1969	–	£20.00

WILBUR-SUCHARD CHOCOLATE CO. (U.S.A.)

35/36	Flags	1918	£2.50	£87.50

WILCOCKS & WILCOCKS LTD. (Tea)

25	Birds	1965	£2.50	–
25	British Cavalry Uniforms Of The 19th Century	1963	£0.50	£12.50
25	Garden Flowers	1964	–	£6.50
25	Passenger Liners	1967	£0.80	£20.00

WILCOCKS & WILCOCKS LTD. (Tea) – cont.

Qty		Date	Odds	Sets
25	People & Places	1966	–	£3.00
24	The Island Of Ceylon	1955	£5.00	–
25	Tropical Birds	1965	–	£12.50
25	Wonders Of The Deep	1965	–	£3.50
25	Wonders Of The World	1971	–	£5.00

A.S. WILKIN LTD. (Confectionery)

25	Into Space	1960	–	£8.50

W.R. WILKINSON & CO. (Confectionery)

M25	Popular Footballers	1956	£40.00	–

ROBERT J. WILSON

L6	Railway Engines	2004	–	£3.00
L10	Traditional Lincolnshire Country Life	2002	–	£6.25
L10	Vintage Tractors	2002	–	£4.50

WIMPY (RESTAURANTS)

M20	Super Heroes Super Villains	1979	£1.40	£28.00

WOMAN'S FRIEND (Periodical)

K52	Fortune Telling Cards	1925	£3.00	–

WOMAN'S OWN (Periodical)

F8	Film Stars	1955	£6.50	£54.00

E. WOODHEAD & SONS (Tea)

25	Types Of British Soldiers	1916	£28.00	–

WOOLWORTH (Stores)

M24	Fascinating Facts	1989	–	£4.00

WORTHINGTON (Brewers)

36	Sportsmen (Imperial Tobacco Reprints)	1992	–	£40.00

WRIGHTS BISCUITS LTD.

24	Marvels Of The World	1954	–	£2.50
24	Mischief Goes To Mars ("Mischief Club")	1954	–	£8.00
24	(Wright At Side)	1954	–	£4.00
24	(Wright At Base)	1954	£0.60	£16.00

YOUNG BRITAIN (Periodical)

MF15	Favourite Cricketers Series (In Pairs)	1922	£7.00	£105.00

NOTES